The Future of Children

PRINCETON-BROOKINGS

VOLUME 26   NUMBER 1   SPRING 2016

Children and Climate Change

Children and Climate Change: Introducing the Issue

Janet Currie and Olivier Deschênes

According to the US National Oceanic and Atmospheric Administration, 2015—with an average global temperature 1.6° Fahrenheit warmer than the twentieth-century average—was Earth's warmest year since record keeping began in 1880, continuing a half-century-long trend of rising temperatures. The debate about climate change and appropriate policy response is often framed in terms of the likely impact on our children. Children born in 2016 will be 34 in 2050 and 84 in 2100. How will the probable rise in temperature (3.6 to 7.2° Fahrenheit, or 2 to 4° Celsius), rising sea levels, and the increasing likelihood of extreme weather affect the course of their lives and the lives of their children? This issue of *The Future of Children* outlines the likely consequences of climate change on child health and wellbeing and identifies policies that could mitigate negative impacts.

Four interrelated themes emerge from the issue.

1. Climate change will fundamentally alter Earth's climate system in many ways that threaten children's physical and mental wellbeing.

2. Today's children and future generations will bear a disproportionate share of the burden of climate change, which will affect child wellbeing through many direct, indirect, and societal pathways.

3. Children in developing countries and countries with weak institutions face the greatest risks.

4. The uncertainties associated with climate change and its mitigation—coupled with the fact that the costs of climate change mitigation policies need to be paid now, but the benefits will accrue in the future—make it difficult to enact appropriate policies.

In the past decade, the science of climate change has progressed rapidly. By combining evidence from direct observation, climate modeling, and historical sources (such as ice cores that can reveal information about climate centuries ago), scientists have become virtually certain that human activities are altering our climate in ways that will have drastic effects for future generations through mechanisms such as sea-level rise, warmer

www.futureofchildren.org

Janet Currie is the Henry Putnam Professor of Economics and Public Affairs, chair of the Department of Economics, and director of the Center for Health and Wellbeing at Princeton University. Olivier Deschênes is an associate professor in the Department of Economics at the University of California, Santa Barbara.

temperatures, and a higher frequency of natural disasters.

Children are largely left out of discussions about appropriate responses to climate change, but they ought to be central to these debates because they—as well as future generations—have a much larger stake in the outcome than we do.

Compared with adults, children are physically more vulnerable to the direct effects of extreme heat, drought, and natural disasters. Climate change's indirect effects can also derail children's developmental trajectories—for example, through conflict, vector-borne diseases, economic dislocation, undernutrition, or migration—making it harder for them to reach their full potential. As some of the most vulnerable members of society, children generally suffer whenever there is social upheaval. Given the profound changes to society that may accompany climate change, it is likely that children will be especially severely affected.

Our third theme is that children are especially vulnerable in developing countries, where 85 percent of the world's youth currently live. Children in those countries are already facing the impacts of climate change. The World Health Organization estimates that children suffer more than 80 percent of the illness and mortality attributable to climate change. So, for a large share of the world's population, climate change is here and now and not merely some future problem. Moreover, to the extent that children in developing countries are already more likely to face other threats to their health and welfare, they may have less resilience to confront the additional problems caused by climate change.

At the same time, given that so many factors contribute to children's development, there may be many ways to either exacerbate or compensate for the harm caused by climate change. Governments bear major responsibility for adopting policies that respond to climate change. However, governments in developing countries are less likely to represent children's interests effectively, leaving children at even greater risk of harmful consequences.

Our fourth theme is that decision making surrounding climate change is greatly complicated by the high degree of uncertainty involved in virtually all of its aspects. Yet waiting for uncertainty to be resolved before acting is not a viable option, given the risk of allowing irreversible changes to the planet to be "baked in." Climate science has made great strides in recent years, but estimates of climate change's likely effects still span a broad range, and it's important to consider worst-case scenarios as well as median forecasts.

Just as important is the uncertainty surrounding human responses to climate change. Technology can help us both mitigate climate change (for example, by capturing and storing carbon emissions or increasing our reliance on renewable energy) and adapt to it (via cooling technologies such as air conditioning, changes in urban building design, flood control, and so on). Individual behavioral responses, such as migrating or spending more time indoors, also represent possible adaptations to climate change. Moreover, such responses can work either to prevent the effects of climate change or to mitigate them after the fact. But until we invest in, develop, and disseminate new technologies, it's impossible to know how well they would work or how much they would cost. And it's still uncertain whether governments have the political will to act, though the 2015 Paris Agreement was encouraging in that respect; adopted by all 195 member states of the United Nations Framework Convention on Climate Change, it laid out a framework for each country to reduce carbon emissions based on a national target.

Overall, then, even if we knew the precise magnitude of future shifts in global climate, we would still have trouble forecasting the likely effects on children. Much of what we know about, for example, the effects of high temperatures on children comes from extrapolating from short-term variations in weather to long-term variations in climate. In the short term, though, our capacity to adapt to, compensate for, or reinforce such effects is limited. Thus estimates based on short-run variations could either overstate or understate the likely longer-term effects of climate change.

A related problem is that it's hard to identify the causal impacts of changes in weather or climate. Correlation is not causation, in part because many factors typically change at the same time, and some of them may not be captured in the types of data we study. If, for example, a local drought coincided with a global drop in the production of a locally grown commodity, we might erroneously attribute negative economic effects to the drought rather than to global markets. Similarly, if everyone living in a floodplain were moved to higher ground, then increases in periodic flooding due to climate change wouldn't mean greater loss of life or property. However, the move itself would involve costs and foregone opportunities, and those costs would ideally be considered costs of climate change. Throughout this issue of *The Future of Children*, then, we asked authors to pay careful attention to the credibility of the available causal evidence and the extent to which that evidence captures all of the

relevant costs and benefits of climate change, including those caused by adaptation or mitigation efforts.

Findings of the Issue

Here we highlight key findings from the individual articles.

The opening article, "The Science of Climate Change," by Michael Oppenheimer and Jesse Anttila-Hughes, offers a primer emphasizing the features of climate change that are likely to have the greatest impact on children. Oppenheimer and Anttila-Hughes consider four broad sources of knowledge about climate change: direct observation of weather and climate records over time; paleoclimate work based on such things as ancient tree rings or air bubbles trapped for thousands of years in Antarctic ice; chemical and physical analysis; and climate modeling. One broad conclusion is that although climate change will be felt globally, its effects will be very different in different places. Overall, however, the effects of climate change on human wellbeing—either directly, through exposure to changing climate, or indirectly, through climate-induced changes in society and the economy—are predicted to be extremely negative. A moderate example comes from studying the El Niño phenomenon, a relatively mild periodic climate shock that causes a great deal of disruption globally, with local effects that range from torrential rains to heat waves to droughts. The likely effects of climate change include changes in the distribution of temperature toward greater warmth, hydrologic stress and a resulting increase in food insecurity, more-frequent extreme weather events, sea-level rise, and damage to ecosystems. The long atmospheric life of most greenhouse gases that cause climate change—hundreds to thousands of years—

combined with the lag between actions to reduce the extent of climate change and their effects, suggests that our children and our children's children are already on track to suffer those effects.

In the second article, Joshua Graff Zivin and Jeffrey Shrader zero in on how rising temperatures (global warming) affect children. They review evidence that high temperatures increase mortality, especially among fetuses and young children (as well as the elderly). When combined with other conditions—such as high humidity, disease vectors, or pollution—heat can be even deadlier. And even when it isn't fatal, exposure to high temperatures reduces learning and worker productivity. Graff Zivin and Shrader also discuss a range of policy responses—from air conditioning to better preparation for emergencies—that could mitigate those effects.

In the next article, Richard Akresh considers the relationship between conflict and climate change. A growing contingent of researchers has been examining the relationship between climate shocks, especially higher temperatures and extreme weather events, and conflict at all scales, from interpersonal violence to war. Children are especially vulnerable to conflict and suffer impacts from exposure in the short, medium, and long term. Akresh discusses evidence that those effects can spill over to the next generation and beyond, leaving long-run damage to the affected countries' ability to develop human capital. In addition to its direct effects, conflict generally leaves many additional problems in its wake, including malnutrition, famine, disease, and economic and social dislocation. Akresh points out that conflict is a great leveler in that its negative effects are seen among both rich children and poor children, among boys as well as girls, and in all stages of childhood.

Carolyn Kousky focuses on how children may be affected by the increased frequency of natural disasters that climate change is expected to produce. Kousky considers three types of harm: negative health impacts, interruption in schooling, and negative psychological impacts. Disasters can harm children's physical health disproportionately—for example, through malnutrition or diarrheal illness—and can decrease access to medical care even for non-disaster-related illnesses. Like conflicts, disasters can displace populations, destroy school facilities, and push families to send children into the labor force to help with the economic shock the disaster causes. Finally, the trauma of disasters can cause mental health problems later on. Kousky notes that children living in low-income areas are particularly vulnerable to a disaster's effects.

Allison Larr and Matthew Neidell's article explores the complex relationship between pollution and climate change, as well as the relationship between pollution and children's health and human capital development. Many people assume that policies to reduce climate change will also reduce pollution (and vice versa), but that's not necessarily the case. Concentrations of some ambient pollutants are linked to temperature and other climatic variables through complex, nonlinear relationships. As a result, higher temperatures caused by global warming may increase ozone levels, but the increased rainfall that's predicted to occur in some areas could reduce levels of particulate matter in the atmosphere. On the other hand, fossil fuel power plants are major sources of carbon dioxide, but they also emit high levels of nitrogen dioxide and sulfur dioxide—which play a role in forming ozone and particulate matter—suggesting that if we reduced fossil fuel consumption, we would not only reduce emissions of greenhouse gases but also reduce ambient pollution. In that way, Larr and Neidell project, mitigating the emissions that produce climate change would produce significant improvements in child wellbeing. More children would survive into adulthood, experience healthier childhoods, have more human capital, and be more productive as adults. The authors' calculations focus exclusively on the United States, which has the most-complete data available to make such calculations. Yet, they point out, the expected costs of climate change are likely to be largest in developing countries.

Rema Hanna and Paulina Oliva delve into the likely implications of climate change for children in developing countries. Such children already face severe challenges, which climate change will likely exacerbate. In particular, most people in developing countries still depend primarily on agriculture as a source of income, and so anything that reduces crop yields is likely to directly threaten the livelihoods of developing-country families and their ability to feed their children. Children in developing countries also face more-severe threats from pollution of both the air and the water and from water- and vector-borne diseases. And the fact that many developing countries have high birth rates and high ratios of children to adults (known as *high dependency ratios*) means that proportionately more children are at risk in developing countries.

In their article on the costs of mitigating climate change, Billy Pizer, Ben Groom, and Simon Dietz lay out a framework for thinking about the costs and benefits of climate change policies. A central question, given that climate change is a multigenerational

problem, is that of who should pay the costs relative to who will reap the benefits. For example, one formulation of the problem is that the current generation must pay to reduce the risks of climate change for future generations. But depending on the progress of technology and economic growth, it might well be the case that future generations will be much wealthier than we are; if so, perhaps it's not fair to demand that current generations pay. That type of trade-off is at the heart of discussions about whether current children in developing countries should pay for climate change policies, as they would if measures are adopted that reduce current economic growth. Another difficult issue has to do with how to value the welfare of generations that are yet unborn and that may never be born in some possible states of the future world. In their discussion of those issues, the authors bring to bear insights from burgeoning research on intergenerational equity and the appropriate way to discount future costs and benefits.

The last article, by Joseph Aldy, describes the political economy that underlies the current state of global efforts to mitigate climate change. Aldy frames the political challenge associated with crafting a meaningful climate policy in the context of a model of business capital and societal capital that includes the environment and global climate as components of societal capital. A key implication of Aldy's framework is that the near-term costs of climate change mitigation will be borne disproportionately by the owners of existing business capital—especially incumbent firms in fossil-fuel-intensive sectors—whereas the benefits of such policies would accrue primarily to future generations.

Aldy argues that the current lack of a national climate change policy in part reflects this distributional imbalance in costs and benefits. He then draws lessons from successful US policy reforms in the past whose costs and benefits accrued to different groups. His analysis highlights some of the key characteristics of long-term, durable, successful public policies in American history—for example, the 1935 Social Security Act and the 1970 Clean Air Act Amendments. Those policies addressed contemporary problems that were already imposing direct costs on a significant portion of the population. A major difference between such policies and effective climate policy is that those past policies tackled domestic issues, whereas climate change is a global problem that will require some form of coordination across countries. The recently adopted Paris Agreement is an example of a promising policy framework centered on multilateral collaboration and engagement.

Implications for Research and Policy

The effects of global climate change on child wellbeing are expected to be extensive, geographically varied, and, to a large extent, reinforced by current economic and social inequities. On June 25, 2013, while announcing his Climate Action Plan, President Barack Obama said: "Someday, our children, and our children's children, will look at us in the eye and they'll ask us, Did we do all that we could when we had the chance to deal with this problem and leave them a cleaner, safer, more stable world?"

The findings in this issue have clear implications for researchers and policy makers trying to tackle the many challenges climate change poses.

1. The continuous emission of greenhouse gases since the dawn of the Industrial Age has already begun to alter the global climate system, and it will continue to do so even if we significantly reduce global emissions. Establishing a large-scale international and coordinated policy response has proven difficult. Children and future generations lack a presence in the debate. The 2015 Paris Agreement, the positive outcome of more than 20 years of international climate negotiations, may prove to be a fundamental step in addressing the threat of climate change, but at best we won't know whether it's effective until two to three decades from now. This state of affairs highlights the fundamental uncertainty that characterizes the issue of climate change as well as the need to find a way to act despite that uncertainty.

2. Even as we increase our efforts to reduce emissions of greenhouse gases that cause climate change, the climate system will continue to grow warmer for a significant period of time. Thus policies must be developed to prepare and adapt in the face of inevitable climate change. States, cities, and communities all over the world must promote preparedness and resilience. For example, the 2015 Paris Agreement includes a plan to give developing countries $100 billion a year to adapt to and mitigate the impacts of climate change. In the United States, federal agencies have released adaptation plans that lay out strategies to protect their programs from the effects of climate change.

3. Large-scale adaptive responses to climate change entail significant societal impacts. For example, in 2008, extreme weather events displaced 20 million people. Future forecasts suggest that by 2050 there could be 200 million environmental migrants, many of whom could be

children. Countries and communities need to prepare for such possible large-scale relocation of poor and vulnerable populations. The 2015 European migrant crisis highlights the complex and difficult nature of responding appropriately to such mass migrations.

4. We need additional public health investments and interventions to educate people about the risks climate change poses to children and to protect individuals and communities from its effects. Advance warning of excessive heat, outreach, and air-conditioned cooling shelters and community centers have succeeded in mitigating the impact of extreme heat. Education and warnings are especially important because the populations most vulnerable to the health effects of climate change are young children and the elderly. Climate change may therefore place increased demands on already financially fragile public policies such as Medicare and Medicaid. In another vein, although the US Environmental Protection Agency's Indoor Air Quality in Schools program includes the maintenance of acceptable temperature and relative humidity in its definition of good indoor air quality management, no federal standard establishes maximum temperatures in schools. Based on the evidence in this issue, temperature standards or air-conditioning requirements for schools would provide sizable benefits, especially for children in disadvantaged urban communities.

5. We need more research across the entire spectrum of disciplines, from improving climate science and climate modeling to better measuring climate change impacts and identifying possible adaptation strategies to developing new methods for effective decision making in the face of long time horizons and deep uncertainty. Both the public and the private sector must stimulate additional research by funding new initiatives and by collecting and disseminating the required data.

United Nations Secretary-General Ban Ki-moon has called climate change "the defining challenge of our age." The 2015 Paris Agreement gives us reason for cautious optimism, but only time will tell whether that optimism is justified.

The Science of Climate Change

Michael Oppenheimer and Jesse K. Anttila-Hughes

Summary

Michael Oppenheimer and Jesse Anttila-Hughes begin with a primer on how the greenhouse effect works, how we know that Earth is rapidly getting warmer, and how we know that the recent warming is caused by human activity. They explain the sources of scientific knowledge about climate change as well as the basis for the models scientists use to predict how the climate will behave in the future. Although they acknowledge the large degree of uncertainty that surrounds predictions of what will happen decades or even centuries in the future, they also emphasize the near certainty that climate change has the potential to be extremely harmful to children.

Most children around the world will face hotter, more extreme temperatures more frequently. Higher temperatures will directly affect children's health by increasing the rates of heatstroke, heat exhaustion, and heat-related mortality. Excessive heat is also likely to affect children indirectly by disrupting agricultural systems, driving up prices, and increasing food scarcity.

Many of the world's children may see local demand for water outstrip supply, as shifting precipitation patterns dry out some regions of the world, make other regions wetter, and increase the frequency of both unusually dry periods and unusually severe rains. Mountain glaciers will recede further, significantly reducing storage of winter snows and thus springtime runoff, which has traditionally been used to water fields and recharge reservoirs. Melting ice will also raise sea levels, triggering direct physical threats to children through flooding and erosion and indirect threats through migration and expensive adaptation.

Climate change is also expected to make weather-based disasters more frequent and more damaging. This is particularly worrisome for children, not only because of the physical peril disasters pose but also because disasters can have debilitating long-term indirect effects on children. Damage to ecosystems from climate change may also harm children; for example, acidification the world's oceans will reduce food supplies, and disease-carrying insects will invade new areas in response to changing rains and temperatures.

In the face of such dire forecasts, Oppenheimer and Anttila-Hughes argue, climate change forces us to directly confront the value we put on future children's wellbeing. Fortunately, we have reason for hope as well as for concern: "History," they write, "has demonstrated time and again that humans can tackle uncertain threats in times of need."

www.futureofchildren.org

Michael Oppenheimer is the Albert G. Milbank Professor of Geosciences and International Affairs in the Woodrow Wilson School of Public and International Affairs and the Department of Geosciences at Princeton University; he is also the director of the Program in Science, Technology and Environmental Policy at the Woodrow Wilson School and a faculty associate of the Atmospheric and Ocean Sciences Program, Princeton Environmental Institute, and the Princeton Institute for International and Regional Studies. Jesse K. Anttila-Hughes is an assistant professor in the Department of Economics at the University of San Francisco.

Geoffrey Heal of Columbia University reviewed and critiqued a draft of this article.

Michael Oppenheimer and Jesse K. Anttila-Hughes

Understanding how humanity's accumulated greenhouse gas emissions will alter Earth's climate over the next few centuries requires a broad perspective, so climate change is usually discussed as a global issue. But understanding how climate change will affect children who live through it requires a narrower focus—one that pushes directly against the limitations of that global view. Geographic variation in climate change's effects over time, uncertainty stemming from scientific complexity, and, more than anything, the inherent impossibility of forecasting future human behavior combine to make climate change's eventual impacts on children both very different from place to place and extraordinarily difficult to predict with any certainty. Climate change will influence children's lives in few "global" ways. Rather, during the coming decades, children will face myriad interactions between changes in the climate and social, economic, and cultural forces.

A defining theme of this article is the need to balance high uncertainty in some areas with relative certainty in others. As we will show, we now have overwhelming evidence that human emission of greenhouse gases has already begun to change the climate and that it will continue to do so unless emissions are halted; hence we call this climate change *anthropogenic*, from the Greek for *human influenced*. Moreover, ample evidence indicates that we can expect many changes in the weather and the climate that will fall outside the range of human experience. Unless we reduce emissions drastically, those changes are expected to have pervasive impacts worldwide, including, in some cases, the destabilization or destruction of ecological and social systems. Thus the costs of inaction are high. At the same time, enormous uncertainty surrounds any forecast of specific outcomes of climate change. Which regions will be affected and in what ways, how quickly changes will occur, and how humans will respond are all impossible to know with certainty, given the complex natural and social forces involved. From a risk management perspective, the possibility of extremely negative outcomes means climate change has much in common with other large-scale global threats such as conflict between nuclear powers, wherein the potential for highly undesirable and irreversible outcomes is real but very difficult to predict with precision. We will return to this theme many times.

Origins of Understanding

The greenhouse effect is a prerequisite for life as we know it because without it, Earth would be much colder (by about 32° Celsius, or 57.6° Fahrenheit) and drier: a frozen desert. Nobel Prize–winning Swedish chemist Svante Arrhenius laid out the greenhouse "problem" in an 1896 paper. He showed that a rise in atmospheric concentrations of carbon dioxide—a by-product of combustion, caused by burning coal as an energy source in the emergent industrialized countries—would make the planet warmer, although he saw that warming as beneficial rather than problematic. Other notable nineteenth- and early-twentieth-century scientists also contributed to our understanding by linking earlier, natural changes in atmospheric carbon dioxide to the comings and goings of ice ages.

After Arrhenius, interest in the problem lagged until the 1950s, when a few scientists began exploring in detail how carbon dioxide traps infrared radiation. They provided the first credible estimates of the fraction of emissions that remain in the atmosphere rather than dissolving in the ocean. The advent of modern computing advanced weather forecasting and led to an interest in modeling the general circulation of the atmosphere. An offshoot of those studies examined the effect of carbon dioxide and, in the 1960s, produced the first computer-based models for estimating future climate change. By the 1970s, scientists had come to understand that the *cooling effect of particulate matter*, which is a by-product of dirty, fossil fuel combustion techniques, had been substantially offsetting the *warming effect of carbon dioxide*. The roles played by water vapor, clouds, and minor atmospheric gases other than carbon dioxide were also elaborated in great detail. By the late 1980s, the scientific consensus that carbon emissions would warm the climate was sufficient to become a major political issue, leading to the 1992 negotiation of the United Nations Framework Convention on Climate Change treaty, which was dedicated to stabilizing greenhouse gas concentrations in the atmosphere "at a level that would prevent dangerous anthropogenic interference with the climate system." Today, carbon dioxide has increased by more than 40 percent from its preindustrial level because of the mining and burning of fossil fuels, the cutting and burning of forests, certain agricultural practices that emit greenhouse gases, and the output of certain industries, such as those that produce cement and halocarbon refrigerants.

The terms *climate* and *weather* are sometimes confused with each other, and that confusion can have serious implications. *Weather* denotes the actual behavior of Earth's oceans and atmosphere over a given short period; the term *weather* refers to the temperature, precipitation, wind, storminess, and so forth that we experience during any given day, week, month, or year. *Climate*, on the other hand, refers to the behavior of weather over longer periods, such as decades, from a statistical perspective (for example, annual mean temperature or mean daily maximum temperature, averaged for a geographic region). *Climate change* thus refers to an increase in *average global temperature*, along with all of the ways such an increase affects the characteristics of climate and weather.

Failure to differentiate between weather and climate can lead to serious misunderstandings. We easily recall weather, and that readiness of perception (or *availability*, as psychologists call it) often dominates our assessment of risk: If this winter is cold, what happened to global warming? If this summer is hot, we'd better hurry up and fix the problem! Obviously, such misunderstandings can be manipulated to fit political agendas, and we must act to decouple our understanding of the larger, global problem from the random weather experienced on any given day.

The Physical Problem

Concern about climate change has grown over the past 25 years. Today, thousands of climatological scientists and researchers across related fields are conducting research on topics ranging from the specifics of obscure climate processes to the likely impacts of climate change on everything from alpine ecosystems to financial markets. The pace of discovery and the growth in understanding have been sufficiently rapid, the breadth of impacts sufficiently wide, and the implications of social concern sufficiently broad that a major international organization was created to synthesize scientific evidence on climate change. The Intergovernmental

Panel on Climate Change, or IPCC, operates under the auspices of the United Nations Environment Programme and the World Meteorological Organization. Every six years or so, the panel publishes assessment reports that summarize the state of the research on climate change science, impacts, and policy.[1] Many other organizations, too, have assessed aspects of the problems inherent in climate change, resulting in projects ranging from the 2007 *Stern Review*—a UK government study emphasizing the economic benefits of early action against climate change—to the 2014 philanthropically funded American Climate Prospectus, which summarizes the expected economic risks of climate change in the United States.[2]

Perhaps the most important point about the science of climate change is that our knowledge arises from four very different sources: direct observations of the climate system and changes within it, including everything from almanac records to satellite-based imaging; paleoclimate evidence of Earth's climate in the distant past—for example, what we can deduce by examining air bubbles trapped in the Antarctic ice sheet by snow that fell hundreds of thousands of years ago, or by analyzing the chemical composition of fossilized marine animal shells trapped in sedimentary layers at the sea bottom for tens of millions of years; laboratory studies of the chemical and physical processes that take place in the atmosphere; and—perhaps most important for forecasting—numerical, computer-based models of climate circulation and other climate properties, which in many respects are similar to the meteorological models used for generating weather forecasts. Our understanding of climate change is based on all four of these sources, which together paint a consistent picture of carbon's current and future warming effects on the planet.

Scientists are nearly certain that climate change is occurring and has the potential to be extremely harmful. Climate change nonetheless has several unique characteristics that combine to present a very challenging mix for policy makers. Climate changes—both those already observed and those anticipated—will affect different countries and different regions very differently. But, eventually, the changes will affect humans in every nation on the planet; in no place will climate remain unchanged. Moreover, every country's carbon dioxide emissions affect the climate in every other country because carbon dioxide's long lifetime means that it achieves a nearly uniform distribution in the atmosphere. Thus climate change is a global commons problem at the largest conceivable scale; the atmosphere is an easily damaged, open-access resource whose preservation will demand increasingly active coordination across the full complexity of human social interactions. Climate change's global nature thus distinguishes it from almost every other major environmental policy problem—except, perhaps, the effects of ozone depletion or large-scale nuclear warfare.

Another implication of carbon dioxide's very long lifetime is that a significant fraction (about 25 percent) of today's emissions will remain airborne even a millennium from now unless we invent a technology to affordably capture and bury the carbon dioxide, meaning that many expected changes are effectively irreversible. Furthermore, the huge mass of the oceans is absorbing a large portion of the climate's thermal energy as Earth warms, and the resulting thermal inertia means that the effects of today's emissions will take several decades to appear.

Even if we could eliminate emissions entirely today, enough greenhouse gases have already been released to gradually warm the planet for the rest of the current century and beyond.

Policy makers will need an unusual degree of foresight, extraordinary powers of judgment, and a willingness to act without getting credit for the outcomes.

Climate change science is also rife with uncertainty. Even though scientists are increasingly certain about the general characteristics of global climate changes under certain emissions scenarios, extensive uncertainties remain when it comes to details of how the climate will respond at time and spatial scales relevant to humans. The answers to such questions as how fast the sea level will rise are so uncertain that scientists can offer policy makers only a very limited basis for making decisions, much less tell them with confidence how high to build a seawall. When combined with the fact that, in the coming years, humans will change their emissions behaviors in response to changes in energy supply and economic development, uncertainty about what will happen becomes daunting.

The combination of universality; effective irreversibility; lags between emissions, policy actions, and system responses; and general uncertainty means that policy makers will need an unusual degree of foresight, extraordinary powers of judgment, and a willingness to act without getting credit (or

suffering opprobrium) for the outcomes. It's no wonder that many leaders have resisted grappling with climate change—all the more so because of the potential costs of reducing greenhouse gas emissions.

A natural question is whether all of climate change's impacts on children's wellbeing must necessarily be bad. Generally speaking, most scientists say climate changes will disrupt and damage both natural and human systems in most places around the world; the IPCC, for example, acknowledges eight risks associated with climate change, ranging from increases in rates of death and illness during periods of extreme heat to loss of rural livelihoods.[3] Certain regions are predicted to be more mildly affected, and cooler countries closer to the poles, such as Canada and Russia, may actually see a variety of benefits under climate change (at least temporarily), thanks principally to longer growing seasons and milder winters. However, those beneficial effects are expected to be dwarfed by a variety of negative impacts around the world, particularly in poorer countries, and especially after factoring in certain indirect effects of the increased stress that climate change will exert on socioeconomic systems.

Scholars have made strides in understanding how social and economic systems respond to climate changes, often using variability in historical weather patterns to provide insights into what future climate change might mean for human society. Readers who want to learn more about such research should consult a recent review by economists Melissa Dell, Benjamin Jones, and Benjamin Olken in the open-access *Journal of Economic Literature* or the Impacts, Adaptation, and Vulnerability section of the most recent IPCC report.[4]

In general, the fact that climate change's impacts are expected to be mostly negative reflects the speed and intensity with which human activity is expected to change the climate. Although the climate is constantly in flux, natural variations on such a large scale normally occur many times more slowly than the current rate of change. The rapid pace of anthropogenic climate change limits our ability to respond smoothly and gradually to changes in risk, and it hampers the efficacy of slow-moving policy options for mitigating climate risk—such as improving infrastructure or developing new technologies—thereby potentially forcing populations and food systems to change at speeds far faster than normal.

What Can Past Climates Tell Us about Climate Change?

Natural climate variation has arisen from (1) a host of small changes in the amount of light the sun emits, (2) fluctuations in the amount of volcanic dust in the atmosphere (which cools Earth by reflecting sunlight), and (3) a spectrum of other variations, including some that are chaotic and therefore unpredictable. Taken together, these factors have caused global average temperature to vary by a few tenths of a degree Celsius through the decades—less than the current level of human-influenced warming.

One lesson science can draw from the recent past stems from the effects of the El Niño Southern Oscillation, a suite of climatological changes tied to an increase in the surface temperature of the eastern tropical Pacific Ocean that occurs every three to seven years. El Niño and similar oscillations are associated with changes in weather patterns around the world, including changes of a few tenths of a degree in the global average temperature. Even that small a variation in the global climate is enough to seriously influence human wellbeing; strong El Niño events are associated with punishing droughts and heavy floods throughout the world, including in major agricultural regions like California and eastern Australia. One vivid albeit imperfect way of conceptualizing climate change's magnitude would be to think of a permanent shift in the global climate regime several times stronger than El Niño, though at a much slower pace.

We can extend our understanding of the climate further into the past by analyzing data related to the paleoclimate. Air bubbles trapped in ice that froze millennia ago, tree rings that capture growing-season conditions, microscopic fossils millions of years old buried beneath the ocean floor, and plentiful other data let scientists infer what the atmosphere and climate were like in ages past and to chart climate history. Scientists now know that the causes of natural, preindustrial climate changes included very gradual shifts in Earth's orbit and axis of rotation relative to the sun over tens and hundreds of thousands of years. Those cycles alter the pattern of sunlight that reaches Earth's surface and thereby affect the level of photosynthesis, the melting of ice sheets, and many other processes that determine both the amount of greenhouse gases in the atmosphere and, ultimately, the behavior of Earth's climate. In the past million years, at the climatic minimums of such cycles—which we call ice ages—glaciers covered much of the Northern Hemisphere, and global surface temperature averaged around 5°C (9°F) below its value during periods of peak warmth, called interglacials. The entirety of human civilization, starting at the dawn of agriculture, has taken place during the most recent interglacial.

Much earlier, about 65 million years ago, when the age of the dinosaurs came to an end, temperatures averaged 8–10°C (14.4–18°F) higher than today. About 55 million years ago, during the Eocene, global average temperature jumped relatively rapidly, to 12°C (21.6°F) higher than today, possibly because of unusually high atmospheric levels of methane, a potent greenhouse gas. During the period of sustained warmth 50 million to 55 million years ago, the Arctic latitudes were home to alligators, tapirs, and rain forests.[5] In other words, the projected warming for this century is modest in terms of the very long span of climate history but is comparable in magnitude to changes of the past million years that remade Earth's surface; in our case, however, changes are occurring much, much more quickly than the natural rate. Sea level also varies naturally, but the trend associated with global warming, about 6–8 inches of sea level rise over the past century, now exceeds natural variations. Eight inches may not seem like much, but it is sufficient to erode and permanently submerge about 60 feet landward from the typical US East Coast beach tide line.

Observed Global Changes

Earth's average temperature since the mid nineteenth century is known with fair precision. By that point, enough ground- and ship-based thermometers were in place and readings were being reported with sufficient reliability that scientists today can retrospectively establish a credible record of global average temperature by using modern analytic techniques; that record is supplemented by satellite-based measurements beginning around 1980. Similarly, global sea level measurements using tide gauges go back to the late nineteenth century and are supplemented by satellite-based observations of sea surface height beginning around 1990.

Together, our climatic records indicate that Earth's average temperature has gradually increased during the past century and a half by 0.85°C, or about 1.5°F. That increase has been uneven, with alternating intervals of one to three decades of above-average or (as was the case for the most recent 16 years) below-average warming or even complete cessation (1940–70), a natural consequence of the climate system's highly complex and variable nature. In the inland areas of continents, the warming observed so far has been greater than the global average because coastal areas experience the moderating effect of the oceans. Warming has also been greater than average in the northern polar regions, where melting sea ice increases the oceans' absorption of the sun's rays. Global mean sea level, meanwhile, has risen about 15–20 centimeters (6–8 inches) during the past century. Warming has melted the land ice of mountain glaciers and polar ice sheets and simultaneously caused the thermal expansion of water already in the oceans; both factors have raised the oceans' height.

Such changes in mean temperatures and sea levels are already worrisome. To provide context, a further 1°C increase in global average temperature above today's levels, which many scientists say is already inevitable, would put Earth clearly outside the range of global temperature experienced in the entire 10,000-year history of civilization. In addition—and critically important when considering impacts on humans and infrastructure—are changes in climatic extremes, which are expected to increase as the planet warms. The frequency of extremely hot days and nights has already surpassed the historical record, as have the frequency and duration of heat waves. Very cold days have become less common. Because more heat means more evaporation of water from the ocean surface to drive the hydrologic cycle, more land areas are seeing increases rather than decreases in the frequency and intensity of extreme precipitation. When the excess ocean vapor encounters conditions under which precipitation would normally occur, it adds to the moisture available for storms; and heavy rainfall, which causes damaging inland flooding, only becomes heavier. In addition, even minor changes in average sea level can produce major changes in the likelihood of coastal flooding, dangerously high tides, and storm surges, all of which have increased. For example, in the mid nineteenth century, a flood level of about four feet occurred about once every 10 years in New York Harbor. Since then, the local sea level has risen 1.3 feet. That seemingly small shift in average sea level means that the 10-year flood level now reaches 6.4 feet, topping the seawall that protects much of lower Manhattan.[6]

Scientists have documented many other phenomena in the past few decades consistent with unusual climate changes, ranging from rapid loss of mountain glaciers and ice caps known to be thousands of years old to migrations of species toward cooler climates, to changes in annual ecological cycles such as the flowering and fruiting of plants. Many of these changes are subtle for now, but together they paint a consistent picture of a planet that's warming with unprecedented speed. At the same time, scientists still can't prove that some of the climate's more complex behaviors—such as the rate of formation and the intensity of tropical cyclones or large-scale oscillations such as El Niño—have been altered by

climate change, although they say changes are likely to occur in the future.

How Do We Know Humans Are Responsible?

A variety of evidence establishes that humans are the primary culprits causing climate change. Humans emit 35 billion metric tons of carbon dioxide into the atmosphere per year. Under natural conditions, Earth's ocean and land areas, including organic and inorganic material, emit about 20 times that amount, and they also naturally absorb an almost equal amount via dissolution in the ocean and photosynthesis. Without human interference, the gains and losses in the carbon cycle would be more or less in balance, and the amount of carbon dioxide in the atmosphere would vary very slowly over thousands of years. Human additions to the cycle can be absorbed only so fast, however, making it fairly straightforward to connect the recent, rapid buildup of carbon dioxide to human activity. The isotopes of atmospheric carbon dioxide (that is, heavy and light forms of carbon dioxide that carry different numbers of neutrons in their carbon atoms) carry distinctive fossil carbon signatures, making it easy to demonstrate the amount of carbon in the atmosphere that comes from fossil fuels versus the amount that comes from natural processes. Legal records for the major fossil fuel extraction companies dating back more than a century make total emissions from a supplier's perspective easy to calculate. Even the nearly uniform distribution of carbon dioxide in the atmosphere is broken slightly by a pattern of geographic variation that can be traced to the distribution of emission sources around the world. In sum, there is no doubt that humans have radically altered the carbon cycle.

It's harder to ascribe responsibility for changes in temperature and precipitation because human forcing is only one of many things that influence the climate's complex behavior. On a grand scale, observed average global temperatures have been increasing in time with emissions and in line with our understanding of climate. But that average state masks wide-ranging variability. Although scientists say they're certain that we're changing the climate overall, it's hard to show that any specific climatic event happens "because of" climate change. To infer that climate change bears some of the responsibility for a specific event or shift in the climate involves sophisticated statistical optimal-fingerprinting techniques, which compare observed geographic distribution of warming, precipitation, and other factors with climate models that either include or exclude the buildup of anthropogenic greenhouse gases and particulate matter. The optimal-fingerprinting method estimates the effect of an increase in greenhouse gases, thereby enabling scientists to calculate the odds that certain events, such as an unusual heat wave, would not have occurred in the absence of climate change. Simpler techniques compare the time series of observed warming with a model projection method that yields best estimates of how climate variables would have changed continent by continent or region by region. In both cases, models that account for increasing amounts of greenhouse gases substantially agree with what we've actually observed, whereas models that don't include rising greenhouse gases do not agree. Moreover, direct observations since about 1980 have ruled out the possibility that other factors might be responsible for climate change; compared with anthropogenic factors, neither variations in the sun's activity, which can slightly alter the amount of solar radiation reaching Earth, nor changes in the amount of volcanic particulates in the upper atmosphere, which can cool the planet after eruptions, have produced anything but small effects on the planet's temperature.

Projecting Future Climate and Scientific Uncertainty

To the best of our understanding, climate change's impacts on humans have so far been small and subtle compared with variations in other environmental factors that affect human welfare. Under business-as-usual scenarios whereby we continue to emit vast quantities of carbon dioxide, however, the impact of climate change is expected to grow markedly, eventually becoming a significant drag on human wellbeing all over the planet. To understand the full scope of the problem, we need to predict climate change decades into the future. The most reliable tools for such predictions are climate-modeling computer programs called atmosphere-ocean general circulation models (AOGCMs). These models solve complex systems of equations embodying the known physical and chemical laws that describe how the atmosphere and the oceans behave under the influence of sunlight, Earth's rotation, and changes in the chemical composition of the climate system, including emission of greenhouse gases. AOGCMs take as input the historical record of Earth's climate and make predictions subject to past constraints, thereby producing a long-term climate forecast not unlike weather forecasts provided daily by the world's meteorological organizations. Earth system models expand on AOGCMs by adding descriptions of how the ocean, atmosphere, and climate interact with surface vegetation.

Even the most advanced models can only approximate the climate's behavior, and they often disagree about specific aspects. That uncertainty stems from two sources. First, our understanding of the physical and biological world is incomplete and must be approximated in ways that compromise accuracy. Second, the equations that underpin AOGCMs must be solved numerically on computers with finite capacity, resulting in low (but rapidly improving) spatial and temporal resolutions on even the fastest computers. Together, those uncertainties mean that most models agree fairly well about large changes over long periods of time, but they disagree about smaller-scale changes. For example, projections of how mean temperature will change in an area the size of half of North America can be taken as fairly defensible— unlike projections of specific changes in a small area and a short time frame, such as the intensity of windstorms in Beijing in the winter of 2051.

Differences in how models project global mean temperature arise from a variety of sources, the most influential which is the modeling of feedback factors—complex responses to warming that either amplify or dampen the heat-trapping effect of greenhouse gases. For example, water vapor is a potent greenhouse gas, but it's so abundant in the air that direct human emissions don't alter its concentrations. However, the indirect effect of ocean surface warming that results from climate change causes more evaporation from the oceans and an even greater greenhouse effect, leading to increased warming, or a positive feedback. Similarly, about 30 percent of the sunlight that strikes Earth is reflected back into space under natural conditions without being absorbed—an effect called *albedo*. Changes in albedo lead to changes in the amount of solar energy that Earth absorbs, so changes

that make Earth more or less reflective can influence warming. The clearest example involves ice: land-based glaciers and ice sheets—in particular, Arctic sea ice—reflect more light back into space than do the surfaces underlying them. As the planet warms and surface ice coverage shrinks, Earth will absorb more sunlight, thereby warming the planet further still and melting even more ice.

Clouds, too, make predictions more difficult. Sunlight is reflected from the tops of clouds, especially opaque clouds from which precipitation falls, thereby altering albedo. But clouds—especially cirrus clouds, which are high and thin—can also absorb infrared radiation, much like greenhouse gases. Because we poorly understand many aspects of cloud formation, it's hard to say how, on balance, cloud changes feed back into warming. As a result, each climate model represents cloud processes in a distinct way and thus produces a level of cloud feedback different from that of other models. Differences in cloud feedback are the main cause of disagreement among the models when it comes to projecting global mean temperature. However, there is consensus that cloud feedback would at least modestly amplify warming rather than help lessen it.

The uncertainty that various kinds of feedback cause in climate models, dominated by the uncertainty in cloud feedback, has been summarized by a gross property of each model called its *climate sensitivity*, or the amount of warming the model predicts if carbon dioxide concentrations were to double from their preindustrial levels. The range of model sensitivities is 1.5–4.5°C (2.7–8.1°F); that is, average projected future global warming is 3°C (5.4°F), with uncertainty ranging from 50 percent below to 50 percent above that value.

Differences in how models project global mean temperature arise from a variety of sources, the most influential which is the modeling of feedback factors—complex responses to warming that either amplify or dampen the heat-trapping effect of greenhouse gases. Those differences mean that estimated uncertainty increases when we make predictions that are regional rather than global, sometimes producing high geographic variability. For example, a moderate emissions scenario predicts that by the last two decades of this century, the globe will warm 1.2–2.7°C (2.2–4.9°F) compared with recent temperatures; the same model predicts average warming in the broad range of 1.7–4°C (3.1–7.2°F) in central North America and Asia, with a narrower range in Africa and South America. Predictions of mean precipitation increases vary even more, ranging from 0 percent to 3 percent and 3 percent to 9 percent, respectively, for North America and Asia, to minus 9 percent to plus 9 percent for Africa. The uncertainties make projections more or less meaningless for areas smaller than about 1,000 square kilometers (386 square miles, or about the size of San Diego). The uncertainties also affect shorter time scales. A 4°C (7.2°F) increase in average temperature in an American Midwestern state like Kansas would shift the temperature distribution enough to lead to dozens more days per year of dangerously high temperatures exceeding 35°C (95°F), but trying to predict how such local-scale changes would evolve from year to year is simply too complex a task for current models.

The comparison of observed warming with reconstructed weather data, discussed earlier, offers strong evidence that the models perform reasonably well for conditions not so different from today's—that is, when greenhouse gas concentrations in the atmosphere range from 280 to 400 parts per million. For concentrations beyond that range, paleoclimate data enhance the models' credibility; such data include correlations between atmospheric temperatures and greenhouse gas concentrations that we can infer from ancient ice cores retrieved from deep under the Antarctic and Greenland ice sheets. Not only are the *correlations* consistent with our understanding of how geophysical and climatological processes have evolved over time, but the *magnitude* of the changes is consistent with model-based estimates of how large the temperature difference should be between cold, glacial periods and warm, interglacial periods (like our current epoch). The warming that followed the most recent glaciation, which substantially remade Earth's surface, was about 3–5°C (5.4–9°F), comparable to the higher end of projections for warming by the year 2100.

We've shown that the climate's complexity makes prediction difficult. An even bigger problem is uncertainty about future emissions. To accurately estimate emissions would involve an unimaginable degree of foresight about future technologies, economies, cultures, and policies, including emission abatement policies. Science's answer has been to create hypothetical scenarios in the form of estimates of different, plausible ways that humanity might choose to increase or decrease carbon emissions over the next several decades— generally guided by economic, technical, and political experts. The highest emissions scenario is usually characterized as the likely outcome of business as usual, wherein countries carry on with using carbon-intensive fuel sources for decades. The lowest emissions scenario represents a world with strict climate policies and rapid attempts to drastically reduce emissions and prevent further changes. The differences between those two scenarios are sufficiently large that they have a far greater influence on the uncertainty of future temperature predictions than do model uncertainties themselves. Put differently, models disagree about the difference between temperature predictions in low-emissions scenarios by a little more than one degree over this century, but the difference between projected temperature in any one model between low- and high-emissions scenarios is on the order of three degrees.

The many sources of uncertainty in projecting the future climate could mean huge differences in the eventual impact on human lives. If change is relatively modest, then this century's warming would increase the global average temperature by about 2°C (3.6°F). Under this scenario, a child born in the United States in 2080 would experience a climate markedly different from the one children born today experience; 2080 would see hotter summers, more extreme precipitation, and various other changes outlined later in this article. But those effects pale in comparison to what we can expect if climate changes are substantial. A child born into a 2080 world that is 4°C (7.2°F) warmer would experience a global average temperature higher than anything seen in the past several million years of Earth's history. That scenario would produce a climate radically different from the one we currently live in. Serious droughts, extreme heat waves, and rising sea levels would expose children to a range of risks unprecedented in human experience.

Regime Shifts in Planetary Systems

Scientists see a significant chance that certain changes in the physical climate system could be so rapid, and their impact so widely distributed geographically, that they would radically alter human society. Examples include a multi-meter sea level rise from the melting of ice sheets; a rapid release of methane (a potent greenhouse gas) from melting Arctic ocean sediments and permafrost, that would in turn produce several extra degrees of warming; a shift from moist tropical forest to savannah in the Amazon, causing large losses of ecosystems and species and substantial warming feedback from release of carbon dioxide from soils and biota; and shifts in precipitation and temperature large enough to drastically reduce agricultural productivity.

These possibilities are relatively less likely than other, less extreme changes. But should they occur, their impact will be high. We likely won't face them in this century, but they are nonetheless plausible outcomes of extreme warming that policy makers should take into account. Low-probability but high-impact risks, such as those stemming from cancer-causing chemicals, nuclear accidents, or geopolitical missteps are often viewed as threatening enough to require major shifts in policy. While the risk of a 4°C rise in global average temperature is low, it is not zero, and some estimates put the likelihood of even a 6°C rise in temperature at greater than one percent by the end of the century under a business-as-usual scenario. From a risk management perspective, the threat of less likely but extremely damaging regime shifts may thus be even more important than the threat of more likely but less damaging outcomes.

How Will Children Be Vulnerable to Climate Change?

The many climate changes expected to occur in the coming century are expected to threaten children's wellbeing in a variety of both overt and subtle ways. Of particular concern are changes in environmental risk that could influence children's development both directly—through increasing levels of exposure to a given hazard—and indirectly: through intermediate effects on social and economic systems. For example, an increase in the number of heat waves threatens children directly by exposing them to higher temperatures, increasing their risk of heatstroke and other heat-related illnesses, and making it harder to learn, play, and exercise outdoors. Heat waves' indirect effects are more subtle. More heat waves will make crop failures more likely, driving up prices in market economies and potentially depriving children of food in rural parts of the world. Heat waves also interact with emissions from local industry and transportation systems to increase atmospheric concentrations of gases like ozone (the central component of smog) that harm children's health. And high temperatures increase rates of interpersonal violence such as murder and abuse, as well as group violence such as war.

Climate change's indirect effects are in many ways more worrisome than the direct ones because so much of children's wellbeing is conditioned by social and economic factors. The climate's influence on a child's life doesn't occur in isolation but, rather, in combination with specific social circumstances. For example, a middle-class child in the Midwestern United States might be well insulated from many of climate change's direct effects by technologies such as air conditioning and modern sanitation systems. The indirect effects, however, will include everything from changes to the global food system that threaten to raise prices and induce shortages, to geopolitical changes that occur because climate change destabilizes social relations, thereby increasing conflict and migration. Moreover, children will experience the indirect effects of climate change as people and institutions respond not only to actual changes but also to climate-driven risks—from governments' decisions about urban development to families' decisions about where to rear children. Such adaptive choices are difficult to predict because they will be influenced by complex political, economic, and social factors.[7]

Poverty and development add more complexity. Children in poor countries are particularly vulnerable and exposed to climate-driven threats such as crop failures, heat waves, and tropical storms, and they won't be able to draw on the more sophisticated adaptation mechanisms available to children in rich countries. Moreover, in developing countries, families tend to rely more directly on the environment for their livelihoods—particularly through agriculture, meaning that climate change may cause serious harm to family livelihoods. In their article in this issue, Rema Hanna and Paulina Oliva cover the threats that climate change poses to children in developing countries.[8]

Wherever children live, climate change is likely to affect their development in ways that last well into later life. In recent years, researchers such as Douglas Almond and Janet Currie, who is one of the editors of this issue, have amassed evidence demonstrating that even relatively mild disturbances to a child's developmental trajectory may have effects that last into adulthood, particularly when the disturbances occur during pregnancy and infancy.[9] Economists Sharon Maccini and Dean Yang, for example, have demonstrated that women in rural Indonesia who were born during wetter rainy seasons are taller, better educated, richer, and in better health than their counterparts born during drier rainy seasons.[10]

Lastly, some of the most psychologically important losses that children can expect to incur from climate change involve the destruction of aesthetic and cultural heritage. Although such losses are difficult to quantify, climate change is expected to submerge islands and coastlines, eradicate or permanently change a number of ecosystems, threaten many traditional ways of life, and combine with other human social forces to lead the world through what many biologists say is already the sixth mass extinction of species in Earth's history. Many of the changes will be irreversible, potentially leaving this century's children a world bereft of a host of iconic species, delicate ecosystems, and culturally relevant sites. Cultural practices that depend on the environment—such as skiing, camping, hunting, and fishing—are likely to be permanently altered in many areas, and they may disappear entirely from certain areas. Climate change will thus reshape the very cultural fabric in which children develop, albeit in ways we can't yet know for certain.

What Will Changes Relevant to Children Look Like?

Uncertainties and caveats aside, a variety of changes in the climate are expected to influence social and economic outcomes that are particularly relevant for children. Climate models agree that at high latitudes and in the interiors of continents, warming will be greater than the global mean change,

whereas oceans will heat more gradually— much like the pattern that has already been observed. Similarly, the world as a whole will be wetter because of evaporation from the warmer ocean surface, but the excess moisture will be unevenly distributed and generally restricted to high latitudes and parts of the tropics. Broad areas at the historically arid horse latitudes (belts of high pressure roughly 30–35 degrees north and south of the equator) are expected to become even drier. Precipitation overall will become more variable: wet areas and periods will generally become wetter, and dry areas and periods drier, especially in the middle of continents. Ice will continue to melt worldwide; melting will reduce drinking water sources for areas like Lima, Peru, that depend in part on mountain glaciers for their water supplies, and it will increase sea level rise. Extremes of heat, precipitation, coastal flooding, and drought are all likely or very likely to continue to increase, and the strongest tropical cyclones (that is, hurricanes and typhoons) are more likely than not to grow even more intense. All of these factors can be expected to influence children's welfare over the next century in a variety of ways.

Changes in Temperature Distribution

The increase in average temperatures, including the higher likelihood of extremely hot days, is one of the most direct ways that children will be affected by climate change. Regional forecasts vary, but most children around the world will face hotter, more extreme temperatures more frequently in a variety of forms, ranging from heat waves to higher nighttime temperatures to warmer winters. Assuming that future population centers don't radically shift, a typical American family will experience 45–96 days above 35°C (95°F) each year, on average, if emissions don't abate during this century; that's somewhere from four to eight times as many as we've experienced in the past 30 years.[11] The higher temperatures will directly affect children's health and physiology in potentially serious ways, increasing the rates of heatstroke, heat exhaustion, and heat-related mortality and reducing children's basic ability to enjoy the outdoors. Health economists Joshua Graff Zivin and Jeffrey Shrader examine heat's effects on children's health and human capital in their article in this issue.[12]

Heat will also affect children indirectly in a variety of ways. For example, many crops are vulnerable to high temperatures, and even relatively small increases in heat exposure can cause huge reductions in crop health above certain threshold temperatures. Under business-as-usual warming scenarios, by the end of the century the United States may produce more than 50 percent less of such key crops as corn.[13] Higher temperatures will likely disrupt food systems, drive up prices, and increase scarcity, particularly when combined with increased stress on water supply due to population growth and drought. The changes may be particularly damaging in developing countries, where poor growing-season conditions can cause marked increases in death and illness among children.

Heat has other indirect effects that may be more subtle but are no less worrisome. Scientists from a range of disciplines have shown that increased temperatures and more-variable rains are broadly associated with increased rates of violent conflict, both interpersonally and societywide. A variety of mechanisms seem to explain those results, ranging from heat-wave-induced crop failures that lead to poverty and unrest to the

physiological effects of high temperatures on aggressive behavior. In his article in this issue, Richard Akresh reviews that research.[14] More generally, many studies have found that the combined influence of higher temperatures on everything from crop productivity to the human body's ability to work means that economies grow less quickly than they otherwise would, which reduces GDP growth, especially in poorer countries. If that's true, then climate change will likely mean that children around the world will be less prosperous than they otherwise would.

Hydrologic Stress

A second defining aspect of climate change that will influence children's welfare is a global increase in hydrologic stress. Even without climate change, many areas of the world already face serious water shortages because of rapid population growth, migration into cities, increasing pollution, and other processes that have hugely increased global demand for water. Climate change will worsen the situation in three major ways. First, it will shift precipitation patterns around the world, drying out certain regions and making others wetter. Second, it will increase the variability of precipitation in many places, making both unusually dry periods and unusually severe rains more likely. Third, it will reduce the mass of mountain glaciers in ranges such as the Himalayas, the Rockies, and the Andes, significantly reducing storage of winter snows and thus springtime runoff, which has traditionally been used to water fields and recharge reservoirs.

As climate change interacts with increasing future water needs, much of the world's population may see local demand for water outstrip supply. Municipal water and sanitation systems will be increasingly stressed, increasing the cost of access to clean water for consumption and sanitation. Agricultural systems already threatened by more frequent extreme heat will see damage exacerbated by insufficient water, particularly in areas where crops are fed by rain rather than irrigation. Water scarcity will threaten a variety of water-intensive industrial processes such as power generation and, in the long run, may put serious pressure on people to migrate out of drier regions.

Technological advances such as heat-resistant genetically modified crops, cheaper ways to remove salt from seawater, and improved efficiency of water use could help avert those difficulties. But such technologies may not come to fruition fast enough.

Changes in Extreme Events and Hazards

Climate change is expected to alter the behavior of hydrometeorological and climatological disasters, partly because of the increased variability of precipitation and temperatures. More frequent extreme rainfalls will bring more flooding to many parts of the world, while in other areas, higher temperatures combined with decreased rainfall will raise the risk of drought. Extreme temperatures and hydrologic stress will cause more wildfires, and more-intense rains will cause more landslides in mountain areas. There is no consensus as to whether tropical cyclones— the large storms we call cyclones, typhoons, or hurricanes, depending on the ocean basin—will occur any more or less frequently, and the physics behind them is complex. But they will more likely than not increase in average intensity over the coming decades, with stronger, more damaging storms becoming more common in some areas.

The increased potential for large disasters is particularly worrisome for children, not only because of the physical peril they pose but also because a growing number of studies have found that disasters can have debilitating long-term indirect effects on children through everything from households' ability to earn a living and feed their children, to urban planning and infrastructure investment decisions that may fundamentally determine children's living environments. In her article in this issue, Carolyn Kousky reviews the expected impacts of increased natural hazards on children.

Sea Level Rise

Rising seas will increase both (1) long-term land loss, thus reducing the amount of land available for settlement, and (2) episodic coastal inundation. At current rates of sea level rise, for example, the portion of New York City at risk for a one-hundred-year flood will double under high emissions scenarios from just over 10 percent of the city today to 20 percent by 2100.[15] Rising sea levels are also expected to increase erosion and to interact with tropical and extratropical cyclones to worsen storm surges, all of which pose direct threats to children's wellbeing. Less directly, sea level rise will affect children by forcing coastal settlements to adopt expensive adaptive urban planning systems and infrastructure such as seawalls. Sea level rise will also increase the likelihood of large-scale migration and extremely costly relocation of urban centers.

Damage to Ecosystems

Damage to ecosystems is itself a result of climate change and in turn poses threats to children. Climate change is expected to reduce or fundamentally alter major ecosystem services provided by the planet, such as regeneration of soil, pollination of crops, and regulation of erosion. Many of those effects will have the potential to harm children's wellbeing indirectly—for example, by working with other factors to reduce agricultural yields or by increasing the cost of access to clean water. In less-developed countries, where more people depend on ecosystem services, the impacts promise to be more devastating than in wealthy countries.

Biodiversity loss caused by climate change will present further indirect threats to children's wellbeing. Biodiversity makes ecosystems resilient, and the stress that rapid climate change places on animal and plant species will further reduce ecosystem services such as pollination and pest control. More broadly, loss of biodiversity poses a serious threat to cultural heritage for children in many countries. Many threatened species with high aesthetic, cultural, patriotic, or religious value, such as polar bears or coral reefs, will face increased risk of extinction, potentially depriving future generations.[16]

One source of ecosystem damage that deserves special mention is the gradual acidification of the world's oceans, which has already begun under climate change. The oceans naturally absorb carbon dioxide from the atmosphere as part of the global carbon cycle. Carbon dioxide forms a mild acid, called carbonic acid, when dissolved in water, and adding anthropogenic carbon dioxide to Earth's climate has slowly begun to acidify the oceans. Acidification poses a major threat to the many invertebrates, including coral, that harvest calcium dissolved in seawater to form their shells. If it isn't slowed and eventually stabilized or reversed, the gradual increase in acidity would reduce calcium concentrations sufficiently to threaten populations of many ocean invertebrates,

ranging from human food sources like lobsters and clams all the way down the food chain to the zooplankton that form the foundation of the ocean ecosystem. Coral reefs, which are home to much of the oceans' biodiversity and a critical habitat for commercially fished species, are at risk from both acidification and warming, as well as from several nonclimate threats. Unless we reduce emissions, more than half of fish species are expected to be harmed by ocean acidification alone during this century.

Climate-driven changes in Earth's ecosystems are also expected to influence key aspects of the complex disease interaction between humans and the natural environment. Disease vectors such as the *Anopheles* mosquito are expected to move to new areas in response to changing rains and temperatures, which would expose new populations to diseases ranging from malaria to dengue to chikungunya. Changes in the distribution and migration behaviors of birds and other animals are potentially more worrisome because these animals serve as frequent sources of diseases passed on to humans. Pandemic influenzas, for example, are believed to occur when different influenza viruses recombine in the same host; some evidence suggests that flu pandemics may be sparked partly by climate-driven shifts in migratory bird patterns.

Pollution

Air pollutants such as carbon monoxide and ozone have such harmful effects that the World Health Organization has named air pollution as the single greatest environmental health risk, and children are more vulnerable than adults. The major sources of greenhouse gas emissions typically also emit common air pollutants known to damage health; moreover, temperature and precipitation affect whether and how those emissions become smog. Economist Matthew Neidell and research analyst Allison Larr, in their article in this issue, review the pollution impacts of climate change.[17]

The Policy Response

Scientists and policy makers broadly agree that without large-scale international cooperation, economic development and technological progress on their own will not slow emissions enough to save us from large changes in the global climate, which creates a clear need for active international climate policies. Unfortunately, for many reasons, we haven't yet seen an adequate global policy response. The uneven global impacts of climate change and the unequal emission histories of developed versus developing nations produce political divides that have made it hard to find common ground on issues ranging from who should begin reducing emissions first to how much rich countries should pay poor countries not to increase deforestation (a secondary source of carbon dioxide emissions).

The long delay between emissions and their eventual impact on the climate means that effective climate policy must simultaneously satisfy a wide variety of global stakeholders today while maintaining a point of view sufficiently farsighted to incur nontrivial costs that will not show benefits for decades. Uncertainty and scientific complexity make the problem difficult for policy makers to deal with and the public to understand. Attempts to reach binding agreements, most notably the 1997 Kyoto Protocol, have had mixed results at best. Recent moves by the leaders of the United States, China, and certain other main greenhouse-gas-emitting nations indicate that those leaders have begun to see the matter as more pressing, but

some nations with growing emissions, such as India, remain hesitant. The international agreement at the December 2015 Paris Climate Conference provides at least some promise that key emitter nations will take meaningful steps over the next five to ten years.

At this writing, there is relatively little indication that world leaders are considering world carbon emission trajectory changes of the size needed to achieve a two-degree target; economist Joseph Aldy, in his article in this issue, reviews the political aspects of climate change. We have nonetheless seen substantial progress in the broader field of climate policy. Policy makers and researchers generally divide the social response to climate change into two complementary halves: mitigation and adaptation. Mitigation policies seek to insulate society from climate change by preventing it via emission reductions—for example, by replacing fossil fuels with renewable energy or by reversing deforestation. Adaptation policies seek to protect society from climate changes that have already occurred or will occur; such policies can consist of anything from improving disaster response to making agricultural systems more drought resistant.

Most experts agree that limiting warming to no more than 2°C (3.6°F)—governments' chosen benchmark of danger—is technologically feasible and would likely serve to avoid many types of disruptive changes. That agreement implies that there's a limit on how much additional carbon can be emitted—that is, a carbon budget for the planet—before the 2°C target is exceeded. If humans stay within the carbon budget, adaptation will be feasible, although potentially costly. If the carbon budget is exceeded and if climate changes become

The Future
of Children

P R I N C E T O N - B R O O K I N G S

The Future of Children
Princeton University
267 Wallace Hall
Princeton, NJ 08544

ADDRESS SERVICE REQUESTED

Non-Profit
Organization
U.S. Postage
PAID
HANOVER, PA
PERMIT NO. 4

*********************AUTO**5-DIGIT 20036
PHIL SHARP
RESOURCES FOR THE FUTURE
1616 P ST NW STE LL1
WASHINGTON DC 20036-1400
18 7

sufficiently severe, policies could expand to include geoengineering projects intended either to reduce the carbon dioxide in the atmosphere or to reduce the average temperature. Such efforts could range from seeding the atmosphere with sulfate particles to increase albedo and thus cool the planet, to injecting billions of tons of carbon dioxide into old oil and gas deposits and other geologic formations—a process called *carbon capture and sequestration*. Albedo modification is widely regarded as a concept rather than an established technology, and it would be risky for several reasons, including the potential for unforeseen interactions with Earth's complex climate system. Many experts see albedo modification only as a last resort.[18]

Climate Change and Future Generations

It's easy to feel overwhelmed by the scope and scale of climate change as a problem. The uncertainty that stems from our incomplete knowledge about climate and our inability to forecast future human behavior suggests a practically unknowable future, in which potentially huge losses caused by climate change compete with technological advances, economic growth, and social and cultural shifts to determine children's welfare for the rest of the century. That said, history has demonstrated time and again that humans can tackle uncertain threats in times of need. The insurance industry exists to help us manage risks, and businesses in many industries perform risk analyses and adopt policies to reduce risks. On a larger scale, international frameworks are in place to manage global safety risks. International agreements adopted to reduce the risk of nuclear war constitute one such example; the Montreal Protocol prohibiting the manufacture of ozone-layer-destroying

chemicals is another. Climate change has much in common with those uncertain but very real global threats. We must understand that scientific uncertainty about the specifics of a complex problem can go hand in hand with broad agreement about the overall riskiness of an outcome.

At the heart of the climate change problem lies a tension that forces us to directly confront the value we put on future children's wellbeing. The long lag between the emission of a greenhouse gas and its eventual warming effect means that costly decisions to reduce emissions today will bring benefits largely through reduced harm to future generations born many years hence. There is much debate over the best way to approach decisions when costs and benefits are distributed over time, and many deep philosophical and ethical issues surrounding how we justify those decisions are not easily settled. In their article in this issue, economists William Pizer, Ben Groom, and Simon Dietz review discounting and intergenerational decision making.

In the remainder of this issue, leading experts on the social effects of climate change examine issues relevant to climate change's impacts on children. In each case, readers can find ample cause for concern, as well as ample reason for hope that children's lives will continue to improve throughout the current century as they did during the previous one. Taken together, these reports make it clear that ensuring that children's futures are adequately protected from the hazards of climate change will require unprecedented effort, innovation, and coordination, suggesting that few of our decisions about any other issues will come close to having as strong an influence on children's lives.

ENDNOTES

1. Intergovernmental Panel on Climate Change (IPCC), *Climate Change 2014: Impacts, Adaptation, and Vulnerability* (Cambridge: Cambridge University Press, 2014).

2. Nicholas Stern, *The Economics of Climate Change: The Stern Review* (Cambridge: Cambridge University Press, 2007); Trevor Houser et al., *Economic Risks of Climate Change: An American Prospectus* (New York: Columbia University Press, 2015).

3. IPCC, *Climate Change* 2014.

4. Melissa Dell, Benjamin F. Jones, and Benjamin A. Olken, "What Do We Learn from the Weather? The New Climate-Economy Literature," *Journal of Economic Literature* 52(2014): 740–98, doi: 10.1257/jel.52.3.740; IPCC, *Climate Change 2014*.

5. Jaelyn J. Eberle and David R. Greenwood, "Life at the Top of the Greenhouse Eocene World—A Review of the Eocene Flora and Vertebrate Fauna from Canada's High Arctic," *Geological Society of America Bulletin* 124 (2012): 3–23, doi: 10.1130/b30571.1.

6. Stefan A. Talke, Philip Orton, and David A. Jay, "Increasing Storm Tides in New York Harbor, 1844–2013," *Geophysical Research Letters* 41 (2014): 3149–55, doi: 10.1002/2014gl059574.

7. Michael Oppenheimer, "Climate Change Impacts: Accounting for the Human Response," *Climatic Change* 117 (2013): 439–49, doi: 10.1007/s10584-012-0571-9.

8. Rema Hanna and Paulina Oliva, "Implications of Climate Change for Children in Developing Countries," *Future of Children* 26, no. 1 (2016): 113–130.

9. Janet Currie and Douglas Almond, "Human Capital Development before Age Five," in *Handbook of Labor Economics*, vol. 4B, ed. David Card and Orley Ashenfelter (Amsterdam: North Holland, 2011), 1315–1486, doi: 10.1016/s0169-7218(11)02413-0.

10. Sharon Maccini and Dean Yang, "Under the Weather: Health, Schooling, and Economic Consequences of Early-Life Rainfall," *American Economic Review* 99 (2009): 1006–26, doi: 10.1257/aer.99.3.1006.

11. Houser et al., *Economic Risks*.

12. Joshua Graff Zivin, "Temperature Extremes, Health, and Human Capital," *Future of Children* 26, no. 1 (2016): 31–50.

13. Wolfram Schlenker and Michael J. Roberts, "Nonlinear Temperature Effects Indicate Severe Damages to U.S. Crop Yields under Climate Change," *Proceedings of the National Academy of Sciences* 106 (2009): 15594–8, doi: 10.1073/pnas.0906865106.

14. Richard Akresh, "Conflict and Climate Change," *Future of Children* 26, no. 1 (2016): 51–70.

15. Talke, Orton, and Jay, "Increasing Storm Tides"; Houser et al., *Economic Risks*.

16. Ove Hoegh-Guldberg and John F. Bruno, "The Impact of Climate Change on the World's Marine Ecosystems," *Science* 328 (2010): 1523–8, doi: 10.1126/science.1189930.

17. Allison Larr and Matthew Neidell, "Pollution and Climate Change," *Future of Children* 26, no. 1 (2016): 91–111.

18. National Research Council, *Climate Intervention: Reflecting Sunlight to Cool Earth* (Washington, DC: National Academies Press, 2015).

Temperature Extremes, Health, and Human Capital

Joshua Graff Zivin and Jeffrey Shrader

Summary

The extreme temperatures expected under climate change may be especially harmful to children. Children are more vulnerable to heat partly because of their physiological features, but, perhaps more important, because they behave and respond differently than adults do. Children are less likely to manage their own heat risk and may have fewer ways to avoid heat; for example, because they don't plan their own schedules, they typically can't avoid activity during hot portions of the day. And very young children may not be able to tell adults that they're feeling heat's effects.

Joshua Graff Zivin and Jeffrey Shrader zero in on how rising temperatures from global warming can be expected to affect children. They review evidence that high temperatures would mean more deaths, especially among fetuses and young children (as well as the elderly). When combined with other conditions—such as high humidity, diseases, or pollution—heat can be even deadlier. Even when it doesn't kill, high heat directly causes heat-related illnesses such as heat exhaustion; worsens other conditions, such as asthma, by increasing smog and ozone pollution; and harms fetuses in the womb, often with long-term consequences. High temperatures can also make learning more difficult, affecting children's adult job prospects.

What can we do to protect children from a hotter climate? Graff Zivin and Shrader discuss a range of policies that could help. Such policies include requiring air conditioning in schools; heat wave warning systems coupled with public infrastructure that helps people stay indoors and stay cool; and readjusting schedules so that, for example, children are mostly indoors during the hottest time of day or the hottest season of the year.

www.futureofchildren.org

Joshua Graff Zivin is a professor of economics at the University of California, San Diego. Jeffrey Shrader is a PhD candidate in economics at the University of California, San Diego.

Alan Barreca of Tulane University reviewed and critiqued a draft of this article

By burning fossil fuels and thereby releasing carbon dioxide and other gases, we are reshaping the global climate.[1] The changes we expect globally will both increase average temperatures and shift the climate toward greater and more frequent extreme temperatures. Already, average Americans experience more hot days per year than they did 60 years ago, and the number is expected to rise dramatically in the coming decades (see figure 1).

Rising temperatures and the increasing frequency of extremely high temperatures are likely to cause more death and illness and to diminish children's ability to learn and adults' ability to perform mental tasks.[2] Children, including fetuses in the womb, will likely suffer especially severe effects from climate change because they are more sensitive to temperature and rely on others to adapt. For a variety of reasons, the negative effects of more heat will outweigh the benefits of reduced exposure to cold, and heat is thus the focus of this article.

In this article, we assess a warming climate's likely effects on child wellbeing, limiting our attention to temperature's direct effects

Figure 1. Projected number of summer days above 90°F in four US cities

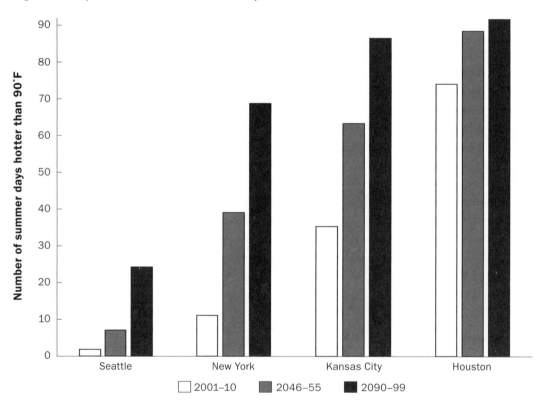

Note: Each projection is the ensemble average of business-as-usual scenario forecasts for the continental United States.

Sources: Katherine Hayhoe et al., "Development and Dissemination of a High-Resolution National Climate Change Dataset," *Final Report for United States Geological Survey,* USGS G10AC00248 (2013); Anne M. K. Stoner et al., "An Asynchronous Regional Regression Model for Statistical Downscaling of Daily Climate Variables," *International Journal of Climatology* 33 (2013): 2473–94; Melinda S. Dalton and Sonya A. Jones, comps., *Southeast Regional Assessment Project for the National Climate Change and Wildlife Science Center, U.S. Geological Survey* (Reston, VA: U.S. Geological Survey, 2010).

on health. Direct effects include physical or mental impairment from heat stress on the body. Examples include death caused by heat stroke, cardiovascular disease, respiratory impairment, or malformed fetal brains, but we also consider more general bodily stress caused by heat. We largely ignore indirect health effects that could arise from a hotter climate due to food insecurity, natural disasters, or increased global conflict; those matters are covered by other authors in this issue.[4] When possible, we rely on studies of the temperature–health relationship that have focused explicitly on children. But such studies leave substantial gaps in the evidence, so we also make use of studies about the general population to help complete the picture. To ensure that our conclusions are relevant for policy, we concentrate on studies that focus on the causal relationships between temperature and human wellbeing (see box 1).

We've organized our discussion around three broad impacts on health: death, illness, and human capital. Human capital involves the skills, knowledge, and abilities that an individual can use to create economic value. Most of heat's effects on wellbeing are acute; heat-related deaths, for example, happen within hours of a heat wave. Heat's effects aren't limited to acute events, however. Research increasingly shows that exposure to warmer days in the womb or during infancy can cause long-lasting, often lifelong harm.[5]

We have compelling evidence that short-lived temperature shocks can damage a child's health, but the key policy issue regarding the health effects of climate change is how a permanent shift in the overall distribution of weather would play out. A sustained shift toward more extreme temperatures could have even more profound impacts than current estimates indicate. On the other hand, if the effects of climate change move slowly, we have a better chance to limit their impact through adaptation. Some recent evidence suggests that we may indeed be able to adapt, calling into question the generalized conclusions often drawn from studies that rely only on short-term variations in weather to predict the long-term effects of heat. Laboratory studies have particular

---

What is Causal Analysis?

Imagine that you're a parent trying to decide whether to enroll your child in a charter school, or that you're a doctor deciding whether to prescribe a certain medicine for a patient, or that you're a senator deciding whether to lower the tax rate. In each case, you want an answer to the question: Would my action actually cause an improvement in outcomes? If my child goes to a charter school, would she have a better chance of attending a good college? Would the medicine make my patient healthier? Would lowering taxes make the economy grow faster? In each case, it's not enough just to know that there's an association or a correlation between an action being considering and the outcome of the action. Two events may be likely to occur at the same time or place, but if we don't know how one influences the other, then the fact that they're associated doesn't tell us whether our action would do some good.

Causal analysis sheds light on questions like those by determining when an action is simply *associated* with an outcome versus when the action indeed *causes* the outcome. A simple example serves to illustrate the difference between correlation and causation: Death often occurs after a hospital stay. Therefore, a hospital stay is correlated or associated with dying. But, in general, hospital stays don't cause death. Rather, some very sick people seek care at hospitals and then die. It's the fact that sick people seek care at hospitals that creates the relationship, and a policy maker would be making a grave misjudgment by closing all hospitals in an effort to reduce the number of citizen deaths. Numerous statistical and scientific techniques have been developed to distinguish causality from correlation, and applying and refining those techniques is a major component of empirical research in the social sciences.

limitations, because they don't consider how adaptive actions could limit negative effects over the long run.

It's clear that public policy can and must help minimize the damage to children's health caused by climate change. The immediate and compounding impacts of harm to children should carry great weight when it comes to encouraging action to cut greenhouse gas emissions. Public information campaigns and alert systems will also become increasingly important in helping us minimize exposure and take action to avoid exposure in the first place. Investing more in emergency response can also help us minimize the damage when we do experience extreme temperatures. Children are vulnerable, and they have little choice about how and where they spend their time, so policies expressly designed to protect them and the adults who care for them may be especially important.

Extreme Temperatures Kill

Although humans are very well adapted to high temperatures, heat can and does kill. It does so through direct effects such as heat stroke, cardiovascular failure, or other physical disease and through indirect effects such as starvation after crop loss or the spread of infectious disease.[6] Research indicates that children are especially vulnerable to heat-related death—partly because of their physiological features, but, perhaps more important, because they behave and respond differently than adults do.

How Heat Kills

Generally, heat directly causes death through cardiovascular failure—often made worse by respiratory disease—or by overheating the body and causing a heat stroke. Studies that examine specific causes of death often focus on cardiovascular impairment, which is generally more relevant for the elderly than it is for children.[7] Among infants, evidence from heat waves suggests that in addition to cardiovascular illness, blood disorders and failures of the digestive system are leading causes of death.[8] As temperatures rise in developing countries, so does the prevalence of gastrointestinal illnesses.[9] Heat-related deaths among children are also increased by many of the indirect impacts of rising temperatures, including disease transmission by insects like mosquitoes.

One of the main ways heat kills is by limiting the body's ability to regulate its own temperature. When body temperature rises as a result of ambient heat, physical exertion, or fever, more blood flows to the skin and we sweat to dissipate body heat. If the ambient temperature is too high, those mechanisms can't cool the body efficiently and may even work to warm the body further. Adverse weather conditions like high humidity magnify that effect by reducing cardiovascular efficiency.[10]

Children are a special case. Infants' and children's vulnerability to cold temperatures is well established, and humans have evolved physical features to combat that susceptibility, including extra fatty tissue in infancy and reduced sweating during childhood. Children may also be physiologically more vulnerable to high temperature because they regulate their body temperature less efficiently, although the evidence here is less conclusive.[11]

At least one mechanism by which heat kills is unique to the very young. In a series of studies starting in the early 1990s, high heat has been linked to sudden infant death syndrome (SIDS).[12] Because the infant body is relatively more vulnerable to heat loss, it compensates with higher fat and reduced sweating. An infant who is wrapped or covered heavily might be unable to shed excess heat, producing brain trauma. Brain trauma can also occur when infants sleep in the same bed as a warm adult, or when they suffer from fever, or when they're exposed to high ambient air temperature.

Behavior, too, may contribute to the disproportionate number of heat-related deaths among children. Children are less likely to manage their own heat risk and may have fewer ways to avoid heat than adults do. For instance, children playing sports often don't hydrate sufficiently.[13] Also, because children don't usually choose their daily schedule, they typically can't avoid activity during hot portions of the day. We'll return to that issue in more detail when we discuss adaptation.

Estimating the Relationship between Heat and Death

Much of the research on heat's direct health impacts has focused on death, partly because death is an important topic and partly because it's easy to measure. The abundant research documenting the relationship between temperature and death provides good estimates of the overall effect of the relationship and explores in detail the mechanisms by which heat kills. Moreover, in contrast to studies of most other temperature effects on health, many studies of heat deaths explicitly examine impacts on children, which lets us clearly compare them with adults.

Studies that classify their results by age group tend to find that death rates are highest among the elderly and second highest among children. A recent review of public health studies concluded that children younger than 15 years have a higher risk of dying from heat than adults do; infants and children younger than five years are particularly at risk.[14] The review estimates that in developed countries, adults experience a 2 to 3 percent increase in mortality with every 1°C (1.8°F) rise in temperature above a threshold of 27°C (80.6°F) to 29°C (84.2°F). For children, the mortality rate is estimated to be 50 to 100 percent higher than for adults.[15]

Economists Olivier Deschênes (one of the editors of this issue) and Michael Greenstone show that death rates increase dramatically at temperatures above 32°C (89.6°F): a day above 32°C sees triple the death rate of a day at 26°C (78.8°F) to 32°C. As in the review of public health studies, they found that infants suffer the second-highest heat mortality rate among all age groups, after the elderly. Deschênes and Greenstone predict that, given the current understanding of how climate change will unfold, infants constitute the age group likely to experience the greatest increase in mortality rates.[16]

Very few studies examine how heat interacts with other climatic and atmospheric conditions, and therefore we know little about those potentially important relationships. One exception is Tulane University economist Alan Barreca's work on the interaction of heat with humidity.[17] Barreca shows that high humidity independently leads to more deaths and that humidity interacts with heat, making high heat even deadlier. Barreca also shows that humidity levels are associated with increases in infant deaths: three additional days of high humidity increase the average monthly infant mortality rate by 1.1 percent.

High heat can also harm health when it interacts with air pollution. Such interaction isn't generally that important, but the formation of ozone pollution depends on high temperatures, and high ozone levels have been proposed as one explanation for the particularly deadly European heat wave of 2003.[18] Ozone is also a significant predictor of childhood asthma.[19]

In contrast to records of the deaths of infants and children, fetal mortality isn't well recorded, so the extent of heat-related deaths in the womb is not clear. The fact that exposing unborn children to extreme temperatures has measurable impacts on their health after birth, which we discuss in the next section, lends credence to the idea that heat can also kill the unborn.

Heat and Death in Developing Countries

Outside the United States and Europe, estimates of deaths caused by heat are sparse. In a review of 36 epidemiological studies, only eight contained any data from countries outside the Organisation for Economic Co-operation and Development, and of those eight studies, most were from a single country: Brazil.[20] Developing-country studies can shed light on how income and infrastructure help mitigate damage from heat. A recent study of weather-related infant mortality in a group of African countries showed that in poorer countries, temperature can kill through many channels. In particular, malaria infection as a result of increased mosquito activity was one of the main sources of temperature-based infant deaths.[21]

A study of temperature-related deaths in India found that heat's average effect on mortality there is more than 10 times greater than in the United States, largely because crop failure arising from excessive heat leads to losses of real income. Urban residents in India experience temperature-related mortality rates similar to rates among residents of the United States, suggesting, first, that deaths caused directly by heat may be relatively few in number compared with those caused by heat's effects on productivity and, second, that the possibilities for adaptation are extensive across the globe.[22]

In developed countries, infant and child mortality from heat is higher among low-income groups, suggesting that wealthier households can make investments that offset at least some of the damage from high heat.[23] Death rates associated with high temperatures are also higher in the northern United States than in the southern United States—likely because of the adoption of air conditioning in areas that routinely experience high heat.[24] This gap has narrowed, however, because over time, heat-related mortality rates have fallen faster in the northern states relative to those in the South.[25] We return to that issue later, when we discuss adaptation and avoidance.

In summary, high temperatures are strongly associated with increases in death rates among all age groups, and the very young are particularly at risk. Heat kills in many ways, varying with location, level of development, and degree of acclimatization. Without investment in infrastructure to protect people from heat, we can expect child mortality associated with high temperatures to rise as the globe warms. Also, because the majority of developing countries already have warmer climates than the United States and Europe do, we should expect to see fewer gains from reduced low temperatures in those countries, making the net effect of climate change there even more severe. To learn more about heat's effects on children in developing countries, see the article by Rema Hanna and Paulina Oliva elsewhere in this issue.

Illness

Even when it doesn't kill, high temperature can cause illnesses or worsen existing medical conditions to the point that sufferers must be hospitalized. Compared with studies of heat-related deaths, however, we've seen fewer studies of how temperature affects illness—partly because of data limitations. For example, detailed hospitalization data can be difficult to obtain, and data on physician and pharmacy visits are even scarcer.[26] Moreover, many heat-related illnesses may be socially costly without producing doctor or emergency room visits, because the symptoms are treatable at home—for instance, through rest and hydration. Access to health insurance coverage (in places like the United States, where coverage is not universal) may also limit doctor and pharmacy visits, making it hard to infer how income shapes the relationship.

How Heat Impairs Health

Heat exhaustion and heat stroke are the most serious illnesses caused directly by heat. They generally result from dehydration associated with exposure to or physical activity during periods of high heat. As it regulates heat, the body loses water and salt in the form of sweat. If the water and salt don't get replaced over time, the body can overheat, leading to the dizziness, muscle cramps, and fever that characterize heat exhaustion. At the extreme, heat exhaustion becomes heat stroke, which, even when it doesn't kill, generally leads to permanent neurological damage.[27]

High heat also strains the heart and can make breathing difficult. Combined with high humidity and behaviors like exercise or wearing inappropriately heavy clothing, high temperatures can cause heart attack, stroke, and respiratory failure.[28] Medical conditions that impede the circulatory or respiratory system—such as asthma, heart disease, or a previous stroke—increase the likelihood of those acute episodes.[29]

Pregnant women and their fetuses are especially vulnerable to high temperatures for several reasons, including higher core temperature because of the pregnant woman's increased fat deposition, her diminished capacity to sweat, and the additional thermal stress associated with fetal maintenance.[30] Warmer temperatures increase both the proportion of preterm births and the incidence of low-birth-weight babies.[31] Shocks to the fetus often have lifelong consequences.[32] And the negative relationship between fetal health and temperature may mean that early life exposure to extreme temperatures can have long-lasting effects, discussed next.

Linking Heat and Illness

The vast majority of evidence on heat and ill health focuses on adults. For example, for each 1°C above 29°C (84.2°F), adult hospitalizations for respiratory disease rise by about 3 percent. Cardiovascular illness rates also rise in many cases, with effects concentrated among older people.[33] Recent research from Germany showed that hospital admissions rise by up to 20 percent on hot days, although, again, the effects occur predominantly among people older than 60 years.[34]

The evidence on how heat affects children's health is more nuanced. A study from Spain found that hospital admissions in general rose dramatically above 34°C–36°C

(93.2°F–96.8°F) and that children younger than nine years were slightly more likely to be admitted than were adults aged 18 to 44 years. Moreover, admissions of children appeared to be higher during periods when high heat was combined with elevated levels of particulate matter, although that finding is not universal.[35] In contrast, a recent study in New York about how hot weather affects hospital admissions due to cardiovascular and respiratory diseases found no significant link between high temperatures and either cardiovascular or respiratory diseases for people from birth to 19 years old. In fact, in the New York study, the estimated magnitude of temperature effects for that age group was the lowest among all groups.[36] But the wide age range in the study could be masking larger effects on the very young by averaging them in with older children and adolescents.

In contrast to heat's effect on fetal mortality, its health effects on fetuses have been better studied. A study that summarized several investigations into how temperature affects mammalian fetuses found that a wide range of less than fatal outcomes could occur. The study's authors cautioned that even though healthy thermal ranges vary among other mammalian species and are not always reliable models for human biology, we can learn some general lessons from them. For example, elevating fetal temperature by 2°C–2.5°C for as little as one hour can cause moderate to severe damage to the nervous system and impede neural development. Physical exertion combined with elevated ambient temperature could trigger potentially dangerous internal temperature spikes, although a stationary, healthy woman would likely be able to avoid them.[37]

Research on humans has focused on preterm births and birth weight. A recent study concluded that the adverse effects of high temperature were consistently stronger for birth weight than for early birth.[38] Another study compared infants' birth weights with the temperatures their mothers were exposed to during each trimester of pregnancy. It found that in all trimesters, high temperatures were associated with reduced birth weight but that the effect was slightly larger during the third trimester.[39] Birth weight is a proxy measure of fetal health that can be linked to illness in childhood and later in life.[40]

The evidence for heat effects on children's ill health is less conclusive than in the case of childhood mortality, but the impacts on fetal health appear to be unambiguously negative. Children appear to be less susceptible than adults or the elderly to some of the more dramatic heat-induced illnesses, perhaps because they tend not to suffer from the combinations of conditions that can lead to adult hospitalizations. On the other hand, children may be more at risk for heat exhaustion and related illnesses because they are less able to monitor and respond to signs of their own dehydration. But because parents or caregivers can treat children's dehydration fairly easily, we may be less likely to see those effects in the data. Studies of heat-related illness thus likely understate the true rate among children.

Heat and Human Capital

In addition to causing illness and death, extreme temperatures may also make it harder to learn and thus may limit children's educational attainment and economic prospects in the long run. Though we have little direct evidence of such a relationship, studies of the fetal period establish the linkage indirectly—through impacts on birth outcomes that prove important for education and work later in life.

How Heat Hinders Human Capital Formation

Excess heat in the womb can produce physical defects, delay brain development, and lead to a host of central nervous system problems that make it harder to accumulate human capital in the long run.[41] As we've seen, low birth weight is a common proxy measure for fetal setbacks and has been shown to significantly affect education and work outcomes later in life. Reduced fetal nutrition may be one important mechanism behind that relationship.[42]

In addition to how temperature affects birth weight and central nervous system functioning, it may also play an important role in gene expression. We now know that environmental stress can affect how genetic code gets translated into observable human traits and that gestation is a particularly susceptible period for such effects.[43] Exposure to high temperatures has been implicated as a source of environmental stress in a wide range of plants and animals.[44] Vertebrates' brains and other central nervous system structures are particularly sensitive to such sources of environmental stress, suggesting that cognitive development may be vulnerable to such exposures.[45]

Once outside the womb, the developing brain is still sensitive to heat on chemical and electrical levels.[46] Rapid brain development, which can be disrupted by extreme heat, continues through early childhood.[47] In more mature children, ambient temperature, as well as the heat generated by the brain itself, can impede mental processes, thereby creating the potential for heat to hinder learning. Although it represents

only 2 percent of the mass of a typical body, the brain generates 20 percent of the body's heat.[48] The body is generally able to efficiently discard heat created by the brain, but when the weather is warm and humid or when we engage in heavy physical activity, our bodies can struggle to regulate temperature, leading to spikes in brain temperature of up to 2.5°C.[49]

Evidence on the Heat–Human Capital Relationship

Experimental evidence supports the notion that heat can directly impair cognitive function. For example, soldiers exposed to hot environments perform worse on complex cognitive tasks, are more prone to error, and are less able to carry out physical tasks.[50] Other studies show that heat exposure reduces performance on multitracked tasks that mimic real-world school and office duties, impairs working memory, and lowers test scores.[51] A review of a number of studies of office workers' productivity estimated that performance declines rapidly when temperatures go above or below 21°C–22°C (69.8°C–71.6°F). For instance, at 27°C (80.6°F), office workers' performance declines by 5 percent relative to their performance at 21°C.[52]

Though heat appears important to human capital formation and productivity, its real-world effects on those areas have been poorly documented, likely because it's hard to observe the relevant outcomes. But the gains from such studies would be immense. The effects are likely to be substantially important, and low-level temperature impacts are, by definition, much more widespread than the extreme temperatures that lead to the majority of hospitalizations and deaths. Thus, from the standpoint of total welfare, human capital effects might be more important than the relatively well-understood, direct temperature effects we discussed in previous sections.

Studies of pollution's impacts have analyzed school attendance, and we could do the same for temperature.[53] Researchers have documented a link between school attendance and indoor air pollution, outdoor air pollution, and ventilation rates.[54] We aren't aware of any studies by economists that show a similar link between temperature and school attendance, although the data needed to do so are relatively available. We know that high temperatures reduce the adult labor supply, so it's certainly plausible that heat also increases school absenteeism.[55]

Student test scores offer a more direct way to assess the human capital effects of temperature. Economists Joshua Graff Zivin (one of the authors of this article), Solomon Hsiang, and Matthew Neidell have shown that a temperature above 26°C (78.8°F) on the day of a math test can diminish students' performance.[56]

Heat and Human Capital in the Long Run

The studies and hypotheses we've discussed focus largely on acute responses to temperature. Temporarily impaired brain function that leads to absenteeism or reductions in test scores, however, doesn't necessarily affect either cognition or human capital attainment in the long term. Do the acute effects we've identified translate into poorer outcomes in school or work later in life? When it comes to estimating the impact of climate change, the question of long-term effects becomes even more important. Simple aggregation of short-lived, acute-impact estimates might

overstate the true damage associated with long-run temperature changes. On the other hand, multiple acute responses could have substantial long-term impacts by hampering children's acquisition of skills, an issue we discuss later in the context of adaptation.[57]

The study that found a link between temperature and test scores also offers evidence of climate's long-term effects on human capital formation. In particular, the authors found that longer-term weather averages are not strongly associated with student performance. The authors suggest that compensatory adaptive behaviors—particularly, additional investments in learning that are made after heat events—might be mitigating the short-term effects.[58] But we have evidence that temperature can have long-term effects on national wealth. We don't know whether that result is driven by changes in human capital or by something else, but the big differences in aggregate output that are associated with differences in climate suggest that high heat may cause at least some loss of human capital or some decline in productivity.[59]

Short-run shocks can also be linked to long-run outcomes through fetal exposures that reduce birth weight. For example, low-birth-weight children in Britain were significantly less likely to pass standardized tests as teenagers.[60] A sample of Californians found similar effects on school attainment and adult poverty.[61] Studies of twins, which let researchers control for genetic endowments and other family characteristics, have also consistently found that low birth weight diminishes educational attainment, IQ, and even earnings.[62]

Put simply, it seems that temperature extremes can impair cognitive functioning in children. The evidence for long-run effects from those impairments is inconclusive, however. One study that directly examined the relationship found no effect, but another that focused on wages—an implicit measure of cognitive attainment—found that extreme heat has a negative effect.[63] The long-run effect of temperature exposure in the womb has not been well studied, but evidence from studies of pollution and other fetal health shocks suggest that in utero heat exposure might have long-run impacts from reductions in fetal nutrition, genetic damage, or other causes.[64] Such impacts may represent climate change's greatest threat to children's long-term prosperity and wellbeing.

Adaptation

How will the magnitude of the effects we've talked about change in the future? As figure 1 shows, under business-as-usual emissions scenarios, current climate models predict that the average number of summer days above 90°F (32°C) will increase dramatically. Across the United States, the average person currently experiences 1.4 such days per year, but by the end of this century, he or she is expected to experience more than 40.[65] If heat's short-run effects can be generalized to a setting wherein extreme heat is routine and commonplace, then simply extrapolating from those effects, the change would dramatically increase the number of deaths, the number of hospitalizations, and the loss of productivity associated with high heat. We believe, however, that such simple extrapolation doesn't accurately predict the future. On one hand, adaptation and technological development could lessen many of those impacts. On the other, if the impacts of heat are nonlinear—such that damage is much more severe at greater temperature extremes—then the impacts

may be even worse than current estimates suggest.

Adaptation to climate change will likely mitigate some of the damage from high heat. The extent to which adaptation can offset harm from anticipated temperature extremes under climate change—and at what cost—is a crucial issue. Moreover, the difference in adaptation to the total level of heat versus relative change in heat becomes important. Figure 1 shows that cities in the southern United States will experience many more hot days than will cities in the north, but those cities already experience some hot days now. Will people who live in places where many hot days already occur suffer more? Or will the effects be worse in places where hot days are expected to be less frequent but where extreme heat is currently not a problem?

One technological development—air conditioning—has already greatly reduced temperature-related deaths in the United States, especially among children and older people.[66] Indeed, air conditioning may also help explain differences in the relationship between heat and death in developing countries and developed countries.

Unfortunately, air conditioning makes climate change worse. First, air conditioning is a major consumer of energy in developed countries, which will likely be the case around the world in coming decades. Given our current reliance on fossil fuels to produce energy, air conditioning contributes to greenhouse gas emissions and therefore to warming the planet.[67] Air conditioning also directly raises urban air temperatures. A high level of air conditioner use in cities is associated with warming of up to 0.5°C during the day and 1.5°C at night.[68] Because of the potentially greater health impacts of nighttime temperature, that fact is particularly worrisome. It may also exacerbate inequality in urban areas because the poorest people can't shield themselves from the increased heat generated by their wealthier neighbors.

Choosing where to live is another adaptation strategy that can influence exposure to climate extremes.[69] Most climate-related migration in the past four decades has seen population shifts from colder, northern areas to warmer, southern areas.[70] That migration has resulted in much lower cold-related mortality, but it could exacerbate future damage from a warming climate. The same areas that have experienced increased migration are also those with the fastest-growing populations of children. Whether the same pattern holds for other countries is an open question.

Shifting the timing of activities during the day—a less drastic strategy than migration—can also help reduce exposure to climatic extremes. Many cities worldwide warn citizens to limit outdoor activities during periods of excessive heat. Some countries systematize that avoidance through cultural norms that dictate the timing of the school year and through siestas, which suspend the workday during the hottest part of the day.[71] Those strategies can be quite effective, but they're usually limited in scope and potentially costly because, for instance, keeping children from exposure to high ambient temperature might reduce their physical activity. Perhaps compensating investments in children's health and human capital to limit heat-related impacts after exposure rather than preventing it in the first place may prove to be a more useful adaptation.[72] For such actions to be successful, however, timing is crucial. Small

losses in attainment during early childhood can become compounded over time, making early intervention important.

Evidence for acclimatization points to biological adaptation's limited role in both the short and the long run.[73] Small-scale medical studies of performance of physical tasks have shown that adults can partially acclimatize to even very high heat (above 40°C [104°F]). But studies on how acclimatization affects cognitive performance have been inconclusive.[74]

Adaptation is especially complicated when it comes to children, who generally can't choose their own adaptation strategies. Children don't purchase air conditioners, decide where to live, or even set their own schedules. Instead, children must communicate their temperature-related discomfort to caregivers, who must then take action on children's behalf. Effectively communicating that information is challenging for very young children, but even those able to clearly convey their discomfort may not have their needs met if adult caregivers don't perceive heat or experience temperature-related physical impairment in the same way children do.

The appallingly routine incidents of children being left in hot cars illustrate the problem viscerally. Each year in the United States, about 40 children die from being locked inside a hot vehicle. According to a recent study, in 43 percent of cases the caregivers simply forgot they were transporting children; being aware of the presence of children is obviously a clear prerequisite for thinking through the steps required to manage children's exposure to extremes.[75]

Conclusions

The extreme temperatures expected under climate change will affect human health, and they may have especially harmful impacts on children. But public policy can help. First, we have many tools that encourage reducing greenhouse gas emissions with a view to averting the worst of the warming scenarios. The immediacy of the health impacts we've discussed—in contrast to effects that depend on slow-moving climate changes rather than weather extremes—could energize international climate negotiations. Threats to human capital, which is generally viewed as an engine of economic growth, should offer additional motivation.

Public policy can also do more to encourage adaptation. Government policies could encourage many of the private responses we detailed in the previous section. Currently, national policy doesn't require schools to maintain specific temperatures for students, although the Centers for Disease Control and Prevention has issued nonbinding recommendations.[76] Many states have their own regulations regarding temperature and humidity in schools.[77]

Lack of air conditioning has forced schools to close. For instance, in 2014, heat forced the San Diego school system to close or alter the operating schedules of 120 schools; many schools in the district that lacked air conditioning saw temperatures in excess of 90°F (32.2°C).[78] In Des Moines, Iowa, the public schools have kept records of school closures since 1972; not until 2000 did they begin closing because of excessive heat.[79]

As the planet warms, it will become increasingly beneficial to require universal air conditioning for schools. Such a policy would also let schools stay in session during summer and move breaks to cooler seasons, thereby keeping children indoors in a climate-controlled environment during the most dangerous part of the year. Those benefits may be especially important for children of poorer families, who are less likely to have air conditioning at home.

Many places in the United States have heat wave warning systems. When weather forecasts predict extremely high heat, the systems inform the population about the risks.[80] Such warning systems can be effective in places like the United States, where many people have air conditioners or where public infrastructure lets people avoid the heat. In places like Europe, however, where fewer people have air conditioners, disseminating information might not be sufficient.

When the 2003 heat wave hit Europe, causing up to 40,000 deaths, only Lisbon and Rome had effective early warning systems. Lisbon and Rome still experienced very high numbers of excess deaths during the heat wave (although Lisbon fared relatively better than other cities), underscoring the need to combine information about heat risks with public infrastructure to mitigate the effects of heat.[81] As an example, in some cities, public buildings with air conditioning stay open longer during heat waves to let people take refuge.[82] Incentives to buy cooling systems might also help, but they should encourage investment in energy-efficient technologies that limit additional contributions to climate change.

Sociocultural institutions shape adaptive responses by dictating norms about the timing of workdays and school days. Restructuring schedules to avoid the hottest parts of the day requires a huge amount of social coordination that we may be able to achieve only with government assistance. Even with such policies, though, eliminating exposure to climate extremes seems unlikely. So we'll also need public investment in emergency preparedness and medical infrastructure.

Individuals and policy makers must consider the constraints that children face. In particular, it may be harder for children to mitigate their own heat exposure.[83] Children may also be at greater physiological risk of overheating, which makes it harder for their caregivers to assess when they're in danger of suffering from heat-related illnesses. Medical professionals such as emergency room doctors—who are likely to treat acute heat-related illness in children—need proper pediatric training. Even when the general care recommendations for adults and children don't differ, as they do in the treatment of heat exhaustion, the doctor's actions should be tailored to children. For instance, for heat stroke, the American Heart Association provides a series of child-specific recommendations, including alternative cardiopulmonary resuscitation procedures as well as warnings against common drugs used for treating adults.[84] In addition to caregivers' possible difficulty in recognizing heat's effects on children, the children themselves might have trouble communicating their needs. When combined with children's reduced ability to take personal action, this is a thorny problem in developed countries and a potential disaster in less developed ones with low levels of literacy and poor infrastructure.

Although we've relied on the best evidence available, research on nonlethal impacts from high heat exposure is surprisingly thin. Evidence of how heat's impacts on children are different from its impacts on adults is particularly sparse, and many basic relationships remain poorly understood. To what extent do temperature extremes affect children's health? How much of children's heat-related illness is treated outside the health-care system? What explains heat's potential impacts on school performance and human capital formation more generally? The evidence on adaptation is also incomplete, especially with regard to our options for limiting heat's impacts through avoidance and compensatory behaviors. We must assess the costs of those impacts and of all of the efforts undertaken to minimize them. Together, they compose an important future research agenda.

ENDNOTES

1. Michael Oppenheimer and Jesse K. Anttila-Hughes, "The Science of Climate Change," *Future of Children* 26, no. 1 (2016): 11–30.

2. Joshua S. Graff Zivin, Solomon M. Hsiang, and Matthew J. Neidell, "Temperature and Human Capital in the Short- and Long-Run," Working Paper no. 21157 (National Bureau of Economic Research, Cambridge, MA, 2015); Marshall J. Edwards, Richard D. Saunders, and Kohei Shiota, "Effects of Heat on Embryos and Foetuses," *International Journal of Hyperthermia* 19 (2003): 295–324, doi: 10.1080/0265673021000039628; and Olivier Deschênes and Michael Greenstone, "Climate Change, Mortality, and Adaptation: Evidence from Annual Fluctuations in Weather in the US," *American Economic Journal: Applied Economics* 3 (2011): 152–85, doi: 10.1257/app.3.4.152.

3. For more details on how cold temperatures affect human health and analysis of net effects, see Olivier Deschênes, "Temperature, Human Health, and Adaptation: A Review of the Empirical Literature," *Energy Economics* 46 (2014): 606–19. The relationship between temperature and mortality is much flatter for low temperatures than for high temperatures in Alan Barreca et al., "Adapting to Climate Change: The Remarkable Decline in the US Temperature–Mortality Relationship over the 20th Century," Working Paper no. 18692 (National Bureau of Economic Research, Cambridge, MA, 2013).

4. See Richard Akresh, "Conflict and Climate Change," *Future of Children* 26, no. 1 (2016): 51–71; Carolyn Kousky, "Climate Change and Natural Disasters," *Future of Children* 26, no. 1 (2016): 71–90; and Allison Larr and Matthew Neidell, "Pollution and Climate Change," *Future of Children* 26, no. 1 (2016): 91–111.

5. Adam Isen, Maya Rossin-Slater, and W. Reed Walker, "Every Breath You Take—Every Dollar You'll Make: The Long-Term Consequences of the Clean Air Act of 1970," Working Paper no. 19858 (National Bureau of Economic Research, Cambridge, MA, 2014).

6. David R. Carrier, "The Energetic Paradox of Human Running and Hominid Evolution," *Current Anthropology* (1984): 483–95; Rupa Basu and Jonathan M. Samet, "Relation between Elevated Ambient Temperature and Mortality: A Review of the Epidemiologic Evidence," *Epidemiologic Reviews* 24 (2002): 190–202; Rupa Basu, "High Ambient Temperature and Mortality: A Review of Epidemiologic Studies from 2001 to 2008," *Environmental Health* 8 (2009): 40, doi: 10.1186/1476-069X-8-40; and Robin Burgess et al., "Weather and Death in India" (Massachusetts Institute of Technology, Cambridge, MA, 2011).

7. Basu, "High Ambient Temperature."

8. Xavier Basagaña et al., "Heat Waves and Cause-Specific Mortality at All Ages," *Epidemiology* 22 (2011): 765–72, doi: 10.1097/EDE.0b013e31823031c5.

9. William Checkley et al., "Effects of *El Niño* and Ambient Temperature on Hospital Admissions for Diarrhoeal Diseases in Peruvian Children," *The Lancet* 355 (2000): 442–50, doi: 10.1016/S0140-6736(00)82010-3.

10. Gavin C. Donaldson, William R. Keatinge, and Richard D. Saunders, "Cardiovascular Responses to Heat Stress and Their Adverse Consequences in Healthy and Vulnerable Human Populations," *International Journal of Hyperthermia* 19 (2003): 225–35, doi: 10.1080/0265673021000058357.

11. The view that children are thermoregulatorily impaired relative to adults is presented in, for instance, Jeffrey R. Bytomski and Deborah L. Squire, "Heat Illness in Children," *Current Sports Medicine Reports* 2 (2003): 320–24, and Robin Knobel and Diane Holditch-Davis, "Thermoregulation and Heat Loss Prevention after Birth and during Neonatal Intensive-Care Unit Stabilization of Extremely Low-Birthweight Infants," *Journal of Obstetric, Gynecologic, & Neonatal Nursing* 36 (2007): 280–87, doi: 10.1111/j.1552-6909.2007.00149.x. Recently, that view has been questioned by some researchers: Thomas Rowland, "Thermoregulation during Exercise in the Heat in Children: Old Concepts Revisited," *Journal of Applied Physiology* 105 (2008): 718–24, doi: 10.1152/japplphysiol.01196.2007, and Bareket Falk and Raffy Dotan, "Children's Thermoregulation during Exercise in the Heat—a Revisit," *Applied Physiology, Nutrition, and Metabolism* 33 (2008): 420–27, doi: 10.1139/H07-185.

12. P. J. Fleming, Y. Azaz, and R. Wigfield, "Development of Thermoregulation in Infancy: Possible Implications for SIDS," *Journal of Clinical Pathology* 45 (1992): S17–S19.

13. Michael F. Bergeron, "Reducing Sports Heat Illness Risk," *Pediatrics in Review* 34 (2013): 270–9.

14. Basu, "High Ambient Temperature."

15. Rupa Basu and Bart D. Ostro, "A Multicounty Analysis Identifying the Populations Vulnerable to Mortality Associated with High Ambient Temperature in California," *American Journal of Epidemiology* 168 (2008): 632–37, doi: 10.1093/aje/kwn170; Nelson Gouveia, Shakoor Hajat, and Ben Armstrong, "Socioeconomic Differentials in the Temperature–Mortality Relationship in São Paulo, Brazil," *International Journal of Epidemiology* 32 (2003): 390–97; and Marie S. O'Neill et al., "Impact of Control for Air Pollution and Respiratory Epidemics on the Estimated Associations of Temperature and Daily Mortality," *International Journal of Biometeorology* 50 (2005): 121–29, doi: 10.1007/s00484-005-0269-z.

16. Deschênes and Greenstone, "Climate Change."

17. Alan I. Barreca, "Climate Change, Humidity, and Mortality in the United States," *Journal of Environmental Economics and Management* 63 (2012): 19–34, doi: 10.1016/j.jeem.2011.07.004.

18. Basu, "High Ambient Temperature," and Ricardo García-Herrera et al., "A Review of the European Summer Heat Wave of 2003," *Critical Reviews in Environmental Science and Technology* 40 (2010): 267–306, doi: 10.1080/10643380802238137.

19. Matthew Neidell, "Information, Avoidance Behavior, and Health: The Effect of Ozone on Asthma Hospitalizations," *Journal of Human Resources* 44 (2009): 450–78.

20. Basu, "High Ambient Temperature."

21. Masayuki Kudamatsu, Torsten Persson, and David Strömberg, "Weather and Infant Mortality in Africa," Discussion Paper no. 9222 (Centre for Economic Policy Research, London, UK, 2012).

22. Burgess et al. "Weather and Death in India."

23. Olivier Deschênes, "Temperature, Human Health, and Adaptation: A Review of the Empirical Literature," *Energy Economics* 46 (2014): 606–19, doi: 10.1016/j.eneco.2013.10.013.

24. Antonella Zanobetti and Joel Schwartz, "Temperature and Mortality in Nine US Cities," *Epidemiology* 19 (2008): 563–70, doi: 10.1097/EDE.0b013e31816d652d.

25. Alan Barreca et al., "Convergence in Adaptation to Climate Change: Evidence from High Temperatures and Mortality, 1900–2004," *American Economic Review* 105 (2015): 247–51.

26. Joshua Graff Zivin and Matthew Neidell, "Environment, Health, and Human Capital," *Journal of Economic Literature* 51 (2013): 689–730, doi: 10.1257/jel.51.3.689.

27. Abderrezak Bouchama and James P. Knochel, "Heat Stroke," *New England Journal of Medicine* 346 (2002): 1978–88, doi: 10.1056/NEJMra011089.

28. US Environmental Protection Agency, *Excessive Heat Events Guidebook,* EPA 430-B-06-005 (Washington, DC: Office of Atmospheric Programs, 2006).

29. Basu and Samet, "Elevated Ambient Temperature and Mortality."

30. Andrew M. Prentice et al., "Energy-Sparing Adaptations in Human Pregnancy Assessed by Whole-Body Calorimetry," *British Journal of Nutrition* 62 (1989): 5–22, and Jonathan C. K. Wells and Tim J. Cole, "Birth Weight and Environmental Heat Load: A Between-Population Analysis," *American Journal of Physical Anthropology* 119 (2002): 276–82.

31. Good reviews are provided in Linn B. Strand, Adrian G. Barnett, and Shilu Tong, "Maternal Exposure to Ambient Temperature and the Risks of Preterm Birth and Stillbirth in Brisbane, Australia," *American Journal of Epidemiology* 175 (2012): 99–107, doi: 10.1093/aje/kwr404, and Linn B. Strand, Adrian G. Barnett, and Shilu Tong, "The Influence of Season and Ambient Temperature on Birth Outcomes: A Review of the Epidemiological Literature," *Environmental Research* 111 (2011): 451–62, doi:10.1016/j. envres.2011.01.023.

32. Douglas Almond and Janet Currie, "Killing Me Softly: The Fetal Origins Hypothesis," *Journal of Economic Perspectives* (2011): 153–72, doi: 10.1257/jep.25.3.153.

33. Paola Michelozzi et al., "High Temperature and Hospitalizations for Cardiovascular and Respiratory Causes in 12 European Cities," *American Journal of Respiratory and Critical Care Medicine* 179 (2009): 383–89, doi: 10.1164/rccm.200802-217OC, and Shao Lin et al., "Extreme High Temperatures and Hospital Admissions for Respiratory and Cardiovascular Diseases," *Epidemiology* 20 (2009): 738–46, doi: 10.1097/EDE.0b013e3181ad5522.

34. Nicolas R. Ziebarth, Maike Schmitt, and Martin Karlsson, "The Short-Term Population Health Effects of Weather and Pollution: Implications of Climate Change," IZA Discussion Paper no. 7875 (Institute for the Study of Labor, Bonn, Germany, 2013).

35. Cristina Linares and Julio Diaz, "Impact of High Temperatures on Hospital Admissions: Comparative Analysis with Previous Studies about Mortality (Madrid)," *European Journal of Public Health* 18 (2008): 317–22, Ziebarth, Schmitt, and Karlsson. "Short-Term Population Health Effects."

36. Lin et al., "Extreme High Temperatures."

37. Edwards, Saunders, and Shiota, "Effects of Heat."

38. Strand, Barnett, and Tong, "Influence of Season."

39. Steven J. Schiff and George G. Somjen, "The Effects of Temperature on Synaptic Transmission in Hippocampal Tissue Slices," *Brain Research* 345 (1985): 279–84.

40. Matthew W. Gillman, "Developmental Origins of Health and Disease," *New England Journal of Medicine* 353 (2005): 1848–50, doi: 10.1056/NEJMe058187, and Almond and Currie, "Killing Me Softly."

41. Edwards, Saunders, and Shiota, "Effects of Heat."

42. Ibid.; Strand, Barnett, and Tong, "Influence of Season."

43. Robert Feil and Mario F. Fraga, "Epigenetics and the Environment: Emerging Patterns and Implications," *Nature Reviews Genetics* 13 (2012): 97–109, doi: 10.1038/nrg3142.

44. Ibid.

45. Alexander Jones et al., "Evidence for Developmental Programming of Cerebral Laterality in Humans," *PLOS One* 6, no. 2 (2011): e17071, doi: 10.1371/journal.pone.0017071.

46. Schiff and Somjen, "Effects of Temperature"; Tom Deboer, "Brain Temperature Dependent Changes in the Electroencephalogram Power Spectrum of Humans and Animals," *Journal of Sleep Research* 7 (1998): 254–62, doi: 10.1046/j.1365-2869.1998.00125.x; and Chris Hocking et al., "Evaluation of Cognitive Performance in the Heat by Functional Brain Imaging and Psychometric Testing," *Comparative Biochemistry and Physiology Part A: Molecular & Integrative Physiology* 128 (2001): 719–34, doi: 10.1016/S1095-6433(01)00278-1.

47. Vania R. Khan and Ian R. Brown, "The Effect of Hyperthermia on the Induction of Cell Death in Brain, Testis, and Thymus of the Adult and Developing Rat." *Cell Stress & Chaperones* 7, no. 1 (2002): 73.

48. Marcus E. Raichle and Mark A. Mintun, "Brain Work and Brain Imaging," *Annual Review of Neuroscience* 29 (2006): 449–76, doi: 10.1146/annurev.neuro.29.051605.112819.

49. Eugene A. Kiyatkin, "Brain Temperature Fluctuations during Physiological and Pathological Conditions," *European Journal of Applied Physiology* 101 (2007): 3–17, doi: 10.1007/s00421-007-0450-7, and Lars Nybo and Niels H. Secher, "Cerebral Perturbations Provoked by Prolonged Exercise," *Progress in Neurobiology* 72 (2004): 223–61.

50. Bernard J. Fine and John L. Kobrick, "Effects of Altitude and Heat on Complex Cognitive Tasks," *Human Factors* 20 (1978): 115–22, doi: 10.1177/001872087802000115; Paul Froom et al., "Heat Stress and Helicopter Pilot Errors," *Journal of Occupational Medicine* 35 (1993): 720–24; and D. Hyde et al., *Quantification of Special Operations Mission-Related Performance: Operational Evaluation and Physical Measures* (Bethesda, MD: Naval Medical Research Institute, 1997).

51. Hocking et al., "Evaluation of Cognitive Performance," and Ioannis Vasmatzidis, Robert E. Schlegel, and Peter A. Hancock, "An Investigation of Heat Stress Effects on Time-Sharing Performance," *Ergonomics* 45 (2002): 218–39.

52. Olli Seppanen, William J. Fisk, and Q. H. Lei, *Effect of Temperature on Task Performance in Office Environment* (Berkeley, CA: Lawrence Berkeley National Laboratory, 2006).

53. Janet Currie et al., "Does Pollution Increase School Absences?" *Review of Economics and Statistics* 91 (2009): 682–94, doi: 10.1162/rest.91.4.682.

54. Mark J. Mendell and Garvin A. Heath, "Do Indoor Pollutants and Thermal Conditions in Schools Influence Student Performance? A Critical Review of the Literature," *Indoor Air* 15 (2005): 27–52, doi: 10.1111/j.1600-0668.2004.00320.x.

55. Joshua Graff Zivin and Matthew J. Neidell, "Temperature and the Allocation of Time: Implications for Climate Change," Working Paper no. 15717 (National Bureau of Economic Research, Cambridge, MA, 2010).

56. Graff Zivin, Hsiang, and Neidell, "Temperature and Human Capital."

57. James J. Heckman, "Skill Formation and the Economics of Investing in Disadvantaged Children," *Science* 312 (2006): 1900–02, doi: 10.1126/science.1128898.

58. Graff Zivin, Hsiang, and Neidell, "Temperature and Human Capital."

59. Melissa Dell, Benjamin F. Jones, and Benjamin A. Olken, "What Do We Learn from the Weather? The New Climate–Economy Literature," *Journal of Economic Literature* 52 (2014): 740–98, doi: 10.1257/jel.52.3.740, and Geoffrey Heal and Jisung Park, "Feeling the Heat: Temperature, Physiology and the Wealth of Nations," Working Paper no. 19725 (National Bureau of Economic Research, Cambridge, MA, 2013).

60. Janet Currie and Rosemary Hyson, "Is the Impact of Health Shocks Cushioned by Socioeconomic Status? The Case of Low Birthweight," *American Economic Review* 89 (1999): 245–250, doi: 10.1257/aer.89.2.245.

61. Janet Currie and Enrico Moretti, "Biology as Destiny? Short-and Long-Run Determinants of Intergenerational Transmission of Birth Weight," *Journal of Labor Economics* 25 (2007): 231–64, doi: 10.1086/511377.

62. Sandra E. Black, Paul J. Devereux, and Kjell G. Salvanes, "From the Cradle to the Labor Market? The Effect of Birth Weight on Adult Outcomes," *Quarterly Journal of Economics* (2007): 409–39, doi: 10.1162/qjec.122.1.409; Philip Oreopoulos et al., "Short-, Medium-, and Long-Term Consequences of Poor Infant Health: An Analysis Using Siblings and Twins," *Journal of Human Resources* 43 (2008): 88–138; Heather Royer, "Separated at Girth: US Twin Estimates of the Effects of Birth Weight," *American Economic Journal: Applied Economics* 1 (2009): 49–85, doi: 10.1257/app.1.1.49; and Prashant Bharadwaj, Katrine Vellesen Løken, and Christopher Neilson, "Early Life Health Interventions and Academic Achievement," *American Economic Review* 103 (2013): 1862–91, doi: 10.1257/aer.103.5.1862.

63. Isen, Rossin-Slater, and Walker, "Every Breath You Take," and Graff Zivin, Hsiang, and Neidell, "Climate, Human Capital, and Adaptation," respectively.

64. Arturas Petronis, "Epigenetics as a Unifying Principle in the Aetiology of Complex Traits and Diseases," *Nature* 465 (2010): 721–27.

65. Deschênes and Greenstone, "Climate Change."

66. Barreca et al., "Adapting to Climate Change."

67. Lucas W. Davis and Paul J. Gertler, "Contribution of Air Conditioning Adoption to Future Energy Use under Global Warming," *Proceedings of the National Academy of Sciences* 112 (2015): 5962–67, doi: 10.1073/pnas.1423558112.

68. Francisco Salamanca et al., "Anthropogenic Heating of the Urban Environment due to Air Conditioning," *Journal of Geophysical Research: Atmospheres* 119 (2014): 5949–65, doi: 10.1002/2013JD021225.

69. David Albouy et al., "Climate Amenities, Climate Change, and American Quality of Life," Working Paper no. 18925 (National Bureau of Economic Research, Cambridge, MA, 2013), and Olivier Deschênes and Enrico Moretti, "Extreme Weather Events, Mortality, and Migration," *Review of Economics and Statistics* 91 (2009): 659–81, doi: 10.1162/rest.91.4.659.

70. Deschênes and Moretti, "Extreme Weather Events."

71. Graff Zivin and Neidell, "Temperature and the Allocation."

72. Heckman, "Skill Formation," and Graff Zivin, Hsiang, and Neidell, "Climate, Human Capital, and Adaptation," respectively.

73. Graff Zivin, Hsiang, and Neidell "Temperature and Human Capital."

74. Bodil Nielsen et al., "Human Circulatory and Thermoregulatory Adaptations with Heat Acclimation and Exercise in a Hot, Dry Environment," *Journal of Physiology* 460 (1993): 467–85, doi: 10.1113/jphysiol.1993.sp019482; Carl Gisolfi and Sid Robinson, "Relations between Physical Training, Acclimatization, and Heat Tolerance," *Journal of Applied Physiology* 26 (1969): 530–34; and P. A. Hancock and Ioannis Vasmatzidis, "Effects of Heat Stress on Cognitive Performance: The Current State of Knowledge," *International Journal of Hyperthermia* 19 (2003): 355–72.

75. John N. Booth III et al., "Hyperthermia Deaths among Children in Parked Vehicles: An Analysis of 231 Fatalities in the United States, 1999–2007," *Forensic Science, Medicine, and Pathology* 6 (2010): 99–105, doi: 10.1007/s12024-010-9149-x.

76. Federal recommendations for schools are available from the CDC at http://www.cdc.gov/niosh/docs/2004-101/chklists/6indoo~1.htm. The Occupational Safety and Health Administration (OSHA) explicitly can't issue citations for air quality in the workplace; see Richard E. Fairfax, "OSHA Policy on Indoor Air Quality: Office Temperature/Humidity and Environmental Tobacco Smoke" (memorandum to regional administrators, February 24, 2003).

77. The Environmental Law Institute has compiled a database of state-level indoor-air-quality laws regarding schools, available at http://www.eli.org/buildings/database-state-indoor-air-quality-laws.

78. Maureen Magee, "High Temps Force Short School Days," *San Diego Union-Tribune*, September 15, 2014, http://www.sandiegouniontribune.com/news/2014/sep/15/heat-forces-short-school-days/.

79. The history of closures is available at http://www.dmschools.org/about/emergency-weather-closing-info/a-history-of-weather-related-closings/.

80. US Environmental Protection Agency, *Excessive Heat Events Guidebook.*

81. García-Herrera et al., "Heat Wave of 2003."

82. US Environmental Protection Agency, *Excessive Heat Events Guidebook*.

83. Bergeron, "Reducing Sports Heat Illness Risk."

84. American Heart Association, "2005 American Heart Association (AHA) Guidelines for Cardiopulmonary Resuscitation (CPR) and Emergency Cardiovascular Care (ECC) of Pediatric and Neonatal Patients: Pediatric Basic Life Support," *Pediatrics* 117 (2006): e989-e1004.

Climate Change, Conflict, and Children

Richard Akresh

Summary

We have good reason to predict that a warming climate will produce more conflict and violence. A growing contingent of researchers has been examining the relationship in recent years, and they've found that hotter temperatures and reduced rainfall are linked to increases in conflict at all scales, from interpersonal violence to war.

Children are especially vulnerable to conflict, Richard Akresh writes. In addition to directly exposing children to violence and trauma, conflict can tear families apart, displace whole populations, interrupt schooling, cut off access to health care or food, and eliminate the jobs that families depend on for a living. Children caught in a war zone may suffer physical injuries, malnutrition, developmental delays, and psychological damage, with effects on their physical health, mental health, and education that can persist into adulthood and constrict their ability to make a living. Moreover, those effects can spill over to the next generation and beyond, damaging the affected countries' ability to develop human capital.

The likelihood that rates of conflict will increase on a hotter planet, then, poses a serious threat to children's wellbeing—especially in poorer countries, which already see the most wars and other conflicts. Unfortunately, Akresh writes, we still poorly understand the mechanisms that link climate to conflict, and we have almost no evidence to tell us which types of policies could best mitigate the effects of climate change-related violence on children.

www.futureofchildren.org

Richard Akresh is an associate professor of economics at the University of Illinois at Urbana-Champaign and a research associate at the National Bureau of Economic Research (NBER). He thanks Valerie Marin for excellent research assistance, Janet Currie and Olivier Deschênes for detailed feedback, and Prashant Bharadwaj for discussions about the literature.

Solomon Hsiang of the University of California, Berkeley, reviewed and critiqued a draft of this article.

Richard Akresh

T his article reviews the evidence linking climate variability to conflict, broadly defined, and what happens to children after they are exposed to conflict. One challenge in examining that link is the question of how to define conflict. Wars between nations, civil conflicts, genocides, ethnic cleansing, political and neighborhood violence, localized rioting or disputes, interpersonal violence, and suicide have all been examined under the rubric of conflict research. Conflicts vary in many ways: in duration, with some lasting days and others lasting decades; in how many individuals are exposed and/or displaced; in whether deaths are concentrated among soldiers or civilians; and in their underlying causes.

Conditions children experience in the womb or early in life have been shown to be especially harmful because they not only affect health in the short term but also may influence health, education, and socioeconomic wellbeing in adulthood.[1] Children are especially vulnerable to conflict, yet different types of conflict can vary wildly in their effects, and researchers have not yet started to explore that variation in a systematic way. In addition to directly exposing children to violence and trauma, conflict may disrupt child care, family arrangements, educational or health opportunities, and adult employment. Most studies of exposure to conflict focus on how it affects health and education, although researchers are beginning to look at other outcomes, such as political beliefs and adult mental health. Recent studies have also found that exposure to conflict may have different effects depending on a child's age, and some of the evidence suggests that the effects can be particularly pronounced if exposure occurs during adolescence. The negative effects of conflict exposure can carry over to the next generation: children of parents exposed to conflict can experience health and education deficits themselves. It's worth noting that research examining how conflicts affect children is part of a broader research agenda studying how children are affected by different types of shocks, such as weather, famine, epidemics, natural disasters, and pollution.[2]

The possibility that growth disturbances in early life might affect future outcomes is particularly relevant in developing countries, where armed conflict occurs more often than in other regions of the world. During the past 50 years, more than half of all countries have experienced conflicts, but nearly 70 percent of countries in sub-Saharan Africa have experienced armed conflict since 1980.[3] Evidence appears to indicate a strong link between climate variability and increased likelihood of more conflict. If those forecasts are accurate, policy makers will need to understand how conflicts affect children and how households respond to the shocks.

The relationship between climate, conflict, and children could be linear; that is, climate variability may increase the risk of conflict and in turn affect children. However, the relationship could also be nonlinear: conflict could render a population more vulnerable to future climatic events, or climate-triggered conflict could be different from other types of conflict, and those differences could make it more or less harmful for children. Furthermore, although conflicts are clearly bad in the short run, in the long run they may have net benefits for a society (for example, a revolution may overthrow a dictatorship), and we need to keep that in mind when we think about policies that could break the links between climate change and conflict or between conflict and children.

Climate Change and Conflict

Three economists—Marshall Burke, Solomon Hsiang, and Edward Miguel—recently surveyed the research on links between climate and conflict.[4] They considered an enormous range of research on different types of conflict, including interpersonal and intrapersonal conflict, such as domestic violence, road rage, assault, murder, rape, and suicide; and intergroup conflict, such as riots, genocides, land invasions, gang violence, civil wars, and wars between nations.[5] According to the most recent World Health Organization estimates, in 2012 collective violence caused about 119,000 deaths, interpersonal violence caused 505,000 deaths, and 804,000 people committed suicide. Given the large number of suicides, we know surprisingly little about the relationship between climate and suicide.

Burke, Hsiang, and Miguel's review focused on research that uses the best statistical tools to estimate causal relationships. Across the 55 studies they examined, they found that both extreme temperatures and less rainfall (changes in climate toward hotter and drier periods) increase the risk of conflict, although the effect is stronger on intergroup conflict than on interpersonal conflict.

Notably, those results hold across different geographic scales. At the village level, in Tanzania, murders of people accused of being witches increase when droughts are more extreme.[6] In East Africa, looking at cells that are one degree of latitude by one degree of longitude in size, higher temperatures are still linked to more local violence.[7] Expanding to the country level, evidence links temperature and civil wars.[8] And finally, throughout the tropics, the probability that civil conflicts will begin increases as sea-surface temperatures rise.[9]

However, Burke, Hsiang and Miguel find a big gap in the research. We don't understand the *mechanisms* that link climate to conflict or how societies adapt to climate change. For instance, we know relatively little about the economic, noneconomic, and even psychological channels that link climate extremes to conflict. In low-income countries where most people are farmers, a link between extreme temperatures or droughts and reduced income is plausible, and the suggestive evidence is strong. In richer countries, the evidence shows links between high temperatures and increased crime, suggesting that noneconomic channels, such as psychology, might explain the relationship. Many pathways likely lead from climate variability to conflict, and those channels could be highly context specific.

We know relatively little about the economic, noneconomic, and even psychological channels that link climate extremes to conflict.

Climate Change and Intergroup Violence

One of the first economics studies on climate, economic conditions, and conflict estimated the causal relationship between economic conditions and civil war in African countries from 1981 to 1999.[10] Earlier research had found an association between economic conditions and civil wars but had not been able to convincingly establish a causal relationship. Given that most of Africa's economies are based on rain-fed agriculture, the researchers measured the relationship between conflict and years of particularly low rainfall. Their data set had two key limitations. First, its definition of conflict specified that the government of a state must be one of the actors in the conflict; second, it specified that a conflict must result in at least 25 battle-related deaths in a year. Thus their analysis excluded types of organized violence that don't involve the state, such as violent crime or clashes among ethnic groups, as well as smaller conflicts. Keeping those limitations in mind, they found that poor rainfall in a given year lowered economic growth and increased the likelihood of civil wars in the following year. The magnitude of the relationship was large: a five-percentage-point drop in annual economic growth increased the chance of a civil war in the following year by 50 percent.

Building on that work, another study looked at how temperature variability might affect armed conflict in Africa.[11] Most previous research on the link between climate variability and conflict had focused on the role of rainfall, which is certainly appropriate when we consider how rain-fed agriculture influences both economic output and employment in developing countries. However, climate change models are much less certain about future rainfall changes (for Africa, in particular) than they are about temperature changes; they consistently predict higher temperatures in Africa over the next few decades. Agricultural evidence confirms that for every degree Celsius of warming, agricultural yields in Africa would be reduced by 10 to 30 percent, mainly through increased evapotranspiration and quickened crop growth. The researchers found strong historical links between higher temperatures and increased likelihood of civil wars: an increase in the average annual temperature of 1° Celsius (1.8° Fahrenheit) leads to a 4.5 percent increase in civil war in that year and a 0.9 percent increase the next year. If the historical relationship between temperature and conflict holds, the authors calculated, we can expect a 54 percent increase in armed conflicts in Africa by 2030.

Not all scholars agree that climate change is actually linked to civil wars. Halvard Buhaug, a research professor at the Peace Research Institute Oslo, has used alternative measures of drought, heat, and civil war and alternative model specifications to argue that climate variability is not a good predictor of conflict.[12] He blames African civil wars on ethnopolitical exclusion, poor economies, and the collapse of the Cold War patronage system. But his analysis has been shown to be based on faulty econometrics.[13] Despite that, Buhaug makes two convincing points. First, the link between climate change and civil wars in Africa may not hold for smaller-scale conflicts (defined as those with more than 25 but fewer than 1,000 deaths in a year), though that isn't necessarily the question the research he critiqued was attempting to answer. Second, the relationship between temperature and civil wars that existed from 1981 to 2002 no longer holds, according to more-recent data: the incidence of civil wars has fallen as temperatures have continued to increase.

Until recently, research on the links between climate and conflict was limited. But during the past few years, debate over the link has grown. In 2012, a special issue of the *Journal of Peace Research* focused exclusively on climate change and conflict. The 16 studies included in the special issue show varying results, and definite conclusions are hard to draw. For instance, some of the researchers found that in certain contexts, more conflicts and killings take place during seasons of relative abundance or after wet years than during seasons of scarcity; other researchers found that civil war is more likely in dry conditions.[14] Those context-specific results and the lack of definitive conclusions might stem from the fact that many of the studies in the special issue dealt with intergroup violence at levels below the state level rather than the civil wars and interstate conflicts that previous researchers had examined.

While most previous research has compared data on weather and conflicts at the country level, one recent study analyzed civil conflict in Africa at the subnational level (within cells of one degree latitude by one degree longitude) for the years 1997–2011.[15] The researchers used a drought index that takes into account rainfall, evaporation, and temperature; such an index is particularly relevant for agricultural production because it captures within-year variation in the timing of weather shocks and variation in crop cover. They found that weather shocks that affect the main crop grown in a region have a large impact on conflict, but weather shocks that happen outside the main growing season have no relationship to conflict, suggesting that agricultural yields constitute the mechanism linking climate variability to conflict.

Several other more recent studies have also focused on within-country variation in examining the link between climate and conflict.[16] One researcher consulted four centuries of historical data from China at the prefecture level to find that severe droughts increased the likelihood of peasant revolts, though the relationship substantially mitigated when farmers began growing drought-resistant sweet potatoes. Another researcher, looking at insurgency and drought during the early-twentieth-century Mexican revolution, found that municipalities

experiencing severe drought were more likely to see insurgent activity. Finally, another researcher found that poor rainfall in India from 2005 to 2011, measured at the district level, increased a Maoist insurgency's violence against civilians.

A robust and consistent finding was that deviations from normal rainfall and temperature increase the occurrence of conflicts.

In 2013, two years before their more recent review discussed earlier, Hsiang, Burke, and Miguel conducted a meta-analysis of studies on the link between climate variability and conflict, drawing on research from such disciplines as archaeology, criminology, economics, geography, history, political science, and psychology.[17] The 60 primary studies they evaluated used 45 conflict data sets from all regions of the world and covered a range of time periods from 12,000 years ago to the present, examining everything from interpersonal violence to crime, political instability, and the collapse of civilizations. A robust and consistent finding from the 60 studies was that deviations from normal rainfall and temperature increase the occurrence of conflicts. Specifically, an increase in temperature or extreme rainfall that is still within the range we might expect today can raise the likelihood of interpersonal violence by 4 percent and of intergroup violence by 14 percent. Effects of that magnitude are worrisome, given that climate models predict much larger variability in heat and rainfall for some regions in the coming years.

Climate Change and Interpersonal and Intrapersonal Violence

Although the evidence linking climate variability and conflicts between nations is growing, we know much less about how climate change may affect criminal behavior. Recently, a number of researchers have begun to expand the focus of climate–conflict research to see whether there's a relationship between extreme temperatures and murders, assaults, rapes, and suicides. One study used 30 years of monthly county-level US data on crime and weather, finding that extreme temperatures have a strong positive effect on criminal activity.[18] The author used his model to make detailed predictions, although he assumed limited adaptation to climate changes. His model showed that by 2100, US crime rates will be 1.5 to 5.5 percent higher for most crimes, and climate change will have caused an additional 22,000 murders, 180,000 cases of rape, 1.2 million aggravated assaults, 2.3 million simple assaults, 260,000 robberies, 1.3 million burglaries, 2.2 million cases of larceny, and 580,000 vehicle thefts.

A study from India focuses on a particular type of homicide: dowry deaths. These are killings of married women who supposedly didn't bring enough dowry to their marriages.[19] Dowry deaths typically happen after the marriage, when the initial dowry paid at the time of the wedding is already controlled by the husband. In response to poor rainfall, the husband may demand additional transfers from the wife's family; because the stigma associated with divorce in India is extremely high, the wife is not in a strong bargaining position. Husbands (or the husbands' extended families) may resort to killing the wife so that the husband can reenter the marriage market and secure another dowry. The researchers used data from almost 600 districts in India for 2002–07, empirically measuring how rainfall shocks affect dowry deaths. Significant declines in rainfall in a given year led to a 7.8 percent increase in dowry deaths and a 4.4 percent increase in domestic violence against women more generally. They also examined women's political representation in the national parliament as a possible strategy to mitigate the impact of rainfall shocks but found it had no mitigating effect on dowry deaths.

Another study used district-level data from two states in India to estimate the relationship between temporary economic shocks to agriculture caused by poor rainfall and the incidence of suicide in the affected families.[20] When lack of rainfall increased poverty, suicides rose among men—a 1 percent increase in poverty from poor rainfall meant that male suicides rose by 0.6 percent. Among women, however, suicides actually declined under the same conditions.

Mechanisms Linking Climate Change to Conflict

As we can see from the previous section, evidence for a relationship between climate variability and conflicts is quickly growing, and the consensus indicates hotter temperatures and reduced rainfall are leading to more conflicts, broadly defined. But what are the mechanisms that link temperature and rainfall variation to increased conflicts? At the moment, that's probably the biggest gap in our knowledge, and researchers are attempting to answer the question because more-detailed understanding of the mechanisms will lead to better long-run predictions.

One group of researchers used data from Mexico to see whether economic factors might be the main mechanisms linking climate variability and conflict.[21] They explored the relationship between high temperatures and three distinctly different types of conflict: gang killings by drug trafficking organizations, homicides, and suicides. High temperatures produced a large and similar increase in all three types of violence, suggesting that the mechanism linking climate variability and conflict is likely to consist of psychological or physiological factors that are affected by temperature.

Another group of researchers looked at how historical fluctuations in temperature within a given country affected aggregate economic outcomes.[22] In poor countries, but not in wealthier ones, higher temperatures reduced economic growth, growth rates, and both agricultural and industrial output. Specifically, in poor countries, a 1° Celsius (1.8° Fahrenheit) increase in average temperature over a given year lowered economic growth by 1.3 percentage points.

More recently, the same group reviewed research on how temperature and precipitation affect economic outcomes.[23] Taken together, the studies they examined showed that changes in local weather over time can affect agricultural output, industrial output, labor productivity, health, and economic growth. Similarly, but on a planetary scale, another pair of researchers examined whether the El Niño Southern Oscillation, which causes large fluctuations in temperature and rainfall in the tropics, can drive economic volatility in those areas.[24] They found that across the tropics, higher temperatures and lower rainfall tied to El Niño reduced cereal yields and agricultural income in general.

How Conflict Affects Children's Wellbeing

Much of the earlier research on conflict was oriented toward macroeconomic issues and generally focused on understanding

the causes and spread of war and its role in reducing economic growth.[25] Civil wars often cause immediate economic harm by destroying productive capacity and disrupting normal activity. In the long term, however, most countries bounce back after wars are over. For instance, postwar economic recovery was extremely strong in Japan, West Germany, and Vietnam despite the bombings by the Allied forces in World War II and by the Americans during the Vietnam War. In Vietnam, areas bombed more heavily showed no long-term effects on poverty rates, consumption levels, literacy, infrastructure, or population density compared with areas that saw less bombing. In Sierra Leone, households exposed to the civil war turned out to be more rather than less involved after the war in local collective action, including voting, joining political and community groups, and attending community meetings.[26] A study of the aftermath of 41 civil wars that occurred from 1960 to 2003 found that although the wars did significant harm across a range of indicators—such as economic performance, political development, demographic trends, and security—once lasting peace was achieved, stability and the economy improved.[27]

Despite the casualties and destruction that wars cause, until very recently researchers had paid relatively little attention to how wars affect children. Although wars may not generally produce long-term macroeconomic harm, research that looks at the microeconomic impacts of exposure to conflict has consistently found harm among groups of people who were directly exposed.

Wars are generally viewed as bad and worth avoiding, and so research that finds that people exposed to wars can be worse off might seem to state the obvious. However, governments and international organizations need accurate assessments of the full long-term costs of conflicts in order to make decisions with respect to postconflict interventions. Evidence increasingly suggests that the effects of exposure to conflicts are both longer lasting (experienced over the entire life cycle) and more extensive than many might suspect. Knowing which ages are most affected is also critical for targeting remediation in the most effective way.

Evidence increasingly suggests that the effects of exposure to conflicts are both longer lasting and more extensive than many might suspect.

In contrast to research on climate change and conflict, research examining the impacts of conflict on children focuses almost exclusively on intergroup conflict and not interpersonal violence. Most of that research on the impacts of conflict exposure examines health or education impacts in both the short and long run. As more data has become available, researchers have started to examine how conflict exposure affects other outcomes, including the labor market, mental health, and political beliefs. Such research typically exploits variation in the geographic extent and timing of a conflict and the extent to which different birth cohorts are exposed to the fighting.

Short-Term Health Impacts

One of the earliest analyses of how conflict exposure affects children's health examined the civil war that began in October 1994 in Burundi's northwestern provinces and then spread across the country.[28] The fighting caused enormous macroeconomic disruptions; from 1990 to 2002, per capita income in Burundi fell from $210 to $110, making it the world's poorest country. In the same period, the proportion of people living below the nationally defined poverty line increased from 35 to 68 percent, and the spread of the civil war starting in 1994 led to double-digit inflation rates, which peaked at more than 30 percent in 1997.[29]

That study focused on early childhood malnutrition and on stunting as measured by age- and gender-standardized measures of height. Combining data from a nationally representative household survey (the 1998 Burundi Priority Survey carried out by the World Bank and the Burundi Institute of Statistics and Economic Studies) with data on the timing and evolution of the conflict from 1994 to 1998, the researchers found that children who had been exposed to war were shorter than those who hadn't been. Based on other research that links children's height to educational outcomes and returns to schooling, they estimated that the average child exposed to the war would complete 0.7 fewer years of school and earn 21 percent less as an adult.

Much of the research on conflict and health has focused on civil wars, but wars between nations are also common. In many cases, particularly in Africa, conflicts between nations are started or exacerbated by territorial disputes. Using household survey data from Eritrea, one study aimed to estimate how exposure to the 1998–2000 Eritrea–Ethiopia war affected children's health.[30] When Eritrea, formerly a province of Ethiopia, became independent in 1993 following a long guerrilla war, the countries never demarcated certain sections of the new border. Full-fledged fighting over those areas started in May 1998. Though the region has been described as desolate and inconsequential, more than 300,000 troops dug in and deadlocked on both sides of the border. Because most civilians fled the war-torn areas, leaving the armies to fight over empty villages, most of the conflict's casualties were soldiers.

As in the Burundi study, the Eritrea study exploited variation in the conflict's geographic extent and timing and the extent to which different birth cohorts were exposed to the fighting. Helpfully, household survey data included information on each household's region of residence during the war—in addition to region of residence at the time of the survey—thereby improving the accuracy of the results; without that information, war exposure could have been classified incorrectly. The authors found that war-exposed children were shorter, with similar effects on height for children born before or during the war. Because the study was able to accurately record a child's region of residence at the time of the war, the estimated negative impacts of exposure to conflict were 13 percent larger than they would have been if the study had used the child's region at the time of the survey.

Other recent research on conflict and health has attempted to improve measurements of conflict exposure by incorporating GPS data on the distance between survey villages and conflict sites to more precisely capture a household's exposure to conflict.[31] This research builds on the study of the Eritrea–Ethiopia war by using survey data that include households' GPS locations. The GPS-based approach showed that in Eritrea, 24 percent of households within 100 kilometers (about 62 miles) of battle sites had been previously coded as not being in war regions; similarly, 28 percent of Ethiopian households

within 100 to 300 kilometers of conflict sites had been previously coded as not being in war regions; and 2.2 percent of households that were more than 300 kilometers from conflict sites had been coded as being in war regions. Using GPS information, the authors estimated detrimental effects that were two to three times larger than they would have been if exposure had been measured only at the [imprecise] regional level. Specifically, children exposed to the war and living nearest to the battle sites were shorter by approximately 1 to 2 inches; the negative impact diminished as distance from the conflict increased.

Because of the fortuitous timing of the household survey data collection, the researchers were also able to explore whether the conflict had different effects on children who were fetuses in the womb at the time of the fighting compared with those who were in early childhood (ages 0 to 5 years), thereby assessing the relative importance of disturbances during those two critical growth periods. Exposure in the womb may harm children's health for a number of reasons, including poorer maternal nutrition due to disruptions in food supply or income shocks, lack of adequate prenatal care, and the possibility that the conflict reduced the number of deliveries in the presence of trained providers. Though much research finds later-life effects from shocks experienced in the womb, several recent studies have not confirmed those findings; however, this study found that Ethiopian and Eritrean children exposed to the war while in the womb were significantly shorter.[32]

The researchers were also able to examine whether conflict-exposed children in Ethiopia, the nation that won the conflict, suffered smaller health consequences than children in Eritrea. Theoretically, households in a winning nation might suffer less destruction or face fewer disruptions to their economic activities or public health delivery systems. Although children in the losing country, Eritrea, suffered more than those in Ethiopia, the researchers found sizable negative impacts for both boys and girls in both countries, and the effects were comparable in magnitude whether exposure occurred in the womb or during early childhood.

Conflict-exposed children are less likely to be delivered at hospitals and more likely to be very small at birth, and their mothers are more likely to experience postbirth complications.

Researchers have only just begun to explore the mechanisms by which conflicts affect children's health. Looking at health-seeking behaviors and indicators of maternal stress, researchers have found evidence that conflict-exposed children are less likely to be delivered at hospitals, suggesting health service delivery may be compromised in conflict areas. Furthermore, conflict-exposed children are more likely to be very small at birth, and their mothers are more likely to experience postbirth complications. Disruptions in health care delivery and added maternal stress are mechanisms that could explain conflict-exposed children's lower heights. From a policy standpoint, those results suggest that households may not be able to adequately cope with conflicts that disrupt the economy and

displace people, even if the number of civilian casualties is limited.

Although we know a lot about how nonconflict shocks affect children, few studies have compared the effects of exposure to conflict with the effects of exposure to other types of shocks. One group of researchers examined whether exposure at birth to small-scale localized conflict had different effects on Rwandan children's health than did exposure at birth to crop failure.[33] The conflict was an outbreak of localized fighting in northern Rwanda in October 1990, and the crop failure was a localized and extremely severe event in southern Rwanda in 1988–89. The researchers had access to household survey data that asked about agriculture and child health, as well as to reports on the fighting from nongovernmental organizations. They used variation across birth cohorts and region of residence to capture a child's exposure to the shock. Both crop failure and armed conflict harmed children's health. But gender and poverty affected the outcomes differently. Both boys and girls born during the fighting in regions experiencing the conflict were shorter in stature no matter whether they were poor or better off. Conversely, only girls were harmed by the crop failure, and the impact was worse for girls from poor households.

Research on how various kinds of shocks affect children commonly finds evidence of gender bias. For instance, evidence on agricultural shocks in India and China shows better outcomes for boys than for girls when it comes to infant mortality, disability, and illiteracy.[34] Thus, in contrast to findings of gender bias in response to other types of shocks, it's significant that we see no such gender bias in response to conflict. Researchers have consistently found that both boys and girls exposed to conflict suffer negative health effects.

We don't know for certain why conflict and crop failure affect children differently or, more accurately, affect different children. But we do know that the October 1990 fighting in northern Rwanda began suddenly and unexpectedly, which could explain why both boys and girls in both poor and better-off households were harmed by the conflict: Parents couldn't protect any of their children from this type of event. Case studies conducted by local organizations suggest that theft of crops and livestock and families' violence-induced displacement from their homes into the surrounding forests were the principal mechanisms at work. Both of those mechanisms would reduce children's nutrition, and displacement also makes children more vulnerable to illnesses from contaminated water and to diseases transmitted by insects and other pests. In contrast, during the crop failure, households were able to shield boys from harm—consistent with other research demonstrating that households practice gender discrimination by reallocating scarce resources toward boys and therefore only girls suffer the negative effects—and better-off households were able to avoid the shock entirely.

Most of the research on how conflict affects health focuses on wars. Political repression has received much less attention from economists, mainly because we have lacked adequate data. One recent study looked at political and economic repression by the government of Zimbabwe.[35] From 2000 to 2005, Robert Mugabe's government in Zimbabwe violently repressed the opposition party through farm invasions and land theft, leading to an economic crisis, hyperinflation, and an environment of general insecurity.

Looking at data from 1999, before the repression began, and from 2006, after it ended, the study found significant negative effects on children's height. Like exposure to conflict, exposure to political violence appears to harm both boys and girls.

Another study, which looked at the Indian state of Andhra Pradesh, examined the combined effect of exposure to political violence and drought on child malnutrition.[36] Andhra Pradesh has experienced a guerrilla insurgency for decades. At the same time, households there face cyclical climatic shocks that affect their children's nutrition. The study found that drought harmed child nutrition only in villages that saw political violence and that the violence made it harder for households to cope with the droughts.

Though much of the research on childhood exposure to conflict focuses on height as a measure of health, some researchers have examined birth weight as an indicator. In Colombia, for example, one study found that random terrorist land mine attacks occurring during the first trimester of pregnancy reduced children's birth weight and increased the likelihood of a preterm delivery.[37] Another study examined the conflict that began in 2000 between Israel and the Palestinians living in Gaza and the West Bank, during which noncombatants experienced intense psychological stress, which is known to increase the risk of having a low-birth-weight child—that is, an infant who weighs less than 2,500 grams (5.5 pounds), a threshold associated with worse health outcomes in the long term.[38] Each additional conflict-related death to which a pregnant woman was exposed during her first trimester of pregnancy further increased the likelihood that she would have a low-birth-weight child. Similarly, a study of the Mexican drug war found that exposure to violent crime during the first trimester of pregnancy reduced birth weight by an average of 75 grams and increased the risk of having a low-birth weight child by 40 percent.[39] These studies on birth weight suggest that maternal stress may be one of the mechanisms through which exposure to conflict harms children's health.

Even if children's health improves as a tangible peace dividend once a conflict is over, a generation of children exposed to the conflict will continue to suffer adverse effects long after the fighting ends.

Long-Term Health Impacts

Most of the research that examines how children's exposure to conflict affects their health focuses on short-term impacts. Recently, however, several researchers have started to explore the long-term effects. Across many types of conflicts in different regions, research tells us that even if children's health improves as a tangible peace dividend once a conflict is over, a generation of children exposed to the conflict will continue to suffer adverse effects long after the fighting ends.

One group of researchers examined the Nigerian civil war—the first modern war in sub-Saharan Africa after independence and one of the bloodiest—which took place from July 1967 to January 1970 in Biafra, a secessionist region in southeast Nigeria.[40] The war caused widespread malnutrition

and devastation, and 1 million to 3 million people died. The researchers measured the impact of war exposure in the womb or during childhood on adult height, which has been found to be correlated with levels of intelligence and economic success. They found that 40 years after the war ended, its full consequences were still being realized. Women who had been exposed to the war for the average duration between the time they were newborns and 3 years of age were 0.75 centimeters (0.3 inches) shorter than women the same age who hadn't been exposed. Women who were exposed when they were 13 to 16 years old were 4.53 centimeters shorter.

The fact that war exposure in adolescence had the strongest impact is striking. This effect may have stemmed from disruption of the normal adolescent growth spurt. Children's growth in height is fastest during infancy, slows down until around age 3, and then continues at a low rate until peaking again in adolescence.[41] However, we have limited causal evidence of how nutritional deprivation affects children at different ages, and we particularly lack studies that compare how shocks experienced during adolescence differ from shocks experienced during early childhood.[42] Certainly, even if children grow faster in early childhood than they do as teenagers, the increase in food demand that accompanies adolescents' growth spurt may be greater, given their larger size. But because so few researchers have examined children's exposure to conflict at ages older than 5 years, we don't know whether the effect observed in Nigeria is specific to the local context or whether adolescent exposure is systematically different from exposure in the womb or during early childhood. In either case, this is an important avenue for future research.

A follow-up study—the first to explore the impact of conflict on second-generation outcomes—examined the intergenerational transmission of harm from exposure to the Nigerian conflict.[43] The Biafra war was extremely violent. Households in the war-affected regions faced both nutritional deprivation and displacement. The Nigerian government blockaded the region, and starvation reached critical levels. This study analyzed whether mothers' exposure to the Nigerian civil war as children, at any point from before birth to adolescence, had a persistent adverse effect on their children's health. To be clear, this second generation wasn't born during the war, so they weren't exposed to any shock, but their adult mothers had been exposed to the conflict when they themselves were children. The researchers found that the war had significant negative impacts on the mothers' health and education (first-generation impacts), which then led to higher mortality and more stunting among their children (second-generation impacts). However, second-generation impacts were seen only among children of mothers who had been exposed to the conflict during their adolescent years. The fact that exposure during adolescence led to the largest negative effects in the first generation could explain the second-generation impacts, but the authors were unable to rule out alternatives. Future research can help establish whether the results from Nigeria can be seen elsewhere and start to uncover the mechanisms that link impacts across generations.

Short-Term Education Impacts

Exposure to conflict harms children's education as well as their health. Most research on this subject examines school enrollment and years of education completed. An early study looked at how exposure to the 1994 Rwandan genocide affected children's educational outcomes.[44] The Rwandan genocide killed at least 800,000 people, or 10 percent of the country's population, in approximately 100 days.[45] However, the war was short, and the country was taken over by a relatively well-organized regime after the end of the fighting. Armed conflicts typically do immediate economic harm, and Rwanda's experience was no exception. During the genocide, per capita GDP plummeted almost 50 percent and consumer prices increased 64 percent. But by 1996, both had returned nearly to prewar levels.[46] Exports of coffee, the country's predominant export crop, declined 54 percent in 1994 but returned to prewar levels in 1995. Given the rapid return to prewar economic levels, we might expect that long-run impacts wouldn't be severe.

The researchers examined whether and how the genocide affected children's school enrollment and the probability that children would complete a particular grade. They combined two nationally representative household surveys: one collected in 2000, six years after the genocide ended, and one collected in 1992, two years before it began; few studies of conflicts have data from both before and after the event. Overall education rates in Rwanda, on average, improved from 1992 to 2000, as the fraction of people with no education decreased from 30 to 24 percent. However, that overall improvement masked a large negative effect for the children who were school-age when exposed to the genocide in 1994. Using the prewar data to control for baseline schooling levels for a given age group and exploiting variation across provinces in the intensity of killings and in which cohorts of children were school-age when exposed to the war, they found that the genocide had a strong negative effect.

Exposed children completed half a year less of school, an 18.3 percent decline. Following the end of that brutal period in Rwandan history, aggregate measures of the economy as well as overall children's schooling rates have rebounded, although the generation of children exposed to the conflict is still experiencing adverse effects long after the fighting ended.

A study of Tajikistan's 1992–98 civil war also found negative effects on schooling.[47] That study was one of the first to incorporate household-level measures of conflict exposure—specifically, whether individual households experienced any damage to their dwellings during the war—in addition to typically used measures of exposure at the province level. The researcher found that people who were of school age during the conflict were less likely to complete their mandatory education than were people old enough to have finished their education before the start of the war. The impact on schooling had a gendered component: girls exposed to the conflict were less likely to be enrolled in school, but there was no equivalent impact on boys.

On the other hand, a review of the research on how conflict affects education found that either boys' or girls' schooling can suffer greater harm depending on the setting.[48] Factors that can tilt the gendered impacts one way or the other include the specifics of the conflict itself, prewar differences in education levels for each gender, and labor market and educational opportunities in the absence of war. A study of the civil conflict that took place in Nepal from 1996 to 2006 illustrates just how much difference the context can make when it comes to a conflict's effect on education.[49] In districts that saw more casualties from the conflict, girls' educational attainment increased. But

in districts that saw more abductions by the Maoist insurgents, who often targeted schoolchildren, the opposite was true.

Although most researchers have focused on how conflict affects school enrollment, two recent studies examined student academic achievement.[50] The first study found that the 2000–06 Israeli-Palestinian conflict reduced the likelihood that Palestinian students would pass the final high school exam and be admitted to college. The second found that gang warfare in Rio de Janeiro's favelas from 2003 to 2009 reduced fifth-graders' standardized math test scores. Both studies suggested the students' worsening psychological wellbeing as the possible mechanism linking conflict and lower scholastic achievement.

Turning to a broader definition of conflict, researchers have found that domestic violence and school-based violence harm children's test scores and high school graduation rates.[51] Furthermore, evidence indicates that childhood abuse has long-term impacts on the likelihood of committing future crimes, achieving less education, and earning less as adults.[52]

Long-Term Education Impacts

Although the research measuring conflict's short-term effects on education is more extensive, some researchers have examined the longer-term educational impacts. For example, one study found that exposure to Peru's 1980–93 civil war had long-lasting negative impacts on schooling, particularly among children exposed early in life.[53] Specifically, children exposed to the conflict before reaching school age accumulated 0.3 fewer years of schooling by the time they became adults. On the other hand, children who were already of school age when they were exposed to the conflict were able to fully catch up to their peers who weren't exposed. In Germany, school-age children who experienced the destruction caused by Allied bombing during World War II suffered long-lasting harm to their education and, as adults, to their employment outcomes.[54]

Other Impacts

Recently, researchers have looked beyond health and education and started to measure how conflict affects labor market outcomes, mental health, and political beliefs

Labor market. Exposure to Peru's civil war during the first three years of children's lives led to a 5 percent decline in monthly adult earnings and a 3.5 percent reduction in the probability of working in the formal economy; the negative effects were 5 percent larger for women than for men.[55] Survey data shows that Ugandan adults who were abducted as children by rebel groups and forced to become soldiers in the rebel army during Uganda's 1990s civil war had attained almost one year less of schooling, were half as likely to be working in a skilled job, and had one-third less annual earnings.[56] In Tajikistan's 1992–98 civil war, on the other hand, younger women (defined as those who were of school age or who had recently entered the labor force) exposed to the conflict were 10 percent more likely to be employed than were women the same age who lived in regions that had experienced less conflict.[57] There were no such effects for men, nor were there effects on wages for men or women. Thus the only effect of exposure to the conflict was to increase women's participation in the labor force, possibly as a coping strategy during a crisis.

Mental health. Research on how exposure to conflict affects mental health typically faces methodological challenges, including lack of validated mental health scales

in surveys and difficulties in measuring individual exposure to conflict. However, some researchers have overcome those obstacles. A study of the 1992–95 conflict in Bosnia and Herzegovina used a clinically validated scale of mental health and war exposure based on administrative data on war casualties.[58] Surprisingly, the study found no significant differences in adult mental health among people who had experienced different levels of exposure to the conflict. Looking at conflict-induced displacement in Colombia since the mid-1990s, another study found that people who had been exposed to severe violent events suffered feelings of hopelessness and pessimism about their prospects for upward mobility.[59] The authors argued that those changes in mental health create psychological barriers that impede people's recovery after a conflict ends.

Political beliefs. Conflict's effects on preferences and beliefs haven't received as much attention from researchers as have effects on health, education, and labor market outcomes. From a theoretical perspective, because children growing up in difficult circumstances are surprisingly psychologically resilient, conflict exposure might not lead to distrust, factionalism, or disengagement from the political system or to other types of outcomes that could produce continuous violence. Recently, researchers examined whether exposure to conflict-related violence during childhood affected adults' political beliefs and engagement.[60] Reviewing all conflicts in sub-Saharan Africa since 1945, they found that conflict exposure as children had little effect on political attitudes or engagement as adults. Another set of researchers, examining the Burundi civil war, conducted a series of field experiments to measure how conflict exposure affected social, risk, and time preferences and found that individuals exposed to conflict act more altruistically, take more risks, and are less patient.[61]

Conclusions

Research shows strong links between hotter temperatures, reduced rainfall, and more conflict, broadly defined. Despite the fast-growing evidence, however, we still know little about the mechanisms that link temperature and rainfall variation to conflict or about how societies respond and potentially adapt to climate change. In addition, we have almost no evidence on what policies (for instance, foreign aid, refugee support, or cash transfers) could best reduce the effects of climate change-related violence on children. We also don't know whether the fact that climate triggers a given conflict means that we need to adopt different policies to mitigate the impacts. Another open question is the extent to which violence directly causes poor outcomes for children or whether violence is only a symptom of other, unobservable factors, such as mismanagement of resources or poorly run institutions that are themselves harming children.

In the past decade, we've learned a lot more about the impact of exposure to conflicts and violence. We have strong evidence, from different types of conflicts worldwide, that conflict exposure in the womb and during early childhood harms children's health and education. However, because

researchers often rely on geographically large administrative regions to measure conflict exposure or ignore conflict-induced migration/displacement, they may not always accurately measure a given individual's conflict exposure. Given the importance of the issue, we also have surprisingly little evidence about how conflict exposure beyond early childhood affects children and relatively little research examining the long-term and intergenerational impacts of conflict exposure. Often because of limitations in the data, we also know very little about the specific mechanisms that link conflict exposure to particular outcomes, about the behavioral adaptations that households adopt in response to conflict, or about the compensating or reinforcing investments that parents make for their children.[62] Although many researchers have speculated about what those mechanisms might be, convincing evidence is rare. We also know little about how exposure to conflicts is similar or different compared with exposure to other types of shocks, particularly when it comes to how conflict affects different types of children (for example, boys versus girls) or children at different ages. Recent research on natural disasters has started to disentangle the impacts caused by different types of disasters (see the article by Carolyn Kousky elsewhere in this issue); we need similar research with respect to different types of violence.[63]

ENDNOTES

1. See Zena Stein et al., *Famine and Human Development: The Dutch Hunger Winter of 1944–1945* (New York: Oxford University Press, 1975); John Strauss and Duncan Thomas, "Health over the Life Course," in *Handbook of Development Economics*, vol. 4, ed. T. Paul Schultz and John A. Strauss (Amsterdam: North-Holland, 2008), 3375–3474; Janet Currie and Douglas Almond, "Human Capital Development before Age Five," in *Handbook of Labor Economics,* vol. 4B, ed. David Card and Orley Ashenfelter (Amsterdam: North-Holland, 2011), 1315–1486; and Janet Currie and Tom Vogl, "Early-Life Health and Adult Circumstance in Developing Countries," *Annual Review of Economics* 5 (2013): 1–36, doi: 10.1146/annurev-economics-081412-103704.

2. For research on how weather affects children, see Sharon Maccini and Dean Yang, "Under the Weather: Health, Schooling, and Economic Consequences of Early-Life Rainfall," *American Economic Review* 99 (2009): 1006–26, doi: 10.1257/aer.99.3.1006. On famine, see Stefan Dercon and Catherine Porter, "Live Aid Revisited: Long-Term Impacts of the 1984 Ethiopian Famine on Children," *Journal of the European Economic Association* 12 (2014): 927–48, doi: 10.1111/jeea.12088. On epidemics, see Douglas Almond, "Is the 1918 Influenza Pandemic Over? Long-Term Effects of in Utero Influenza Exposure in the Post-1940 U.S. Population," *Journal of Political Economy* 114 (2006): 672–712. On natural disasters, see Janet Currie and Maya Rossin-Slater, "Weathering the Storm: Hurricanes and Birth Outcomes," *Journal of Health Economics* 32 (2013): 487–503, doi: 10.1016/j.jhealeco.2013.01.004, and Germán Daniel Caruso, "The Legacy of Natural Disasters: The Intergenerational Impact of 100 Years of Natural Disasters in Latin America," University of Illinois at Urbana-Champaign, 2014. On pollution, see Janet Currie, Matthew Neidell, and Johannes F. Schmieder, "Air Pollution and Infant Health: Lessons from New Jersey," *Journal of Health Economics* 28 (2009): 688–703, doi: 10.1016/j.jhealeco.2009.02.001.

3. Clionadh Raleigh et al., "Introducing ACLED: An Armed Conflict Location and Event Dataset," *Journal of Peace Research* 47 (2010): 651–60, doi: 10.1177/0022343310378914.

4. Marshall Burke, Solomon M. Hsiang, and Edward Miguel, "Climate and Conflict," *Annual Review of Economics* 7 (2015): 577–617, doi: 10.1146/annurev-economics-080614-115430.

5. Historical research has also shown a link between extreme climatic events and the collapse of civilizations and institutional change; see Brendan M. Buckley et al., "Climate as a Contributing Factor in the Demise of Angkor, Cambodia," *Proceedings of the National Academy of Sciences* 107 (2010): 6748–52, doi: 10.1073/pnas.0910827107; and Gerald H. Haug et al., "Climate and the Collapse of Maya Civilization," *Science* 299 (2003): 1731–35, doi: 10.1126/science.1080444.

6. Edward Miguel, "Poverty and Witch Killing," *Review of Economic Studies* 72 (2005): 1153–72, doi: 10.1111/0034-6527.00365.

7. John O'Loughlin et al., "Climate Variability and Conflict Risk in East Africa, 1990–2009," *Proceedings of the National Academy of Sciences* 109 (2012): 18344–49, doi: 10.1073/pnas.1205130109.

8. Marshall B. Burke et al., "Warming Increases the Risk of Civil War in Africa," *Proceedings of the National Academy of Sciences* 106 (2009): 20670–74, doi: 10.1073/pnas.0907998106.

9. Solomon M. Hsiang, Kyle C. Meng, and Mark A. Cane, "Civil Conflicts Are Associated with the Global Climate," *Nature* 476 (2011): 438–41.

10. Edward Miguel, Shanker Satyanath, and Ernest Sergenti, "Economic Shocks and Civil Conflict: An Instrumental Variables Approach," *Journal of Political Economy* 112 (2004): 725–53, doi: 10.1086/421174.

11. Burke et al., "Risk of Civil War."

12. Halvard Buhaug, "Climate Not to Blame for African Civil Wars," *Proceedings of the National Academy of Sciences* 107 (2010): 16477–82, doi: 10.1073/pnas.1005739107.

13. Marshall Burke et al., "Climate and Civil War: Is the Relationship Robust?" Working Paper no. 16440 (National Bureau of Economic Research, Cambridge, MA, 2010).

14. Wario R. Adano et al., "Climate Change, Violent Conflict and Local Institutions in Kenya's Drylands," *Journal of Peace Research* 49 (2012): 65–80, doi: 10.1177/0022343311427344; Ole Magnus Theisen, "Climate Clashes? Weather Variability, Land Pressure, and Organized Violence in Kenya, 1989–2004," *Journal of Peace Research* 49 (2012): 81–96, doi: 10.1177/0022343311425842; and Clionadh Raleigh and Dominic Kniveton, "Come Rain or Shine: An Analysis of Conflict and Climate Variability in East Africa," *Journal of Peace Research* 49 (2012): 51–64, doi: 10.1177/0022343311427754.

15. Mariaflavia Harari and Eliana La Ferrara, "Conflict, Climate and Cells: A Disaggregated Analysis," Discussion Paper no. 9277 (Centre for Economic Policy Research, London, 2013).

16. Ruixue Jia, "Weather Shocks, Sweet Potatoes and Peasant Revolts in Historical China," *Economic Journal* 124 (2014): 92–118, doi: 10.1111/ecoj.12037; Melissa Dell, "Essays in Economic Development and Political Economy," PhD dissertation, Massachusetts Institute of Technology, Cambridge, MA, 2012, http://dspace.mit.edu/handle/1721.1/72831, especially chapter 3, "Insurgency and Long-Run Development: Lessons from the Mexican Revolution," 139–69; and Oliver Vanden Eynde, "Targets of Violence: Evidence from India's Naxalite Conflict," Paris School of Economics, 2015, http://www.parisschoolofeconomics.eu/docs/vanden-eynde-oliver/version_2015_11.pdf.

17. Solomon M. Hsiang, Marshall Burke, and Edward Miguel, "Quantifying the Influence of Climate on Human Conflict," *Science* 341 (2013), doi: 10.1126/science.1235367.

18. Matthew Ranson, "Crime, Weather, and Climate Change," *Journal of Environmental Economics and Management* 67 (2014): 274–302, doi: 10.1016/j.jeem.2013.11.008.

19. Sheetal Sekhri and Adam Storeygard, "Dowry Deaths: Response to Weather Variability in India," *Journal of Development Economics* 111 (2014): 212–23, doi: 10.1016/j.jdeveco.2014.09.001.

20. Sarah Hebous and Stefan Klonner, "Economic Distress and Farmer Suicides in India: An Econometric Investigation," Discussion Paper no. 565 (Department of Economics, University of Heidelberg, 2014).

21. Ceren Baysan et al., "Economic and Non-Economic Factors in Violence: Evidence from Organized Crime, Suicides and Climate in Mexico," Department of Agricultural and Resource Economics, University of California, Berkeley, 2015.

22. Melissa Dell, Benjamin F. Jones, and Benjamin A. Olken, "Temperature Shocks and Economic Growth: Evidence from the Last Half Century," *American Economic Journal: Macroeconomics* 4 (2012): 66–95, doi: 10.1257/mac.4.3.66.

23. Melissa Dell, Benjamin F. Jones, and Benjamin A. Olken, "What Do We Learn from the Weather? The New Climate-Economy Literature," *Journal of Economic Literature* 52 (2014): 740–98, doi: 10.1257/jel.52.3.740.

24. Solomon M. Hsiang and Kyle C. Meng, "Tropical Economics," *American Economic Review* 105 (2015): 257–61, doi: 10.1257/aer.p20151030.

25. Paul Collier and Anke Hoeffler, "On Economic Causes of Civil War," *Oxford Economic Papers* 50 (1998): 563–73, doi: 10.1093/oep/50.4.563; and Paul Collier, "On the Economic Consequences of Civil War," *Oxford Economic Papers* 51 (1999): 168–83, doi: 10.1093/oep/51.1.168.

26. Donald R. Davis and David E Weinstein, "Bones, Bombs and Break Points: The Geography of Economic Activity," *American Economic Review* 92 (2002): 1269–89; Steven Brakman, Harry Garretsen, and Marc Schramm, "The Strategic Bombing of German Cities during World War II and Its Impact on City Growth," *Journal of Economic Geography* 4 (2004): 201–18, doi: 10.1093/jeg/4.2.201; Edward Miguel and Gérard Roland, "The Long-Run Impact of Bombing Vietnam," *Journal of Development Economics* 96 (2011): 1–15, doi: 10.1016/j.jdeveco.2010.07.004; and John Bellows and Edward Miguel, "War and Local Collective Action in Sierra Leone," *Journal of Public Economics* 93 (2009): 1144–57, doi: 10.1016/j.jpubeco.2009.07.012.

27. Siyan Chen, Norman V. Loayza, and Marta Reynal-Querol, "The Aftermath of Civil War," *World Bank Economic Review* 22 (2008): 63–85, doi: 10.1093/wber/lhn001.

28. Tom Bundervoet, Philip Verwimp, and Richard Akresh, "Health and Civil War in Rural Burundi," *Journal of Human Resources* 44 (2009): 536–63, doi: 10.3368/jhr.44.2.536.

29. All figures are from International Monetary Fund, "Burundi: Poverty Reduction Strategy Paper," IMF Country Report no. 07/46 (International Monetary Fund, Washington, DC, 2007), https://www.imf.org/external/pubs/ft/scr/2007/cr0746.pdf.

30. Richard Akresh, Leonardo Lucchetti, and Harsha Thirumurthy, "Wars and Child Health: Evidence from the Eritrean–Ethiopian Conflict," *Journal of Development Economics* 99 (2012): 330–40, doi: 10.1016/j.jdeveco.2012.04.001.

31. Richard Akresh, German Caruso, and Harsha Thirumurthy, "Medium-Term Health Impacts of Shocks Experienced in Utero and after Birth: Evidence from Detailed Geographic Information on War Exposure," Working Paper no. 20763 (National Bureau of Economic Research, Cambridge, MA, 2014).

32. Skye M. Endara, "Does Acute Maternal Stress in Pregnancy Affect Infant Health Outcomes? Examination of a Large Cohort of Infants Born after the Terrorist Attacks of September 11, 2001," *BMC Public Health* 9 (2009): 252, doi: 10.1186/1471-2458-9-252; Maccini and Yang, "Under the Weather: Health, Schooling, and Economic Consequences of Early-Life Rainfall," *American Economic Review* 99 (2009): 1006–26, doi: 10.1257/aer.99.3.1006; Jason M. Fletcher, "Examining the Long Term Mortality Effects of Early Health Shocks," Paper no. CES-WP-14-19 (US Census Bureau Center for Economic Studies, Washington, DC, 2014).

33. Richard Akresh, Philip Verwimp, and Tom Bundervoet, "Civil War, Crop Failure, and Child Stunting in Rwanda," *Economic Development and Cultural Change* 59 (2011): 777–810, doi: 10.1086/660003.

34. Elaina Rose, "Consumption Smoothing and Excess Female Mortality in Rural India," *Review of Economics and Statistics* 81 (1999): 41–9, doi: 10.1162/003465399767923809, and Ren Mu and Xiaobo Zhang, "Why Does the Great Chinese Famine Affect Male and Female Survivors Differently? Mortality Selection versus Son Preference," *Economics and Human Biology* 9 (2008): 92–105, doi: 10.1016/j.ehb.2010.07.003.

35. Olga Shemyakina, "Political Violence, Land Reform and Child Health: Results from Zimbabwe," School of Economics, Georgia Institute of Technology, Atlanta, 2015.

36. Jean-Pierre Tranchant, Patricia Justino, and Cathérine Müller, "Political Violence, Drought and Child Malnutrition: Empirical Evidence from Andhra Pradesh, India," Working Paper no. 173 (Households in Conflict Network, Brighton, UK, 2014).

37. Adriana Camacho, "Stress and Birth Weight: Evidence from Terrorist Attacks," *American Economic Review* 98 (2008): 511–15, doi: 10.1257/aer.98.2.511.

38. Hani Mansour and Daniel I. Rees, "Armed Conflict and Birth Weight: Evidence from the Al-Aqsa Intifada," *Journal of Development Economics* 99 (2012): 190–99, doi: 10.1016/j.jdeveco.2011.12.005.

39. Ryan Brown, "The Mexican Drug War and Early-Life Health: The Impact of Violent Crime on Birth Outcomes," Department of Economics, University of Colorado Denver, 2015.

40. Richard Akresh et al., "War and Stature: Growing Up during the Nigerian Civil War," *American Economic Review* 102 (2012b): 273–77, doi: 10.1257/aer.102.3.273.

41. Albertine Beard and Martin Blaser, "The Ecology of Height: The Effect of Microbial Transmission on Human Height," *Perspectives in Biology and Medicine* 45 (2002): 475–98.

42. Anne Case and Christina Paxson, "Causes and Consequences of Early-Life Health," *Demography* 47 (2010): S65–85, doi: 10.1353/dem.2010.0007; and Flavio Cunha and James Heckman, "The Technology of Skill Formation," *American Economic Review* 97 (2007): 31–47, doi: 10.1257/aer.97.2.31.

43. Richard Akresh et al., "First and Second Generation Impacts of Nigeria's Biafran War," Department of Economics, University of Illinois at Urbana-Champaign, 2015.

44. Richard Akresh and Damien de Walque, "Armed Conflict and Schooling: Evidence from the 1994 Rwandan Genocide," Discussion Paper no. 3516 (Institute for the Study of Labor [IZA], Bonn, Germany, 2008).

45. Alison Des Forges, *Leave None to Tell the Story: Genocide in Rwanda* (New York: Human Rights Watch, 1999).

46. All figures are from International Monetary Fund, "Rwanda: Statistical Appendix," IMF Staff Country Report no. 98/115 (International Monetary Fund, Washington, DC, 1998), https://www.imf.org/external/pubs/ft/scr/1998/cr98115.pdf.

47. Olga Shemyakina, "The Effect of Armed Conflict on Accumulation of Schooling: Results from Tajikistan," *Journal of Development Economics* 95 (2011): 186–200, doi: 10.1016/j.jdeveco.2010.05.002.

48. Mayra Buvinić, Monica Das Gupta, and Olga N. Shemyakina, "Armed Conflict, Gender and Schooling," *World Bank Economic Review* 28 (2013): 311–19, doi: 10.1093/wber/lht032.

49. Christine Valente, "Education and Civil Conflict in Nepal," *World Bank Economic Review* 28 (2014): 354–83, doi: 10.1093/wber/lht014.

50. Tilman Bruck, Michele Di Maio, and Sami Miaari, "Learning the Hard Way: The Effect of Violent Conflict on Student Achievement," Working Paper no. 185 (Households in Conflict Network, Brighton, UK, 2014); Joanna Monteiro and Rudi Rocha, "Drug Battles and School Achievement: Evidence from Rio de Janeiro's Favelas," Brazilian Institute of Economics, Getulio Vargas Foundation, 2013.

51. Jeffrey Groger, "Local Violence and Educational Attainment," *Journal of Human Resources* 32 (1997): 659–82, and Scott Carrell and Mark Hoekstra, "Externalities in the Classroom: How Children Exposed to Domestic Violence Affect Everyone's Kids," *American Economic Journal: Applied Economics* 2 (2010): 211–28.

52. Janet Currie and Erdal Tekin, "Understanding the Cycle: Childhood Maltreatment and Future Crime," *Journal of Human Resources* 47 (2012): 509–49, and Janet Currie and Cathy Spatz Widom, "Long-Term Consequences of Child Abuse and Neglect on Adult Economic Well-Being," *Child Maltreatment* 15 (2010): 111–20, doi: 10.1177/1077559509355316.

53. Gianmarco Leon, "Civil Conflict and Human Capital Accumulation: Long-Term Effects of Political Violence in Peru," *Journal of Human Resources* 47 (2012): 991–1023, doi:10.3368/jhr.47.4.991.

54. Mevlude Akbulut-Yuksel, "Children of War: The Long-Run Effects of Large-Scale Physical Destruction and Warfare on Children," *Journal of Human Resources* 49 (2014): 634–62, doi: 10.3368/jhr.49.3.634.

55. Jose Galdo, "The Long-Run Labor-Market Consequences of Civil War: Evidence from the Shining Path in Peru," *Economic Development and Cultural Change* 61 (2013): 789–823, doi: 10.1086/670379.

56. Christopher Blattman and Jeannie Annan, "The Consequences of Child Soldiering," *Review of Economics and Statistics* 92 (2010): 882–98, doi:10.1162/REST_a_00036.

57. Olga Shemyakina, "Exploring the Impact of Conflict Exposure during Formative Years on Labor Market Outcomes in Tajikistan," *Journal of Development Studies* 51, no. 4 (2015): 1–25.

58. Quy-Toan Do and Lakshmi Iyer, "Mental Health in the Aftermath of Conflict," Policy Research Working Paper no. 5132 (World Bank, Washington, DC, 2009).

59. Andrés Moya and Michael Carter, "Violence and the Formation of Hopelessness and Pessimistic Prospects of Upward Mobility in Colombia," Working Paper no. 20463 (National Bureau of Economic Research, Cambridge, MA, 2014).

60. Achyuta Adhvaryu and James Fenske, "Conflict and the Formation of Political Beliefs in Africa," Working Paper no. 164 (Households in Conflict Network, Brighton, UK, 2014).

61. Maarten J. Voors et al., "Violent Conflict and Behavior: A Field Experiment in Burundi," *American Economic Review* 102 (2012): 941–64, doi: 10.1257/aer.102.2.941.

62. Richard Akresh et al., "Child Labor, Schooling, and Child Ability," Policy Research Working Paper no. 5965 (World Bank, Washington, DC, 2012).

63. Caruso, "Legacy."

Impacts of Natural Disasters on Children

Carolyn Kousky

Summary

We can expect climate change to alter the frequency, magnitude, timing, and location of many natural hazards. For example, heat waves are likely to become more frequent, and heavy downpours and flooding more common and more intense. Hurricanes will likely grow more dangerous, rising sea levels will mean more coastal flooding, and more-frequent and more-intense droughts will produce more wildfires. Children, particularly the poor and those in developing countries, are at risk.

Carolyn Kousky considers three ways that natural disasters may harm children disproportionately, often with long-lasting effects. First, disasters can damage children's physical health. Children may be injured or killed, but they may also suffer from such things as malnutrition caused by disruptions in food supply or diarrheal illness caused by contaminated water. Moreover, disasters can cut off access to medical care, even for non-disaster-related illnesses. Second, disasters can cause mental health problems. Not only are disasters themselves stressful and frightening, but children can suffer psychological harm from the damage to their homes and possessions; from migration; from the grief of losing loved ones; from seeing parents or caregivers undergo stress; from neglect and abuse; and from breakdowns in social networks, neighborhoods, and local economies. Third, disasters can interrupt children's education by displacing families, destroying schools, and pushing children into the labor force to help their families make ends meet in straitened times.

How can we mitigate the dangers to children even as disasters become more powerful and more frequent? For one thing, we can prepare for disasters before they strike, for example, by strengthening school buildings and houses. Kousky also describes actions that have been proven to help children after a disaster, such as quickly reuniting them with parents and caregivers. Finally, a range of policies not designed for disasters can nonetheless help mitigate the harm disasters cause children and their families. In fact, Kousky writes, using existing safety net programs may be easier, faster, and more effective than creating entirely new programs after a disaster occurs.

www.futureofchildren.org

Carolyn Kousky is a fellow at Resources for the Future.

Emilia Simeonova of Johns Hopkins University reviewed and critiqued a draft of this article.

Kousky would like to thank Stephane Hallegatte, Debarati Guha Sapir, and Vica Bogaerts for helpful early discussions. She would also like to thank all the contributors to this issue for feedback on an earlier draft. Any errors are her own.

Scientists predict that as the climate warms, certain weather-related extreme events may increase in frequency or magnitude. In some regions, for example, heat waves may become more common or hurricanes more intense. Scholarship on natural disasters goes back to the 1960s, and recent concern about how climate change will affect disasters has led more researchers to study the topic. Only a small subset of studies, however, have focused on how natural disasters affect children. Yet, on average, roughly half the people affected by disasters are children, and Save the Children estimates that during the next decade, up to 175 million children will be affected by weather-related disasters connected to climate change.[1] Compared with adults, children may be more vulnerable to disasters or have different needs afterward, warranting special attention.

In this review, I seek to answer several questions.

- Do disasters have a disproportional effect on children?

- If so, what are those effects?

- How long do the effects last?

- What can be done to mitigate the harm disasters do?

Research that examines those questions comes largely, although not exclusively, from the fields of economics, public health, and psychiatry.

A few things to note at the outset: I focus on empirical findings, not theory. I limit the scope to weather-related disasters because they are the disasters most likely to be altered by climate change. Although studies of earthquakes or chemical spills, for example, might hold lessons about the impacts of weather-related disasters, I don't include them here. I also focus on sudden-onset disasters, such as severe storms, and not long-duration events, such as droughts, or annual climatological conditions, such as monsoon seasons. Finally, some places experience chronic disaster conditions, such as annual flooding; the effects of such repeated disasters could be quite different, thanks to the adaptation that has occurred in response, and they, too, are not included here. That said, to identify lessons for improving response in areas likely to see more disasters as the climate warms, researchers could usefully examine the adaptations people have undertaken in areas that experience frequent disasters.

Research on the subject of disasters and children is limited almost exclusively to three impacts, which form my framework for organizing this article: (1) physical health, (2) mental health, and (3) educational attainment and achievement. The studies I review identify, for the most part, correlations—that is, associations between a disaster and a health or educational outcome but not the underlying causes of those associations. Identifying the mechanisms that drive relationships should be a research priority, because it would help guide disaster response policy. Many plausible hypotheses have been put forward with some degree of supporting evidence, and I discuss those. It's also worth noting that many studies examine small samples of children, focusing on a particular disaster and geographic and cultural context, meaning that their findings might not apply elsewhere.

Looking across the research, it's clear that natural disasters can harm children's health, both physical and mental, as well as their education. The effects are often small, but they can be much greater for the severest disasters. Though many impacts seem to subside in the short to medium run, larger effects that occur at critical points in a child's development can persist for a lifetime or even be passed to the next generation. This is particularly true for severe damage to health that occurs in the womb or early childhood. Negative effects are generally greater for the poor and in developing countries. And in many developing countries, children and adolescents constitute a much larger share of the population than they do in developed countries. We need more research on the impact on children not of disasters themselves but of living in areas where disaster risk is high.

Sadly, but also optimistically, many impacts are preventable in the sense that we know ways to lessen the harm disasters do to children. The barriers to more widespread adoption of such practices include different priorities, lack of funding, and lack of political will. Tellingly, general improvements in income and development, along with nondisaster safety-net programs, may be among the best ways to protect children in times of disaster. In addition, there is consensus about what to do after a disaster to protect children, such as quickly reuniting families, providing shelter, and maintaining supplies of clean water. Governments, international agencies, and nonprofit groups continue to work on ensuring that those practices are followed around the world.

How Disasters Affect Children

Scientists increasingly agree that climate change will alter the pattern of many extreme weather events. Heat waves are likely to become more frequent, and heavy downpours more common and more intense. Hurricanes will likely grow stronger, and more-frequent and more-intense droughts will produce more wildfires. Extreme weather events are the disasters most likely to change in response to elevated levels of greenhouse gases, and they are responsible for the majority of disaster losses. The annual average global cost of weather-related disasters ranges from $90 billion to $130 billion.[2] Those figures likely underestimate the full costs of disasters, however. Many types of disaster damage are underreported or not measured. For instance, many nonmarket impacts, such as loss of family heirlooms or environmental degradation, are rarely measured, and some, such as losses from interrupted business, are not fully captured by estimates.

Changes in extremes won't be uniform around the globe.[3] Spatial variation is important for estimating disasters' effects because damage from a disaster is a function not only of the event itself but also of where and how societies build—and the resources available to recover and respond. Those things vary dramatically both across and within countries. On a GDP basis, developing countries sustain greater damage from natural disasters. Developing countries also experience much of the death toll from disasters, although across the globe, fatalities have generally decreased over time, due partly to early warning systems and improved construction techniques.

Impact Pathways

Children may be more vulnerable after a disaster. They rely on caregivers, who may be unprepared or overwhelmed. Very young children may not be able to communicate necessary information if they become separated from their caregivers. Some children require special care, special nutrition, and special supplies. Children's physiology makes them more vulnerable than adults to certain health impacts. For example, children breathe more air per pound of body weight than adults do, and their bodies contain less fluid, making them more susceptible to dehydration. They can also be at a point in their development where health problems today can have long-term consequences. They may have greater trouble processing emotional trauma. For all those reasons, a natural disaster may affect a child quite differently from the way it affects an adult. Indeed, it may affect children quite differently depending on their ages.

Disasters can affect children through many interrelated pathways. First, they cause direct physical harm. A disaster can damage schools and health-care facilities, thus interrupting education and reducing the availability of medical care. Disasters can destroy a household's assets. Children or family members can be injured or killed, or they can contract illnesses from postdisaster conditions. Families may lose income either because employed members of the household lose their jobs due to injury or macroeconomic conditions or because working members of the household are killed. In many developing-country contexts, loss of income—combined with loss of assets and higher expenditures for disaster repairs—could cause a household to send children into the labor force. Families may also have less money to spend on medical care, food, or school supplies—all with negative effects on children. Finally, a disaster can cause children stress and trauma, which can be exacerbated by witnessing their parents' stress. For children, such a situation can lead to mental health problems that can in turn affect physical health and schooling. Stress can also affect the fetuses of pregnant women.

Children who become separated from their parents or primary caregivers during or after a disaster represent another cause for concern, especially on the part of nongovernmental organizations. Such children may be abused, exploited, and neglected. Few researchers have examined those impacts, but I return to them later when I discuss best practices for children after a disaster.

A disaster's effects are mediated by the individual characteristics of children, families, communities, countries, and the disaster itself. Different children in different circumstances will not respond the same way to a particular type of disaster. Impacts on children also vary across countries due to socioeconomic conditions, local institutions, and political realities that influence disaster response and recovery. All these things can make it extremely difficult to identify clear causal linkages, even if we see correlations between a disaster and changes in particular measures of child wellbeing, such as time spent in school or health outcomes.

Though little research has examined whether living in an area at higher risk of a disaster has any effect on children, some studies have explored how living with risk can affect household income and consumption choices. For example, households in risky areas may be more likely to grow crops low in risk but also low in returns, such as a variety that tolerates drought but produces lower yields. On the other hand, households might choose to live in riskier areas that provide other benefits for children, such as proximity to jobs or education, though I don't know of any research on those types of trade-offs and how they might affect children.

Much economic research on disasters focuses on how they reduce the funds a household has available to spend. Such research is related to a subfield of economics called *income and consumption smoothing*, which studies how households can maintain a constant level of income and/or spending in the face of unexpected events. In most developed countries, households achieve smoothing through insurance and access to credit. Insurance and credit markets may not fully function in many developing countries or for certain populations. Other mechanisms could take their place, however, such as liquidating assets, drawing down savings, or reciprocal lending or gift giving. After a disaster, the extent to which households can make use of those mechanisms varies.

If households can't borrow or save, then they must finance all of their expenditures at a given point in time with income from that period. If a disaster reduces their income or requires greater expenditures, then unless they have other sources of funds to cover the difference, households will face trade-offs that could involve reducing consumption of goods that are important for children or using children to help increase income.[4] If, after a disaster, households reduce their investments in children's health and education— particularly at critical periods in children's development—the effects can persist into adulthood and even to the next generation.[5] The sections that follow review research that tests that proposition in relation to natural disasters, but the proposition has also been examined in other contexts, providing further evidence that strategies to smooth income can involve children.

Common Methodological Issues

As I've said, most scholarship about children and disasters focuses on physical health, mental health, and education. It's worth briefly reviewing some of the challenges in studying those relationships. Because

of limited data, most studies are able to estimate only short-run impacts, although a few draw on data sets that follow the same people over many years to examine long-run effects. Studies are also generally able to identify only correlations and cannot uncover the underlying mechanisms at work. Estimated impacts usually include not only the effects of the disaster but also any actions taken in response. For instance, in regard to how a flood affects health, the estimated effect could include both the immediate reduction in the availability of clean drinking water and whether households begin boiling or filtering water before using it. Finally, it's clear that the impact of disasters varies along many dimensions; researchers have identified some of that variation, but it's likely there's more that researchers cannot observe.

The population samples used in some of the studies also have problems. Many studies use only small samples over a short time—which can make it hard to identify effects—and their findings should not necessarily be extrapolated to broader populations. Studies may use data collected for other purposes, meaning that the sample is not representative of the affected group. In addition, most studies look at individual localized disasters, raising questions about whether the findings can be extended to other places and other types of disasters. Only a handful of studies have information about their sample from before the disaster. Many mental health studies, for example, can't account for how predisaster mental health affects impacts after a disaster, although the few that are able to do so show that it matters.

Most studies compare people who experience a disaster with a control group that didn't experience it, because the control group is distant in either space or time. Researchers must ensure that control groups could plausibly be assumed to behave in a disaster the same way that the populations actually affected did. One reason that assumption could be invalid is that households might sort themselves according to the risk of disasters. That is, groups that live in low-risk areas may not be similar to groups that live in high-risk areas, and thus children affected by disasters might have had different educational or health outcomes compared with children living in safer areas even if a disaster hadn't occurred. Researchers use various statistical methods to try to eliminate the influence of sorting, but they may not be able to fully do so. Some studies are able to demonstrate that people who experience a disaster and those who don't are similar when it comes to variables the researcher can measure, which lends some assurance that the findings are valid, but variables that the researcher did not observe might make the two groups different.

Most studies I review are based on survey data. Some people who are present in the first rounds of the survey drop out in later rounds, often because they moved after the disaster. Results could be biased if the people who leave the study by moving have characteristics that are correlated with the variable the researchers are examining. To provide some assurance that any bias from attrition is small, most studies try to minimize the number of people leaving the sample, identify why any attrition occurred, and compare the characteristics of those who leave with those who stay in the sample.

Finally, a study may not have information on variables that influence the outcome being examined—such as years of schooling—but that also influence whether a child is exposed to a disaster. That situation prevents researchers from being able to identify which effects can be attributed directly to the disaster. Scholars use several approaches to reduce the problem, with varying degrees of success. For example, some health studies compare outcomes among siblings because siblings presumably live in the same household environment and are subject to the same parental decisions, thereby preventing those variables from biasing the estimation. But there may still be differences between siblings that the researcher doesn't know about; for example, one sibling may love school and another may hate it, influencing the family's choice of whether to send a child into the labor force after a disaster.

Effects on Physical Health

Following major disasters, children often suffer from a range of health problems. Natural disasters can affect children's health through several channels. First, a disaster can reduce intake of calories and of essential vitamins and nutrients because a family loses food crops or income to spend on food. Second, a disaster can destroy health infrastructure. This can mean that illnesses or injuries caused by the disaster are difficult to treat and become worse, but it also means that non-disaster-related health problems may go untreated. For example, after Hurricane Katrina struck the US Gulf Coast in 2005, a survey of those living in housing subsidized by the Federal Emergency Management Agency (FEMA) found that access to medical care was fragmented or nonexistent.[6] For instance, many children of surveyed families were unable to get asthma medications, and half of the children who had a personal doctor before the storm didn't have one afterward. In another example from Katrina, both during the storm and for days afterward, University Hospital in

New Orleans had to triage care for more than 20 infants in its neonatal intensive care unit without adequate power, supplies, or communication with the outside world.[7] Supplies had to be rationed and decisions made about prioritizing care—all while staff worked without sufficient sanitation, food, or power and while the babies were separated from their parents.

Finally, unhygienic conditions and lack of safe drinking water can cause infectious diseases to spread. During and after floods in Bangladesh, for example, cases of diarrhea, cholera, and other intestinal diseases increased due to lack of safe drinking water.[8] Diarrheal illness can lead to dehydration and malnourishment. Because of their small size, babies and very young children are especially susceptible, and dehydration can become life threatening. Moreover, those pathways can interact; in other words, poor nutrition can exacerbate illness.

Children's health may be more vulnerable in a disaster for a number of biophysical reasons. Their respiratory rates are higher, their immune systems are less mature, and many of their systems are still undergoing rapid growth and development. It has been documented that fetuses in the womb and very young children are particularly susceptible to severer or longer-term impacts from negative health shocks.

This section first reviews studies that focus on what happens when a disaster occurs while a fetus is in the womb; it then turns to disasters' effects on children.

Exposure in the Womb

Studies of exposure during pregnancy generally find that a disaster can worsen a range of birth outcomes, although they don't always agree about which outcomes are most affected and to what degree. We also know that the time of exposure during pregnancy influences the effects, although researchers disagree about which stage of pregnancy is most sensitive. No studies have pinned down the mechanisms behind those associations, though maternal stress may play a strong role. In developing countries in particular, decreased nutrition and poor sanitation are also likely factors. Finally, if they're severe enough, shocks experienced in the womb may have long-term consequences.

Several researchers have focused on disasters in the United States. A study of 300 pregnant women affected by Hurricane Katrina found that those whose experience of the storm was severe or more intense were more than three times as likely to have low-birth-weight babies and more than twice as likely to have preterm births.[9] Most women in the study were early in their pregnancies or became pregnant shortly after the hurricane; we might see different results among women who experienced the storm in late pregnancy.

A careful study of births in Texas from 1996 to 2008 found somewhat different effects among women who experienced hurricanes.[10] The study compared pregnant women who lived within 30 kilometers (18.6 miles) of a hurricane's path during their first or third trimester with pregnant women who lived within 100 kilometers (62.1 miles). The researchers found that living closer to a hurricane increased the probability of labor or delivery complications by 30 percent, and the probability of abnormal conditions—such as the baby's requiring a ventilator for more than 30 minutes—by 60 percent. By looking at variations across siblings, the authors made sure that the differences they saw didn't stem from differences in the types of families living closer or farther from storms.

During the study period, only a very small number of people in Texas experienced direct health effects from hurricanes; the impact on pregnant women, according to the researchers, likely resulted primarily from stress. (They were able to rule out certain other explanations, such as worse medical care or increases in smoking.) Unlike the authors of the Katrina study, they found no impact on birth weight or gestation period.

Turning to another kind of disaster, a study that examined data on more than 37 million US births from 1972 to 1988 found that exposure to heat waves during pregnancy, especially during the second and third trimesters, led to lower birth weight.[11] Linking that finding to predictions of temperature change by the end of this century, the authors estimate that the probability of having a low-birth-weight baby (one that weighs less than 2,500 grams, or 5.5 pounds) will increase by 5.9 percent for whites and 5 percent for blacks; of course, those estimates don't account for adaptation that might take place in response to climate change. Heat stress may also be related to preterm birth.[12]

Studies of births in developed countries tend to suggest that stress can affect birth outcomes; in developing countries, stress may be compounded by deteriorating health conditions following a disaster. One study examining the 1997–98 El Niño, which caused excess rainfall in Peru, found that children born during or immediately following El Niño in homes that were likely to have been flooded (based on soil saturation data) were more likely to experience inadequate growth, though birth and death rates were unchanged.[13] The authors couldn't test mechanisms behind the association between flooding and children's growth, but

flooded areas experienced food shortages, lack of adequate health care, lack of clean water, increases in malaria and diarrheal diseases, and loss of crops and livestock, which led to reduced incomes. The Peruvian government adopted policies in advance of El Niño to try to minimize harm, and the authors note that health outcomes and/or mortality might have been worse without them.

Though I don't review them here, studies that look at the impact of fetal exposure to other types of disasters during pregnancy, such as wars or earthquakes, find that such events are also associated with negative birth outcomes. A word of caution: Many studies of disasters use birth weight as an indicator of health, usually because such data is widely available. But birth weight may not be the most comprehensive or sensitive measure of children's health, and its use may hide other impacts.[14]

Childhood Exposure

Most studies of how disasters affect health during childhood focus on malnourishment in developing countries. They generally examine one or more of three indicators of children's health: stunting (failure to grow adequately in height, an indication of malnourishment), measured by height-for-age z-scores; being underweight, measured by weight-for-age scores; and wasting, measured by weight-for-height scores. Stunting, being underweight, and wasting could be caused by shifts in consumption or decreases in food supply, among other things.

Before I review studies that focus on malnourishment, I should note two other important findings related to children's health after a disaster. First, in very extreme disasters, children may be more likely than adults to be injured or killed. For example, children in Indonesia were less likely than adults to survive the 2004 Indian Ocean tsunami. It may be that greater physical strength increases the chances of survival; children were less likely to die when more prime-age men lived in the household or when households were headed by a prime-age male fisherman.[15]

Second, children could be at higher risk for a range of diseases, some of them involving malnourishment and some not. For example, after the 2004 tsunami, a Red Cross emergency relief hospital in Banda Aceh, Indonesia, found that children were more likely than adults to suffer from acute diseases, particularly upper respiratory and gastrointestinal infections.[16] Poor sanitation or disruption of medical care could be behind those increases in disease.

Researchers have observed poorer nutrition among children in many countries after many types of disasters. For example, in Bangladesh, among a sample of more than 4,400 children from birth to five years old, those older than two who had been exposed to an extreme flood in 1998 had lower height-for-age z-scores (the measure of stunting) than did children who hadn't been affected; moreover, the children in the sample didn't grow faster after the flood to make up the loss.[17] In Ivory Coast, among a sample of 1,600 households, extreme rainfall in 1986 increased by 3 to 4 percent the proportion of children from birth to 10 years old who were malnourished.[18] In Nicaragua—among a sample of 2,764 households, of which 396 were affected by 1998's category 5 Hurricane Mitch—children from birth to four years old who had experienced the storm were four times as likely to be undernourished.[19] Finally, in rural India, a survey-based study

found that children of households affected by floods were more likely to be stunted and underweight.[20] The greatest impact was on children younger than one year old, suggesting that the first year of life is a sensitive period for disaster exposure. The mechanism for the effects isn't clear, though it could have been lack of safe drinking water.

Long-Term Consequences

A good deal of evidence from outside the field of disaster studies documents long-term harm to health from malnourishment in the womb and in early childhood. Malnourishment during those sensitive periods has been linked to higher risk of illness and death among infants; and, among adults, to shorter stature, less strength, less work capacity, high blood pressure, and high cholesterol.[21] Many studies have also linked health shocks early in life to education and labor market outcomes. For example, early-life health shocks are associated with fewer years of schooling, reduced economic activity, delayed motor development, lower IQ, more behavioral problems, and lower test scores.[22] Evidence is also accumulating to show that the effects of early-life health shocks can persist for generations. Women who were undernourished as children have lower-birth-weight children themselves.[23] Not only did women in Tanzania exposed to a severe flood before they were 18 years of age suffer long-lasting negative effects, but their children had lower height-for-age z-scores. (This wasn't the case among children of men exposed to the flood.)[24] Not all impacts may be so persistent, however. For example, stunting in very young children can likely be reversed to at least some degree if a child's environment greatly improves—for example, if the child's level of nutrition increases dramatically.[25]

Effects on Mental Health

Natural disasters can cause myriad emotionally harmful circumstances for children. Not only is the event itself stressful and frightening, but after it passes, stress can be incurred from the damage to children's homes and possessions, from migration, and from breakdowns in social networks, neighborhoods, and local economies. When loved ones are missing or injured, the grief can be profound, and children may have a harder time processing and coping with such losses. Children may become upset when their caregivers' ability to protect them declines or when they see caregivers experience fear and stress. Many studies have found that when parents have high levels of postdisaster symptoms, their children have high levels as well.

The studies I cover here generally focus on one or both of two things: the prevalence of mental health impacts (researchers have lately been very interested in the symptoms of posttraumatic stress disorder, or PTSD) and whether any observable phenomena predict the likelihood of experiencing mental health symptoms. A few comments are warranted on each topic.

A variety of measures could be used to examine the prevalence of negative mental health impacts. Studies often use arbitrary cutoff values to define a mental "disorder," which can lead to widely different conclusions about the rates of incidence of such things as PTSD and depression, particularly in studies of children. Despite the prevalence of studies examining PTSD symptoms, some concerns have been raised about this measure. PTSD symptoms may not be meaningful unless we can compare them with predisaster symptoms, because some symptoms, such as trouble sleeping,

could have many causes other than exposure to disaster.[26] PTSD diagnoses also might not say much about children's daily functioning, might not capture certain anxieties or important features of coping, or might not take account of the cultural context in which children live.[27]

Many researchers go beyond estimating prevalence to try to identify factors that increase the likelihood a child will exhibit symptoms. As we know from everyday life, children (like adults) can be more or less susceptible to mental health problems such as anxiety or depression; similarly, some people react more strongly to a disaster than others do. A disaster's impact on children varies based on their prior exposure to traumatic events, socioeconomic factors, age, gender, personality traits, cognitive skills, and relationships with their parents and families.[28] As a useful framing device, one study grouped factors that predict symptoms into four categories: aspects of exposure (perceived threat of death, losses, etc.), children's characteristics (such as gender and age), social support (for example, the roles of parents and teachers), and children's coping responses (for example, anger, wishful thinking, and talking to someone).[29]

Short-Term Effects

In the United States, many researchers examined children's and adolescents' mental health after Hurricane Katrina. Among those who had experienced the storm, researchers found high rates of PTSD symptoms as well as other negative mental health impacts and behaviors, such as aggression in adolescents.[30] In the survey I mentioned earlier of families living in FEMA-subsidized housing after Katrina, half of parents reported that at least one of their children was having emotional or behavioral difficulties that hadn't been present before the hurricane.[31] Those studies generally have small samples and thus may not be representative either of those who experienced Katrina or of broader populations, such as all of those at risk of experiencing a hurricane. Still, studies tend to agree that people who experienced Katrina had higher rates of mental health problems.

Several studies have tried to learn what determined whether people experienced symptoms. Most of the answers weren't surprising. For example, children and adolescents who experienced worse impacts were more likely to have symptoms.[32] In one study of 52 children for whom prestorm data was available, those who tended toward anxiety before the storm were more likely to experience symptoms of posttraumatic stress and general anxiety disorder afterward.[33] Younger children also appeared to have more symptoms.[34]

The rates of symptoms fell as time passed. One study of 387 children 9 to 18 years of age found decreases in posttraumatic-stress and depression symptoms both two and three years after the storm. That said, almost 28 percent of the children still had symptoms three years after Katrina.[35] The US Government Accountability Office reported that after Katrina, the number of mental health professionals in the area declined substantially and that the lack of providers was the greatest barrier to getting mental health services for children.[36]

Katrina's negative effects on mental health increased with the intensity of the disaster experience; similar effects have been found after other disasters. One early study looked at more than 800 children who experienced a devastating bushfire in Australia that destroyed hundreds of thousands of hectares of land and property and took 14 lives.[37] Twenty-six months later, one-third of the children were still preoccupied with the disaster, for example by dreaming about it, talking about it often, or incorporating it into their play. Among children who experienced the disaster, those who became separated from their parents afterward, those whose mothers continued to be preoccupied with the event, and those whose family functioning changed were all more likely to exhibit posttraumatic symptoms. Similarly, two studies that examined children and adolescents after Hurricane Andrew hit Florida in 1992 found mental health symptoms among some portion of those surveyed three to six months after the hurricane.[38] Surveys of almost 5,700 children three months after 1989's Hurricane Hugo hit the United States found that symptoms of PTSD were related to how severe the children perceived the hurricane to be, how much damage their homes had sustained, whether one of their parents had lost a job, and whether they continued to be displaced.[39] That study found higher rates of PTSD among younger children and girls. Children with a tendency toward anxiety were also more likely to report PTSD symptoms.

Similar findings emerge in studies from developing countries. A survey of 158 adolescents six months after Hurricane Mitch hit Nicaragua found many had symptoms of posttraumatic stress and depression and that symptom levels were higher among those who lived in the most-damaged cities and those who experienced the death of a family member.[40] Three to four weeks after the 2004 tsunami, a study of 264 children aged 8 to 14 years in affected areas of Sri Lanka found that 14 to 39 percent had PTSD symptoms.[41] Factors that predicted the likelihood children would experience posttraumatic symptoms included subjective and objective measures of the severity of exposure to the tsunami, having family members who died in the tsunami, and the number of traumatic events the children had experienced before the tsunami.

Long-Term Effects and Resilience

Mental health symptoms usually decline as a disaster recedes into the past. But when disasters produce severe threats to life or dramatic disruptions, the impacts can persist for years. However, some factors, such as available and supportive parents, have been found to buffer the impacts. Researchers recently have tried to find the protective factors that can promote resilience. Resilience is "an individual's capacity to recover from, adapt, and remain strong in the face of adversity"; we see resilience when an individual demonstrates good outcomes despite high risks, remains competent under threat, and/or recovers from trauma.[42] A review of studies on disasters' psychological impacts found that although disasters can indeed have serious negative impacts on a minority of the population, most people demonstrate resilience, and no more than 30 percent of youth typically experience chronic impacts.[43]

Numerous contextual and individual factors influence whether a disaster is likely to cause long-lasting mental health problems. The review found no dominant predictive factor; all factors studied exhibited small or moderate effects. Thus there is no consensus on what interventions might help most after a disaster, a point I return to in the concluding section. That said, certain basic policies can undoubtedly improve mental health outcomes for children—for instance,

reuniting children with their families as soon as possible and promptly resuming schooling.

Effects on Schooling

Natural disasters can harm schooling in three primary ways. First, the disaster can destroy schools themselves, interrupting children's education. Second, if children are hurt or sick or malnourished, they may not attend school as frequently and/or may perform more poorly in school. Third, in developing countries in particular, a disaster that reduces household wealth or income may lead parents to shift children out of school and into the labor market to help enhance family income. If those impacts on schooling persist—and whether they do is still an open question among researchers—they could reduce earnings later in life.

This section reviews two types of studies on these topics: (1) studies from developed countries that tend to focus on how changing schools, spending time out of school, or the trauma of the disaster itself can affect educational performance and (2) studies from developing countries that focus on whether households move children into the labor market at the expense of schooling.

Studies from Developed Countries

Severe disasters can damage or destroy schools. When schools cannot reopen after a disaster, not only is a child's education disrupted, but the child may have to remain in potentially unsafe conditions. If there is no alternative child care, the child's parents may be prevented from returning to work, thereby creating economic stress.[44] Disruption to schooling occurred on a very wide scale after Hurricane Katrina. In Louisiana, 196,000 public school students changed schools, many of them missing a month or more of schooling along with losing their homes and moving to new ones.[45]

The findings from Louisiana are particularly interesting because the school districts that were hit hardest by the storm were also some of the worst performing in the state. Displaced students thus often ended up in better schools. Two studies found that switching to better schools mitigated the hurricane's negative effects. One reported that the test scores of students forced to switch schools declined in the first year but—after controlling for other factors that could have affected the outcome—showed gains that went above prehurricane levels by the third and fourth year.[46] The study included only students who stayed in the Louisiana public school system; roughly 40 percent of students left the system entirely, and their experiences might have been different. Another study found similar results when it looked at the achievement test scores of students affected by Katrina who reenrolled after the storm in Louisiana's public schools.[47] Overall, impacts on school achievement were negative but small; they were most significant among students who changed schools and didn't return to their original schools for the entire 2005–06 year or who took longer to reenroll in school after the hurricane. Negative effects were mitigated when displaced students enrolled in higher-performing schools. Less-severe US disasters have also produced small negative effects on education.

Studies from Developing Countries

Very few studies from developing countries look at the impact of destruction of school facilities. However, many government and nongovernmental organization programs alike target that avenue of impact. Children spend a substantial amount of time in school

buildings, which often are not constructed to withstand disasters. For instance, the nonprofit group Build Change reports that the 2007 cyclone in Bangladesh destroyed nearly 500 schools and damaged more than 2,000 others. Super Typhoon Durian (known locally as Typhoon Reming) damaged 90 to 100 percent of the schools in three Philippine cities and 50 to 60 percent in two others. Build Change works with other organizations, including the World Bank, to build safer schools not only to protect children while they're in school but also to help prevent disruptions in schooling after a disaster.

Most research focuses on the trade-off between sending a child into the labor force for income in the short term versus the long-term benefits of investing in the child's human capital. Some researchers simply document an association between a disaster and reduced schooling, whereas others go further and also show an increase in labor force participation by children. The degree of that effect varies by context and by children's attributes such as age and gender. Studies that don't focus on disasters specifically also show that when households lose income or face unemployment, children are more likely to enter the labor force and go to school less often.[48] One important question that hasn't been fully answered due to lack of sufficient data is whether children who are pulled out of school and put to work are less likely to reenroll even if household income returns to preshock levels.

Even though a reduction in income or an increase in expenditures after a disaster could lead parents to pull their children from school and put them to work, it's also possible that we might see an increase in schooling should a disaster cause macroeconomic disruption that results in lower wages or fewer jobs. Although such an outcome is plausible, it was not observed in any of the studies I reviewed for this article.

Studies from developing countries generally examine rural households, and they typically find some substitution away from schooling after a disaster. For example, one study found that in rural India, child labor functions as self-insurance for poor households.[49] Another study—of households in Tanzania—found that among children aged 7 to 15 years, income shocks due to crop loss led to increased child labor, largely within the household, and decreased school attendance.[50] Specifically, children in households that experienced a crop loss were 20 percentage points less likely to be enrolled in school (with a mean enrollment rate of 70 percent). In Ivory Coast, school enrollment among children aged 7 to 15 years decreased by about 20 percentage points (more than a third of the original rate) in areas that had experienced rainfall shocks.[51] In Nicaraguan communities affected by Hurricane Mitch, labor force participation by children aged 6 to 15 years increased 58 percent.[52] The proportion of children who were both enrolled in school and working more than doubled, rising from 7.5 to 15.6 percent.

More evidence comes from Mexico, where researchers examined the impact of climate shocks (and other income shocks I don't discuss here) on the schooling of 8- to 17-year-olds from 1998 to 2000.[53] They found that disasters other than droughts reduced school enrollment by 3.2 percentage points during the following six months. The authors also found that primary school children, indigenous children, children of agricultural workers, and girls were all more affected. The authors also found that students who were pulled out of school were less likely

to reenroll in the near term. That effect was stronger for secondary-school children. Participation in the labor force increases among children following a disaster, and more so among older children, providing evidence that the decrease in school attendance is based on a need for income.

We also see educational impacts after Hurricane Mitch in rural households in Honduras.[54] Among 387 adolescents for whom data was available from four years before the storm to three years after, those who lived in households that experienced greater income loss after the hurricane had lower educational attainment scores—but only in households that had little or no access to credit. Thus it's possible that improving credit or liquidity through transfers or loans could help families maintain investments in their children's education.

Mitigating the Effects of Disasters

Climate scientists project that many regions will see increases in the intensity and/ or frequency of certain weather-related extreme events. Some areas that haven't been susceptible to natural disasters in the past may become vulnerable as the climate warms. Thus, unless we take steps to mitigate such disasters, the harm they cause children around the globe is likely to increase. We don't have much research on the efficacy of various policies—including which ones perform better than others in protecting children—but we know that many interventions have a positive impact. That said, lack of funds and a failure to prioritize them often stall the implementation of such policies. Policies could also be enhanced if we better understood the channels through which natural disasters' effects on children operate. Though a full review of various interventions is beyond the scope of this article, I can offer a brief overview of major findings and themes.

First, to increase the odds that negative impacts on children will be minimized, many measures can be taken before a disaster ever strikes. They include building schools, health facilities, and houses that can better withstand disasters. International agencies and nonprofit groups are helping people in developing countries build safer buildings, and local initiatives have emerged around the world. In Kansas, for example, the Wichita Public Schools have created school safe rooms to protect children from tornadoes. In general, schools and health facilities should adopt disaster response plans, ensure that all of their staff members are aware of the plans, and practice them routinely. Unfortunately, much progress remains to be made in these areas. Save the Children found that as of 2013, 28 states and Washington, DC, were falling short of having the best kinds of policies in place to protect children in day care centers and schools from disasters.[55] Children should themselves be educated about disaster risks—with curricula tailored for various ages—and empowered to take action to reduce those risks. Children should also be more directly involved in participatory research that aims to understand their needs and responses.[56]

A range of policies not designed for disasters can nonetheless help mitigate the harm disasters cause children and their families. Such policies include wide access to credit, subsidies for school enrollment, and social insurance policies, which can help maintain consumption of goods critical for children after a disaster. For example, in developing countries, conditional cash transfer programs, which give money to families who keep their children in school, can help ensure that more children stay in school and out of the labor force after a disaster.[57] In the United States, unemployment insurance and public medical spending increase after a disaster; even though those programs aren't designed specifically for disasters, they help mitigate a disaster's negative effects.[58] Using existing safety net programs for disaster response may also be easier, faster, and more effective than creating entirely new programs after a disaster occurs.

In the aftermath of a disaster, numerous actions have been proven to help protect children. One is reuniting children as quickly as possible with parents, families, or other primary caregivers, who can buffer children against the disaster's trauma and keep them safe from neglect and abuse. Governments and nonprofits can work together to reunite families, and several organizations have developed identification systems to speed that process; in the United States after Hurricane Katrina, unfortunately, the authorities did a poor job of reuniting children with their families.[59] In any case, caregivers, too, need support, such as family-friendly shelter and housing and food aid appropriate for infants and children. Direct aid to families is also important. After a disaster, children can benefit from even small cash transfers, which can be used to pay for food, soap, school, or medical care.[60] Managing spikes in food prices or providing food for families in need can also benefit children. Response must be rapid, however, because delays can lead to stress on the family and/or unnecessary deterioration of the situation, causing greater harm.[61] Quickly reestablishing predisaster routines, such as schooling and other normal activities, can also protect children.

The public health sector has developed a set of interventions and practices that can help children after a disaster. They include providing necessities for hygiene to prevent the spread of disease and making safe drinking water available. Breastfeeding of infants should be encouraged. Young children should be targeted for intervention to prevent dehydration and other illnesses, and vaccinations should be dispatched quickly to protect against the spread of diseases such as cholera. There is no consensus, however, on interventions to protect children's mental health, an area that deserves further attention.

Conclusions

I've reviewed the empirical evidence on how sudden, weather-related disasters affect children. Researchers have shown that disasters can harm children's physical and mental health as well as their schooling. Younger children seem most susceptible. The effects of the severest disasters or of shocks to health and schooling at critical periods in children's development can last for years, even into adulthood. That said, children's responses to disaster vary widely depending on the type of disaster; the countries, communities, and families in which children live; and the characteristics of individual children. We're beginning to understand some of that variation—such as critical ages, differences by gender, or the roles of certain social structures or policies in mitigating impacts—but we need much more work to identify what can make a disaster's impacts more or less severe. One area we know too little about, for example, involves differences between rural and highly urbanized areas. If we better understood what drives variation

in people's responses to disaster, we could improve both mitigation policies and coping strategies.

Three other large gaps in our knowledge stand out. First, researchers have carried out very few careful policy evaluation studies to understand which interventions are most effective. Although this is partly because it's difficult to gather the data needed to do such studies well, further work in this area is warranted. Second, although researchers have uncovered many associations between disasters and outcomes, the pathways by which disasters produce the observed effects are largely unknown. I've discussed many hypotheses in this article, but we poorly understand which mechanisms operate when, or to what degree. Research that identifies such mechanisms could help us develop better responses. Finally, we don't know enough about whether and how living with higher risk of disasters can translate into behaviors that affect children's wellbeing.

As climate change alters extreme events, some places may begin to see more-frequent natural disasters, from floods to heat waves. Households could have a harder time recovering from repeated disasters, and the effects on children could be many times more severe than those from a onetime shock. Studying areas that already face repeated disasters could help identify strategies for other areas as the climate warms. For example, Bangladesh has introduced schools on boats to keep children in school even during a flood. On a warming planet, we may need such responses even in areas that until now have been unaccustomed to considering disaster risk.

ENDNOTES

1. Paula McDiarmid, ed., *In the Face of Disaster: Children and Climate Change* (London: International Save the Children Alliance, 2008).

2. Carolyn Kousky, "Informing Climate Adaptation: A Review of the Economic Costs of Natural Disasters," *Energy Economics* 46 (2014): 576–92, doi: 10.1016/j.eneco.2013.09.029.

3. For example: Gerald A. Meehl and Claudia Tebaldi, "More Intense, More Frequent, and Longer Lasting Heat Waves in the 21st Century," *Science* 305 (2004): 994–97, doi: 10.1126/science.1098704; Matthew Ranson et al., "Tropical and Extratropical Cyclone Damages under Climate Change," *Climatic Change* 127 (2014): 227–41, doi: 10.1007/s10584-014-1255-4.

4. Hanan G. Jacoby, "Borrowing Constraints and Progress through School: Evidence from Peru," *Review of Economics and Statistics* 76 (1994): 151–60, doi: 10.2307/2109833; Jonathan Morduch, "Income Smoothing and Consumption Smoothing," *Journal of Economic Perspectives* 9 (1995): 103–14, doi: 10.1257/jep.9.3.103.

5. James J. Heckman, "The Economics, Technology, and Neuroscience of Human Capability Formation," *Proceedings of the National Academy of Sciences* 104 (2007): 13250–55, doi: 10.1073/pnas.0701362104.

6. David Abramson and Richard Garfield, *On the Edge: Children and Families Displaced by Hurricanes Katrina and Rita Face a Looming Medical and Mental Health Crisis* (New York: Mailman School of Public Health, Columbia University, 2006).

7. Brian M. Barkemeyer, "Practicing Neonatology in a Blackout: The University Hospital NICU in the Midst of Hurricane Katrina: Caring for Children without Power or Water," *Pediatrics* 117 (2006): S369–74, doi: 10.1542/peds.2006-0099F.

8. Roy Brouwer et al., "Socioeconomic Vulnerability and Adaptation to Environmental Risk: A Case Study of Climate Change and Flooding in Bangladesh," *Risk Analysis* 27 (2007): 313–26.

9. Xu Xiong et al., "Exposure to Hurricane Katrina, Post-Traumatic Stress Disorder and Birth Outcomes," *American Journal of the Medical Sciences* 336 (2008): 111–15, doi: 10.1097/MAJ.0b013e318180f21c.

10. Janet Currie and Maya Rossin-Slater, "Weathering the Storm: Hurricanes and Birth Outcomes," *Journal of Health Economics* 32 (2013): 487–503, doi: 10.1016/j.jhealeco.2013.01.004.

11. Olivier Deschênes, Michael Greenstone, and Jonathan Guryan, "Climate Change and Birth Weight," *American Economic Review* 99 (2009): 211–17, doi: 10.1257/aer.99.2.211.

12. Mary Carolan-Olah and Dorota Frankowska, "High Environmental Temperature and Preterm Birth: A Review of the Evidence," *Midwifery* 30 (2014): 50–59, doi: 10.1016/j.midw.2013.01.011; Emilia Simeonova, "Out of Sight, Out of Mind? Natural Disasters and Pregnancy Outcomes in the USA," *CESifo Economic Studies* 57 (2011): 403–31, doi: 10.1093/cesifo/ifr005.

13. Heather E. Danysh et al., "El Niño Adversely Affected Childhood Stature and Lean Mass in Northern Peru," *Climate Change Responses* 1 (2014): 1–10, doi: 10.1186/s40665-014-0007-z.

14. Douglas Almond and Janet Currie, "Killing Me Softly: The Fetal Origins Hypothesis," *Journal of Economic Perspectives* 25 (2011): 153–72, doi: 10.1257/jep.25.3.153.

15. Elizabeth Frankenberg et al., "Mortality, the Family and the Indian Ocean Tsunami," *Economic Journal* 121 (2011): F162–82, doi: 10.1111/j.1468-0297.2011.02446.x.

16. Debarati Guha-Sapir, Willem Gijsbert van Panhuis, and Joel Lagoutte, "Short Communication: Patterns of Chronic and Acute Diseases after Natural Disasters—A Study from the International Committee of the Red Cross Field Hospital in Banda Aceh after the 2004 Indian Ocean Tsunami," *Tropical Medicine and International Health* 12 (2007): 1338–41, doi: 10.1111/j.1365-3156.2007.01932.x.

17. Carlo del Ninno and Mattias Lundberg, "Treading Water: The Long-Term Impact of the 1998 Flood on Nutrition in Bangladesh," *Economics and Human Biology* 3 (2005): 67–96, doi: 10.1016/j.ehb.2004.12.002.

18. Robert Jensen, "Agricultural Volatility and Investments in Children," *American Economic Review* 90 (2000): 399–404, doi: 10.1257/aer.90.2.399.

19. Javier E. Baez and Indhira V. Santos, "Children's Vulnerability to Weather Shocks: A Natural Disaster as a Natural Experiment," working paper (World Bank, Washington, DC, 2007).

20. Jose Manuel Rodriguez-Llanes et al., "Child Malnutrition and Recurrent Flooding in Rural Eastern India: A Community-Based Survey," *BMJ Open* 1 (2011): e000109, doi: 10.1136/bmjopen-2011-000109.

21. Reynaldo Martorell, "The Nature of Child Malnutrition and Its Long-Term Implications," *Food and Nutrition Bulletin* 20 (1999): 288–92, doi: 10.1177/156482659902000304; Cesar G. Victora et al., "Maternal and Child Undernutrition: Consequences for Adult Health and Human Capital," *Lancet* 371 (2008): 340–57, doi: 10.1016/S0140-6736(07)61692-4; Almond and Currie, "Killing Me Softly."

22. For example, see: Victora et al., "Maternal and Child Undernutrition"; Martorell, "Nature of Child Malnutrition"; and Janet Currie, "Healthy, Wealthy, and Wise: Socioeconomic Status, Poor Health in Childhood, and Human Capital Development," *Journal of Economic Literature* 47 (2009): 87–122, doi: 10.1257/jel.47.1.87.

23. Victora et al., "Maternal and Child Undernutrition."

24. Germán Daniel Caruso, "Intergenerational Transmission of Shocks in Early Life: Evidence from the Tanzania Great Flood of 1993" (Department of Economics, University of Illinois at Urbana-Champaign, January 31, 2015).

25. Reynaldo Martorell, L. Kettel Khan, and Dirk G. Schroeder, "Reversibility of Stunting: Epidemiological Findings in Children from Developing Countries," *European Journal of Clinical Nutrition* 48 (1994): S45–57.

26. George A. Bonanno et al., "Weighing the Costs of Disaster: Consequences, Risks, and Resilience in Individuals, Families, and Communities," *Psychological Science in the Public Interest* 11 (2010): 1–49, doi: 10.1177/1529100610387086.

27. Jo Boyden and Gillian Mann, "Children's Risk, Resilience, and Coping in Extreme Situations," in *Handbook for Working with Children and Youth: Pathways to Resilience across Cultures and Contexts*, ed. Michael Ungar (Thousand Oaks, CA: SAGE Publications, 2005), 3–27.

28. Ann S. Masten and Angela J. Narayan, "Child Development in the Context of Disaster, War, and Terrorism: Pathways of Risk and Resilience," *Annual Review of Psychology* 63 (2012): 227–57, doi: 10.1146/annurev-psych-120710-100356.

29. Eric M. Vernberg et al., "Prediction of Posttraumatic Stress Symptoms in Children after Hurricane Andrew," *Journal of Abnormal Psychology* 105 (1996): 237–48, doi: 10.1037/0021-843X.105.2.237.

30. For example: Monica A. Marsee, "Reactive Aggression and Posttraumatic Stress in Adolescents Affected by Hurricane Katrina," *Journal of Clinical Child & Adolescent Psychology* 37, (2008): 519–29, doi: 10.1080/15374410802148152.

31. Abramson and Garfield, *On the Edge.*

32. For example: Howard J. Osofsky et al., "Posttraumatic Stress Symptoms in Children after Hurricane Katrina: Predicting the Need for Mental Health Services," *American Journal of Orthopsychiatry* 79, (2009): 212–20, doi: 10.1037/a0016179.

33. Carl F. Weems et al., "Predisaster Trait Anxiety and Negative Affect Predict Posttraumatic Stress in Youths after Hurricane Katrina," *Journal of Consulting and Clinical Psychology* 75 (2007): 154–59, doi: 10.1037/0022-006X.75.1.154.

34. Mindy E. Kronenberg et al., "Children of Katrina: Lessons Learned about Postdisaster Symptoms and Recovery Patterns," *Child Development* 81 (2010): 1241–59, doi: 10.1111/j.1467-8624.2010.01465.x.

35. Ibid.

36. US Government Accountability Office, *Hurricane Katrina: Barriers to Mental Health Services for Children Persist in Greater New Orleans, although Federal Grants Are Helping to Address Them* (Washington, DC: US Government Accountability Office, 2009).

37. Alexander Cowell McFarlane, "Posttraumatic Phenomena in a Longitudinal Study of Children following a Natural Disaster," *Journal of the American Academy of Child and Adolescent Psychiatry* 26 (1987): 764–69, doi: 10.1097/00004583-198709000-00025.

38. Vernberg et al., "Prediction of Posttraumatic Stress Symptoms"; Carol Z. Garrison et al., "Posttraumatic Stress Disorder in Adolescents after Hurricane Andrew," *Journal of the American Academy of Child and Adolescent Psychiatry* 34 (1995): 1193–201, doi: 10.1097/00004583-199509000-00017.

39. Christopher J. Lonigan et al., "Children Exposed to Disaster: II. Risk Factors for the Development of Post-Traumatic Symptomatology," *Journal of the American Academy of Child and Adolescent Psychiatry* 33 (1994): 94–105, doi: 10.1097/00004583-199401000-00013.

40. Armen K. Goenjian et al., "Posttraumatic Stress and Depressive Reactions among Nicaraguan Adolescents after Hurricane Mitch," *American Journal of Psychiatry* 158 (2001): 788–94, doi: 10.1176/appi.ajp.158.5.788.

41. Frank Neuner et al., "Post-Tsunami Stress: A Study of Posttraumatic Stress Disorder in Children Living in Three Severely Affected Regions in Sri Lanka," *Journal of Traumatic Stress* 19 (2006): 339–47, doi: 10.1002/jts.20121.

42. Boyden and Mann, "Children's Risk, Resilience, and Coping," 6.

43. Bonanno et al., "Weighing the Costs."

44. National Commission on Children and Disasters, *2010 Report to the President and Congress* (Rockville, MD: Agency for Healthcare Research and Quality, 2010).

45. John F. Pane et al., "Effects of Student Displacement in Louisiana during the First Academic Year after the Hurricanes of 2005," *Journal of Education for Students Placed at Risk* 13 (2008): 168–211, doi: 10.1080/10824660802350169.

46. Bruce Sacerdote, "When the Saints Go Marching Out: Long-Term Outcomes for Student Evacuees from Hurricanes Katrina and Rita," *American Economic Journal: Applied Economics* 4 (2012): 109–35, doi: 10.1257/app.4.1.109.

47. Pane et al., "Effects of Student Displacement."

48. For example: Suzanne Duryea, David Lam, and Deborah Levison, "Effects of Economic Shocks on Children's Employment and Schooling in Brazil," *Journal of Development Economics* 84 (2007): 188–214, doi: 10.1016/j.jdeveco.2006.11.004.

49. Hanan G. Jacoby and Emmanuel Skoufias, "Risk, Financial Markets, and Human Capital in a Developing Country," *Review of Economic Studies* 64 (1997): 311–35.

50. Kathleen Beegle, Rajeev H. Dehejia, and Roberta Gatti, "Child Labor and Agricultural Shocks," *Journal of Development Economics* 81 (2006): 80–96, doi: 10.1016/j.jdeveco.2005.05.003.

51. Jensen, "Agricultural Volatility."

52. Baez and Santos, "Children's Vulnerability."

53. Alain de Janvry et al., "Can Conditional Cash Transfer Programs Serve as Safety Nets in Keeping Children at School and from Working When Exposed to Shocks?" *Journal of Development Economics* 79 (2006): 349–73, doi: 10.1016/j.jdeveco.2006.01.013.

54. Seth R. Gitter and Bradford L. Barham, "Credit, Natural Disasters, Coffee, and Educational Attainment in Rural Honduras," *World Development* 35 (2007): 498–511, doi: 10.1016/j.worlddev.2006.03.007.

55. Save the Children, *Unaccounted For: A National Report Card on Protecting Children in Disasters* (Fairfield, CT: Save the Children, 2013).

56. Lori Peek, "Children and Disasters: Understanding Vulnerability, Developing Capacities, and Promoting Resilience—An Introduction," *Children, Youth and Environments* 18 (2008): 1–29.

57. De Janvry et al., "Conditional Cash Transfer Programs."

58. Tatyana Deryugina, "The Role of Transfer Payments in Mitigating Shocks: Evidence from the Impact of Hurricanes" (Department of Finance, University of Illinois at Urbana-Champaign, August 8, 2013).

59. Anne Westbrook Lauten and Kimberly Lietz, "A Look at the Standards Gap: Comparing Child Protection Responses in the Aftermath of Hurricane Katrina and the Indian Ocean Tsunami," *Children, Youth, and Environments* 18 (2008): 158–201.

60. McDiarmid, *Face of Disaster*.

61. Ibid.

Pollution and Climate Change

Allison S. Larr and Matthew Neidell

Summary

Childhood is a particularly sensitive time when it comes to pollution exposure. Allison Larr and Matthew Neidell focus on two atmospheric pollutants—ozone and particulate matter—that can harm children's health in many ways. Ozone irritates the lungs, causing various respiratory symptoms; it can also damage the lung lining or aggravate lung diseases such as asthma. Particulate matter affects both the lungs and the heart; like ozone, it can cause respiratory symptoms and aggravate asthma, but it can also induce heart attacks or irregular heartbeat. Beyond those immediate effects, childhood exposure to ozone and particulate matter can do long-term damage to children's health and reduce their ability to accumulate human capital. For example, frequent asthma attacks can cut into school attendance and academic performance, ultimately detracting from children's ability to earn a good living as adults.

Fossil fuel-burning power plants, which are a major source of carbon emissions that cause climate change, also emit high levels of nitrogen dioxide and sulfur dioxide, which play a role in forming ozone and particulate matter. We might assume, then, that policies to reduce climate change by cutting back on carbon emissions from power plants would automatically cut back on these other types of pollution. But it's not quite that simple—atmospheric concentrations of ozone and particulate matter are linked to heat and other climatic variables through complex, nonlinear relationships.

Taking those complex relationships into account and examining a variety of ways to model future air quality, Larr and Neidell project that policies to mitigate the emissions that produce climate change would indeed significantly reduce atmospheric ozone and particulate matter—at least in the United States, which has the most-complete data available to make such calculations. The drop in pollution would in turn produce significant improvements in child wellbeing. Children would be more likely to survive into adulthood, experience healthier childhoods, have more human capital, and be more productive as adults.

www.futureofchildren.org

Allison S. Larr completed a master of public health degree from the Environmental Health Sciences Department at the Mailman School of Public Health, Columbia University, in 2014 and currently works in the Public Finance Department at Citi. Matthew Neidell is an associate professor in the Department of Health Policy and Management at the Mailman School of Public Health, Columbia University, and a research associate at the National Bureau of Economic Research.

Denise Mauzerall of Princeton University reviewed and critiqued a draft of this article.

W e can expect climate change—and policies aimed at curbing it—to affect air quality, among other things. Exposure to pollution during childhood has numerous consequences for wellbeing. In the short term, it can affect health; for example, it can exacerbate children's asthma or even kill them. In the long term, it can alter their human capital (for example, how many years of school they complete) and their labor market productivity. This article spells out and quantifies some of those effects based on our understanding of the relationships between climate change and pollution and between childhood pollution exposure and wellbeing.

We focus on two ways that climate change and efforts to fight it may affect air quality. The first involves policies that aim to reduce the use of fossil fuels, which emit not only carbon dioxide (CO_2) but also many air pollutants that affect health. For example, power plants are major sources of CO_2, but they also emit high levels of sulfur dioxide and nitrogen dioxide, which lead to the formation of ozone and fine particulate matter (particles up to 2.5 microns in size, or $PM_{2.5}$). Therefore, any policies that reduce the use of fossil fuels would also reduce emissions that affect local air quality. (Geoengineering techniques such as carbon capture and sequestration don't generate improvements in local air quality because they don't reduce the amount of CO_2 produced.) The health effects of using less fossil fuel are often referred to as *cobenefits* of climate change policy.

The second way that climate change may affect air quality is through weather's role in determining pollution. For example,

ozone forms when heat combines with volatile organic compounds and nitrogen oxides. Therefore, warmer temperatures are expected to increase ozone levels. The process is complex, however, and some predictions about climate change's net effect on air quality are ambiguous.

To understand how changes in ozone and $PM_{2.5}$ might affect child wellbeing, we review empirical estimates of the relationship, focusing solely on studies that use *quasi-experimental* research designs. We do so because pollution is not randomly assigned across children, and a third factor might cause both more exposure to pollution and worse health outcomes, skewing the results through what's called *omitted variable bias*. For example, because worse air quality is often reflected in lower housing prices, families with higher incomes are more likely to live in areas with less pollution. Those same families are also likely to invest more in their children's health and human capital. Failing to account for that correlation would lead to spurious estimates of pollution's effects. Quasi-experimental studies attempt to overcome that limitation by examining events that produce unexpected changes in air quality in some areas but not in others.

We begin by describing how air pollution may affect child wellbeing. We then review estimates from models that project pollution changes under various climate change and mitigation scenarios. To gauge how climate change–induced pollution might affect child wellbeing, we then combine those pollution changes with estimates from quasi-experimental studies of how childhood pollution exposure affects various outcomes, including infant mortality, respiratory diseases, and labor market productivity. As with all research that projects the effects of climate change, our calculations involve many assumptions. Climate change is a long-term problem, and we need to make decisions in the present based on uncertain outcomes in the future; our estimates of the potential impacts offer suggestive evidence to help make those decisions.

Our projections suggest that mitigating the emissions that produce climate change would lead to significant improvements in child wellbeing. More children would experience healthier childhoods, survive into adulthood, have more human capital, and be more productive as adults. Those projected benefits arise whether we compare air quality under a mitigation scenario with today's air quality or with air quality in the future if no mitigation occurs.

Our calculations focus exclusively on the United States, not because we're interested only in this country but largely because we have sufficient US data, such as forecasts for ozone and $PM_{2.5}$ under various future climate scenarios. Although we can't explicitly quantify the relationship in other developed countries, we suspect that effects would be similar because of generally similar technologies, industrial activity, capacity to implement policy, and projected climate changes. Effects are likely to differ substantially in developing countries, however. For example, many developing countries, such as those in sub-Saharan Africa, already face much warmer temperatures today, and they differ in the likelihood that they would enact mitigation policies. Those and other factors could lead to vastly different air quality projections for developing countries. We'll discuss this topic as it relates to children to some degree, but the article by Rema Hanna and Paulina Oliva elsewhere in this issue analyzes climate change's effects on children in developing countries in depth.

Biological and Behavioral Effects of Pollution

How do ozone and $PM_{2.5}$ affect child wellbeing?[1] Ozone affects the body primarily by irritating the lungs. It can cause various respiratory symptoms such as shortness of breath and coughing; it can inflame and damage the lung lining; and it can aggravate existing lung diseases such as asthma. Those effects can arise anytime from within a few hours of exposure to several days afterward, and they can be produced by quite low concentration levels.

$PM_{2.5}$ penetrates deep into the lungs and passes into the bloodstream, thereby affecting both the lungs and the heart. It can reduce lung function and increase respiratory symptoms such as airway irritation, difficulty breathing, and asthma. It can also induce heart attacks or irregular heartbeat. As with ozone, the effects can appear either quickly or several days after exposure, and they can arise at quite low concentration levels.

Children's rapid biological development suggests that childhood is a particularly sensitive time when it comes to pollution exposure. Children are believed to suffer greater effects from pollution than adults do, and younger children are more affected than older ones, which implies that the same dose of pollution has a greater effect the earlier in life it occurs.

Given the dynamic nature of health and how it interacts with human capital, exposure to these pollutants can harm wellbeing beyond immediate, direct health insults by affecting human capital accumulation and labor market outcomes later in life. For example, a child might experience asthma attacks that cut into her school attendance and academic performance, which later detracts from her performance in the workplace. Alternatively, children's human capital might be affected when their parents make investments to respond to a direct health shock—for example, by providing additional resources. The stream of events that flows from the initial insult through the life cycle represents an important component of childhood pollution exposure's total effects.

In addition to contemporaneous and life cycle effects, latent effects may appear years after pollution exposure. Evidence increasingly shows that the nine months in the womb and the first few years of life are critical periods for physiological development, when toxic exposures can have lasting impacts.[2] In particular, pollution may permanently alter the way genes function, and those epigenetic effects can damage intellectual growth and maturity later in life.[3] Latent effects may be accompanied by contemporaneous impacts as well, though they need not arise. For example, a person with latent epigenetic damage might appear to be in perfect health early in life only to experience observable health problems later on. Such latent effects constitute another important component of childhood exposure.

Sustained exposure to either ozone or $PM_{2.5}$ may also have cumulative long-run effects on child wellbeing. That relationship can be particularly important, but it is more complex and involves more uncertainty. We don't know of any quasi-experimental evidence on the subject, so we don't consider such cumulative effects in our review.

Consequences of Climate Change

As we've said, climate change and mitigation of emissions are projected to affect air quality through two relatively distinct processes. First, weather directly influences the production of some pollutants. Though we don't know many of the net effects that changes in climate will have on pollution, the predicted effect on ozone is unambiguous. Ozone forms when nitrogen oxides and volatile organic compounds interact in the presence of heat and sunlight. Therefore, a warmer planet is likely to have more ozone. Second, policies that limit the use of fossil fuels that lead to climate change will also improve local air quality, because many of the sources that give rise to carbon emissions also give rise to air pollutants, such as sulfur dioxide and nitrogen dioxides, that help form ozone and $PM_{2.5}$. In this section, we focus on the direct effects of climate change; we discuss mitigation of emissions in the following section.

Modeling Methods

To project future surface ozone and $PM_{2.5}$ levels requires a broad set of models and assumptions used to forecast future conditions. The models and assumptions involve carbon emissions, climate change projections, air quality models, and downscaling modeling techniques; we describe each of those below. Table 1 summarizes the methods used across the various studies we review.

Carbon emissions. To model how future emissions will affect climate change, researchers use different emissions assumptions under various future scenarios. For longer-term projections, most studies use one or several emissions scenarios that were developed by the Intergovernmental Panel on Climate Change (IPCC).[4] The scenarios are grouped into four families—A1, A2, B1, and B2—which are further broken down into

Table 1. Model Scenarios for Projecting Ozone and PM$_{2.5}$ under Climate Change

Authors	Emissions scenario	Climate models and downscaling	Air quality models	Projection period
Chen et al. 2004	IPCC A2	PCM/MM5	CMAQ/ MOZART-2	2045–54
Hogrefe et al. 2004	IPCC A2	GISS GCM/ SMOKE/MM5	CMAQ	2053–57
Avise et al. 2009	IPCC A2	PCM/MM5	CMAQ	2045–54
Tao et al. 2007	IPCC A1Fi and B1	PCM/MM5	SAQM	2050
Nolte et al. 2008	IPCC A1B and current emissions	GISS GCM/MM5	CMAQ	2045–55
Tagaris et al. 2007	IPCC A1B and current emissions	GISS GCM/MM5	CMAQ	2049–51
Trail et al. 2014	RCP 4.5	GISS GCM/WRF	CMAQ	2048–52
Penrod et al. 2014	IPCC A1B	WRF	CMAQ	2030

Abbreviations: CMAQ = Community Multiscale Air Quality Model; GISS GCM = Goddard Institute for Space Studies General Circulation Model; MM5 = fifth-generation Penn State/National Center for Atmospheric Research mesoscale model; MOZART-2 = Model for Ozone and Related Chemical Tracers; PCM = Parallel Climate Model; RCP = Representative Concentration Pathway; SAQM = San Joaquin Valley Air Quality Study/Atmospheric Utility Signatures, Predictions, and Experiments Study Regional Modeling Adaptation Project Air Quality Model; SMOKE = Sparse Matrix Operator Kernel Emissions model; WRF = Weather Research and Forecasting model.

a total of 40 unique scenarios. The scenarios differ based on the degree to which we might rely on fossil fuels, on patterns and sizes of economic and population growth, on the energy efficiency of future technology, and on patterns and rates of technological change. The favored scenarios in the studies we review below are the A1B scenario, which assumes rapid economic growth and more-balanced use of fossil fuels and renewable energy sources compared with present levels, and the A2 scenario, which assumes rapid population growth and consistent increases in CO$_2$ emissions.

Climate change projections. The process of modeling climate change typically starts with the results of a general circulation model of physical processes in the atmosphere, in the ocean, and on land, which comprises all of the variables that affect climate on a global scale. Many research teams develop and maintain their own general circulation models, which take into account many variables that affect global climate. Those variables include but aren't limited to temperature, precipitation, wind, sea level rise, and radiative forcing—that is, the difference between the solar energy Earth absorbs and the energy it radiates back to space. One commonly used general circulation model was developed by NASA's Goddard Institute for Space Studies. Researchers may input various greenhouse gas emissions scenarios into the model, whether they come from the IPCC or elsewhere.[5] General circulation models are structured so that the results they produce appear at coarse levels of spatial resolution: each output may correspond to an area that can be as large as hundreds of square kilometers in size. To obtain more-fine-grained results, researchers use downscaling methods, which we describe below.

Air quality. As we've said, air quality is a function of meteorological conditions and emissions. Using the assumptions and results from the models described above, researchers project changes in air quality that are likely to occur under future conditions. One frequently used model is the Environmental Protection Agency's (EPA's) Community Multi-Scale Air Quality model, which simulates the chemical and physical processes involved when chemicals travel through the atmosphere. Developed to help communities project future air quality conditions, it is highly flexible in both space and time.[6]

Downscaling. To generate results for smaller levels of spatial resolution, most if not all climate models require downscaling.[7] Through downscaling, large-scale results are further analyzed to characterize smaller spatial regions—for instance, a state or region of the United States. As with general circulation models and air quality models, researchers have many downscaling methods and techniques at their disposal.

Many methods are available for each step in the modeling process, and many possible combinations of assumptions and modeling techniques can affect the results, all of which contributes to uncertainty when we compare results across studies. However, the general framework for modeling future air quality follows the process outlined above.

Unabated climate change is projected to diminish air quality in the United States both overall and, to a great extent, by region, although projections vary by research team and depend on the assumptions and models a team uses to generate results. Even though projected changes in ozone concentrations across the United States are relatively well documented both regionally and nationally,

projections of $PM_{2.5}$ in the context of climate change are comparatively sparse.

Projections of 2050 US Ozone Levels— Regional and National

Given the way ozone forms, many studies focus on ozone levels during the summer months—when temperatures are higher— looking specifically at the daily maximum eight-hour ozone level, which is the measure through which ozone is regulated under the Clean Air Act. The most comprehensive review of 2050 ozone levels under different climate change scenarios comes from the EPA, whose projections summarize the results of six studies that analyzed how climate change would affect US air quality in areas of various sizes.[8] The EPA projects that if emissions don't decrease, most regions of the country will see higher mean daily eight-hour average ozone levels, though some regions will see little to no change and a few will see ozone levels fall. The studies used a variety of emissions reduction scenarios, which contributed to uncertainty regarding future ozone levels.

It's difficult to accurately synthesize the results of projections by different research teams.[9] The methods teams use differ in a number of ways, which contributes to uncertainty in analyzing the combined results. For instance, a review of studies that projected ozone and $PM_{2.5}$ levels found that of the eight that focused on North America, only three produced results across the United States, and only one team used the same set of assumptions and methods to project both $PM_{2.5}$ and ozone levels and the corresponding health effects. Because of such difficulties, we focus on results from Efthimios Tagaris's team, which projected both ozone and $PM_{2.5}$ under two scenarios—business as usual, defined as emissions conditions under historical 2001 conditions, and a scenario of planned climate change mitigation—thus establishing a baseline set of assumptions that underlie projections for each measure of air quality.[10]

Under the 2001 emissions scenario, climate change was expected to affect atmospheric ozone concentrations variably by region, ranging from a decrease of 1.4 parts per billion in the Midwest to an increase of up to 1.6 parts per billion in the Northeast. Averaging across the United States, however, the team saw no increase in ozone. In contrast, under the decreased-emissions scenario, ozone levels were projected to fall across all regions, by approximately eight parts per billion overall.

Consequences of Mitigating Climate Change

Reducing Emissions

At the federal level, proposed policies aim to fight climate change both directly and indirectly. The policies fall into three broad categories.

- Policies to reduce greenhouse gas emissions by requiring or encouraging greater energy or fuel efficiency standards in vehicles, buildings, and appliances.

- Policies to reduce emissions from power plants, which are the greatest sources of carbon emissions in the United States.[11]

- Policies to encourage the use of renewable and less-carbon-intensive energy sources, including but not limited to wind, solar, and hydropower. These policies aim to mitigate climate change indirectly by displacing emissions-heavy energy sources such as coal, oil, and natural gas.

The EPA's Clean Power Plan is one example of a supply-side policy targeting the power sector. Finalized on August 3, 2015, the Clean Power Plan will mitigate climate change by cutting power plants' carbon emissions to 70 percent of 2005 levels by 2030, using a state-based framework that sets a CO_2 mitigation target for each state. Along with substantially decreasing carbon dioxide emissions, the policy will also decrease emissions of particulate matter, nitrogen oxides, and sulfur dioxide. Thus mitigation policies that seek to reduce emissions are especially important for air quality. Reducing carbon emissions is nearly always associated with reductions in other emissions that directly harm human health or that react in chemical pathways that produce harmful agents.

Projections of 2050 $PM_{2.5}$ Levels— Regional and National

To date, one study has comprehensively analyzed how climate change and climate change mitigation will affect future $PM_{2.5}$ levels in the United States compared with a no-mitigation scenario. Three more studies have compared projected with historical $PM_{2.5}$ levels.

Jeremy Avise and colleagues projected how climate change mitigation policies will affect $PM_{2.5}$ levels in the United States.[12] They characterized $PM_{2.5}$ forecasts in 2050 under six different scenarios. The scenarios that examined only climate change, maintaining current emissions levels, projected that $PM_{2.5}$ would decrease overall in the United States by 0.9 micrograms per cubic meter, with decreases or no change in each region except the Northeast, which was projected to experience an increase in $PM_{2.5}$ of 0.2 micrograms per cubic meter. When they took into account future changes in emissions, land use, and climate change together, however, the researchers projected that $PM_{2.5}$ would increase across all regions by 2 micrograms per cubic meter overall in the United States (a 25 percent increase) and by up to 4 micrograms per cubic meter in the Northeast (a 44 percent increase).

Tagaris and colleagues, in the study we described earlier, projected changes in $PM_{2.5}$ levels in conjunction with ozone levels under two different climate change scenarios. If emissions are reduced compared with 2001 levels, they projected, summer $PM_{2.5}$ would decrease by 2.9 micrograms per cubic meter on average across the United States, with the highest decrease in the Southeast at 6.2 micrograms per cubic meter.

Another team of researchers compared current ozone levels with future summertime ozone concentrations for the United States using a climate change scenario that corresponds to global emissions of greenhouse gases and land use changes that produce a CO_2-equivalent atmospheric greenhouse gas concentration of 650 parts per million by 2100, compared with 481 parts per million in 2014.[13] (CO_2-equivalent atmospheric greenhouse gas concentration is a measure of the aggregate concentration of all atmospheric greenhouse gases, expressed in terms of the amount of CO_2 alone that would be required to produce the same amount of radiative forcing.) In addition to their climate change assumption, the group assumed future air quality conditions that would result if the IPCC's A1B scenario were combined with passing and implementing a number of policies to improve air quality. The group projected pollution levels in 2050 compared with levels for 2006–10 and found that once emissions and climate change

were taken into account, air quality would improve over much of the country, including decreases in ozone and $PM_{2.5}$. When they examined the impact of climate change alone, however, they found that pollution policies' effects on ozone and $PM_{2.5}$ levels were muted, suggesting that climate change would make air quality improvement measures less effective. Although this study is helpful for comparative purposes, it doesn't provide regionally specific results in units we can use for our projections.

A fourth team projected changes in ozone and $PM_{2.5}$ in 2026–30 under the IPCC A1B scenario for the contiguous United States only. The researchers didn't compare a future business-as-usual simulation with that projection; instead, they compared their results with current ozone levels.[14] They found that summer ozone levels would fall across almost the entire country, with the exception of large urban areas. A drop in ozone precursor emissions, such as nitrogen dioxides, would be the leading cause of the drop in summer ozone concentrations. The study predicted that summer $PM_{2.5}$ would fall the most in the central and eastern United States; several areas in the Southwest and the Great Lakes region would actually see increased levels of $PM_{2.5}$.

Geoengineering

Some strategies to mitigate climate change—in particular, geoengineering techniques such as carbon capture and storage—won't improve local air quality. Geoengineering in general encompasses strategies to reduce climate change by managing solar radiation. Carbon capture and storage involves capturing CO_2 at the point of emission and storing it to prevent it from entering the atmosphere. Because geoengineering approaches don't reduce the amount of pollutants other than carbon released into the atmosphere, they don't affect local air quality.

One example of a geoengineering strategy in action is the Boundary Dam Integrated Carbon Capture and Storage Demonstration Project at a coal-fired power plant in Saskatchewan. A recent assessment of the project found that its carbon capture operation would reduce greenhouse gas emissions by 63 percent.[15] But whether local air quality also improves depends greatly on the type of mitigation and not simply on whether mitigation takes place.

Empirical Problems

When we try to identify the causal effects of pollution exposure, the primary problem we run into is called *residential sorting*.[16] Sorting occurs when people vote with their feet by choosing where to live based on such characteristics as school quality, crime rates, and—most relevant here—pollution levels. For such sorting to occur, people need not be directly aware of pollution concentrations; they need only choose where to live based on factors correlated with pollution levels, such as proximity to major roads and industrial production. Major roads and factories are drawbacks by themselves, but they are also major sources of pollution.

High-income families tend to move away from highly polluted areas.

Evidence increasingly suggests that sorting based on environmental quality indeed plays an important role in determining where people live. Researchers have found that high-income families tend to move away from highly polluted areas and that when an area's environmental quality improves, the proportion of pregnant women in that area who are white and college educated increases.[17] Furthermore, areas with higher pollution levels also have lower housing prices.[18]

As a result of this kind of sorting, areas with more pollution may also have other, unobserved characteristics correlated with health, suggesting that omitted variable bias is likely to skew estimates. For example, a more polluted area may also be a more impoverished area, and children there may have less access to medical care. Failing to account for that lack of access can lead to spurious estimates of the relationship between pollution and health. In this example, not accounting for access to care would lead to overestimating the true relationship, but other factors might lead to underestimates. For example, urban and suburban areas typically have greater access to care but also more pollution than do rural areas. Given the way sorting can skew estimates, we focus here on quasi-experimental studies that directly attempt to confront sorting.

A secondary empirical problem stems from avoidance behavior. If people act to protect their children's health when pollution is high, those actions will lead to nonrandom pollution exposure. Such actions require knowledge of pollution levels. Many large cities disseminate pollution information to the public, often accompanied by recommended strategies to avoid pollution, such as staying indoors or shifting activities to times of day when pollution is expected to be lower. Because such avoidance behavior occurs in response to pollution levels, omitting it from analyses doesn't bias estimates per se. Rather, omitting avoidance behavior affects how the estimated relationships are interpreted. Estimates that control for avoidance behavior uncover the direct biological effect of pollution on health. Estimates that don't control for avoidance behavior measure pollution's net effect on health, which consists of the biological effect plus the degree to which avoidance behavior is successful in reducing health effects. Avoidance behavior is an important component of pollution's total welfare cost because avoiding pollution is costly.[19]

Quasi-Experimental Evidence

So that we can project calculations based on climate–pollution forecasts in the next section, we limit ourselves to studies that directly examine ozone and $PM_{2.5}$, though we note that other studies examine emissions that may lead to those pollutants.[20] Most notably, we omit studies that focus on carbon monoxide, another pollutant linked with many measures of wellbeing. Though carbon monoxide is highly correlated with $PM_{2.5}$, it comes predominantly from automobiles rather than from power plants; power plants are the major sources of CO_2 emissions that mitigation policies target.

Because $PM_{2.5}$ has been monitored for a much shorter time than ozone has, we also include studies that look at larger particles—specifically, PM_{10} (particles up to 10 microns in size) and total suspended particles (equivalent to PM_{100})—which have been monitored longer. Many of these studies capture the effects of all particles, of which $PM_{2.5}$ particles are a subset. In fact, the only available evidence on long-run effects comes from studies using total suspended particles. For future projections, we provide a crude approximation by scaling our estimates according to the estimated fraction of particles included in either PM_{10} or total suspended particles that are small enough to be considered $PM_{2.5}$.[21]

Short-Run Effects—Infant Health

The health of newborns is a crucial place to start. Two landmark studies that focused on the effects of air pollution pioneered research designs used by many researchers ever since. The first examined the recession of the early 1980s in the United States.[22] Manufacturing is a key source of emissions, so an economic slowdown can produce far-reaching changes in pollution. Furthermore, manufacturing is not spread evenly throughout the United States, so the shocks to manufacturing from the 1980s recession induced considerable spatial variation in pollution—specifically, in total suspended particles. Because those changes in total suspended particles were caused by a global economic phenomenon, they were unlikely to be related to other factors affecting health. The study found that a decline of 1 microgram per cubic meter in total suspended particles reduced infant deaths by four to seven per 100,000 births.

The second landmark study used the 1970 Clean Air Act Amendments as a source of quasi-experimental variation in pollution. Counties that were out of compliance with pollution thresholds established by the Clean Air Act Amendments were required to lower pollution, whereas counties with pollution levels just below the thresholds were unaffected. By comparing affected and unaffected counties, the researchers estimated that a decline of 1 microgram per cubic meter in total suspended particles led to five to eight fewer infant deaths per 100,000 live births.

Using the same design based on the Clean Air Act Amendments, other researchers examined the effects of pollution on sex ratios at birth.[23] Because male fetuses are thought to be more fragile than female fetuses, a decrease in the ratio of male live births to female live births suggests an increase in fetal deaths. Consistent with that hypothesis, researchers found that a reduction in pollution increases the fraction of male fetuses.

Another way to confront sorting is to use *fixed effects* models, which compare changes in pollution in a set of geographic areas over time with changes in health outcomes in the same areas. That approach thereby controls for all of an area's characteristics that don't vary over time, such as access to health care and underlying health status (if they are in fact constant over time). For example, one study used the primary unit of local government as a fixed effect to examine the relationship between pollution levels in Great Britain from 1998 to 2005 and the deaths of children under 15 years old.[24] It estimated that reducing PM_{10} by 10 micrograms per cubic meter was associated with four fewer deaths per 100,000 children.

Another study used California traffic congestion data as a source of variation in pollution levels, with fixed effects by ZIP code.[25] Traffic congestion temporarily raises pollution levels in a way that isn't correlated with other factors affecting child health. The authors found that reducing PM_{10} levels by 1 microgram per cubic meter led to 18 fewer infant deaths per 100,000 live births. It's important to note that unlike the pioneering studies of the 1980s recession and the 1970 Clean Air Act Amendments, this study focused on the 1990s—a more recent time period.

Only a few studies of pollution and child health have examined less-developed countries. One team of researchers looked at pollution and infant mortality in Mexico.[26] The team used thermal inversions—which trap pollution near the ground—as a source of variation in daily pollution; their model included fixed effects by municipality. The researchers found that an increase in PM_{10} of 1 microgram per cubic meter produced a statistically significant 0.24 more weekly infant deaths per 100,000 births, which is quite comparable to estimates for the United States.

Short-Run Effects—Childhood Health and Human Capital

Beyond its effects on infants, exposure to pollution throughout childhood can also significantly affect health and human capital—for example, by causing respiratory diseases or reducing performance in school. To explore the relationship between ozone and respiratory-related hospitalizations, one researcher confronted sorting by studying military personnel.[27] The relocation of military personnel is based entirely on the needs of the armed forces and not on personal preferences; thus variations in pollution exposure among military families are similar to random assignment. Furthermore, all military families are covered by identical health insurance plans, so access to care isn't a factor. The study found that a 15 percent decrease in annual ground-level ozone exposure decreased the probability of respiratory hospitalizations among children aged 2 to 5 years by 8 to 23 percent.

As we've said, people may take actions to reduce their exposure to harmful pollutants by, say, making changes in daily activities or even moving to a new home in a different area. If people act to lessen their exposure, then estimations that don't take those actions into account may understate pollution's effects. One of the authors of this article, Matthew Neidell, used fixed effects by ZIP code to exploit naturally occurring daily variation in ozone pollution.[28] He accounted for avoidance behavior by controlling for smog alerts—an important source of information about pollution and health. Without taking smog alerts into account, he found that when five-day ozone levels increased by 12.8 percent, child hospital admissions rose by 1.09 percent; when he controlled for smog alerts, the estimate rose to 2.88 percent.

Two researchers studied monthly variations in ozone exposure by following a large cohort of English children over time.[29] Like the children in military families, the English children all had the same access to health care—in this case, via the United Kingdom's universal National Health Service. To avoid skewing the estimates, the researchers used a child fixed effects model, controlling for all of the children's characteristics that didn't vary over time. They found that increases in ozone were associated with statistically significant increases in respiratory treatments among children aged 2 to 6 years. Specifically, a 10 percent increase in a month's ozone levels increased by 2.5 to 3.3 percent the probability that a child would undergo respiratory treatment in that month.

We've seen that exposure to pollution may affect not only children's health but also their performance in school—whether directly through harm to the brain or indirectly through such channels as asthma attacks that cause them to miss school. A study using annual classroom-level performance data from California showed that higher pollution

levels affected scores on annual achievement tests.[30] Because unobserved differences in student populations could be correlated with both pollution and lower test scores, the researchers included in their analysis school fixed effects as well as observable student and family characteristics. They found that when ambient levels of $PM_{2.5}$ fell by 10 percent, students' scores rose by 0.34 percent on standardized math tests and by 0.21 percent on standardized reading tests.

Another study examined whether daily exposure to pollution could affect student performance on high-stakes high school tests.[31] The researchers followed Israeli students over time as they took multiple tests, which allowed the researchers to control for all of the students' time-invariant characteristics. An increase in $PM_{2.5}$ of 1 microgram per cubic meter was associated with a 0.65-point decrease in the students' test scores. Looking further ahead, the researchers also found that the decrease in test scores caused by higher levels of $PM_{2.5}$ affected important college outcomes.

Long-Run Effects

Because we don't have a lot of data that would let us link childhood pollution exposure to later outcomes, only a handful of studies have looked at long-run effects from any pollutant.[32] Two focus on particulate matter, but only for total suspended particles; again, we scale the estimates based on total suspended particles to approximate the projected effects of $PM_{2.5}$. Despite the limited evidence, a consensus is growing that early pollution exposure has significant long-run consequences.

One recent study built on earlier work by using quasi-experimental variation in pollution during the 1980s recession and examining how children who were in the womb when the recession occurred performed on high school tests many years later.[33] Unfortunately, the researcher wasn't able to identify where the women were living when their children were born, so he was forced to assume that the children were born in the same place they attended high school. Despite that potential source of measurement error, which would likely bias his estimates toward no effect, he found that a 21.9 percent decrease in total suspended particles around the time of birth increased high school test scores by 10.3 percent.

Similarly, another team of researchers interested in long-run outcomes recently returned to the 1970 Clean Air Act Amendments as a source of variation in pollution.[34] Unlike the study of children who were in the womb during the 1980s recession, these researchers were able to obtain children's counties and dates of birth. Comparing children born in counties just below the threshold for action under the amendments with those born in counties just above, they found that each 10-unit decrease in total suspended particles during pregnancy and early childhood resulted in a 1 percent increase in annual earnings once the children became adults.

Calculations

In this section, we project future pollution impacts from climate change on several indicators of child wellbeing. To do so, we combine pollution projections under various climate scenarios with selected estimates of pollution's effects on wellbeing to calculate potential impacts throughout the United States, assuming that current air quality policy remains unchanged. We recognize that this exercise is fraught with tenuous assumptions; in the absence of an approach that avoids such limitations, we proceed with caution.

Among the several studies we described earlier that project future $PM_{2.5}$ and ozone, we base our projections on Tagaris and colleagues, for three reasons. First, they use the same set of models to predict both pollutants. Second, they predict what would happen under both a business-as-usual scenario and a mitigation scenario, thereby letting us compare a particular mitigation strategy with no mitigation. Third, they make regional projections, so we can assess the distribution of impacts across the country. Table 2 shows ozone and $PM_{2.5}$ projections under each scenario by region. For all of our calculations, we make three comparisons: mitigation in 2050 versus baseline values in 2001, no mitigation in 2050 versus baseline values in 2001, and mitigation in 2050 versus no mitigation in 2050. The last scenario is the most useful one for thinking about the effects of climate change policy versus the effects of inaction, because inaction is a scenario with no mitigation.

Based on the $PM_{2.5}$ and ozone projections, we calculate three separate outcomes: $PM_{2.5}$ and infant mortality, $PM_{2.5}$ and adult earnings, and ozone and childhood hospitalizations.

Infant Mortality

For infant mortality, we obtain data on the number of births in each region based on vital statistics as of 2012, and we assume that the number of births will remain constant in the future. We then multiply the number of births by (1) the estimated relationship between $PM_{2.5}$ and infant mortality and (2) the difference in $PM_{2.5}$ across the various scenarios. This gives us the change in infant

Table 2. Ozone and $PM_{2.5}$ Projections by Region under Alternative Mitigation Scenarios

	West		Plains		Midwest	
	Ozone (ppb)	$PM_{2.5}$ ($\mu g/m^3$)	Ozone (ppb)	$PM_{2.5}$ ($\mu g/m^3$)	Ozone (ppb)	$PM_{2.5}$ ($\mu g/m^3$)
2001	49.75	4.05	48.25	6.925	45.25	11.725
2050	46.25	3.65	44.25	5.425	40.5	9.025
2050 BAU	49.75	4.15	49	6.875	45.25	12.2

	West		Plains		Midwest	
	Ozone (ppb)	$PM_{2.5}$ ($\mu g/m^3$)	Ozone (ppb)	$PM_{2.5}$ ($\mu g/m^3$)	Ozone (ppb)	$PM_{2.5}$ ($\mu g/m^3$)
2001	46.25	9	54	12.3	48.75	8
2050	41.75	6.425	46.25	8.425	44.25	6.125
2050 BAU	46	9.625	55.5	11.975	49.25	8.1

Note: Projections include a baseline mitigation scenario as well as a business-as-usual scenario (no mitigation). Ozone is the annual average of daily eight-hour maximum ozone. $PM_{2.5}$ is the annual average of the daily $PM_{2.5}$.

Abbreviations: BAU = business as usual; ppb = parts per billion; $\mu g/m^3$ = micrograms per cubic meter

Source: Efthimios Tagaris et al., "Impacts of Global Climate Change and Emissions on Regional Ozone and Fine Particulate Matter Concentrations over the United States," *Journal of Geophysical Research: Atmospheres* 112 (2007): D14312.

mortality in each region under each scenario. We then calculate the percentage change in infant mortality by dividing the change in deaths from pollution by the estimated number of infant deaths from all causes, which is calculated by assuming that the current rate of 6.1 deaths per 1,000 births will remain the same in the future.

After consulting a variety of studies, our best estimate of the relationship between $PM_{2.5}$ and infant mortality is 34 deaths per 100,000 births.[35]

As panel A of table 3 shows, under a 2050 scenario of no mitigation, we see some variation in impacts across the country from the projected change in $PM_{2.5}$, including small decreases in the number of infant deaths in the Plains and the Southwest and

small increases in the West, the Midwest, and the Northeast. The changes are quite small, however, amounting to a total of 133 extra deaths. The percentage changes are likewise generally small, at less than 4 percent by region. The small size of those impacts is not surprising because, unlike ozone, $PM_{2.5}$ isn't expected to be directly affected by climate change, but only by mitigation policies. Figure 1 shows the percentage changes graphically.

Under the mitigation scenario, panel A of table 3 shows infant mortality falling across all regions, with the largest drops in the Midwest, Northeast, and Southeast. Overall, the estimates show a decrease of 2,501 infant deaths, which represents a decrease in overall US infant mortality of 10.5 percent and a decrease as high as 21.6 percent in

Table 3. Projected Pollution Impacts on Child Wellbeing

Panel A. Impacts on infant mortality from contemporaneous exposure to $PM_{2.5}$

	Births	Infant deaths	No mitigation vs. 2001	Mitigation vs. 2001	Mitigation vs. no mitigation	No mitigation vs. 2001	Mitigation vs. 2001	Mitigation vs. no mitigation
West	832,065	5,076	28	−113	−141	0.56%	−2.23%	−2.79%
Plains	635,916	3,879	−11	−324	−314	−0.28%	−8.36%	−8.08%
Midwest	820,761	5,007	133	−753	−886	2.65%	−15.05%	−17.70%
Northeast	835,041	5,094	177	−731	−909	3.48%	−14.35%	−17.84
Southeast	798,891	4,873	−88	−1,053	−964	−1.81%	−21.60%	−19.79%
All	3,922,674	23,928	133	−2,501	−2,634	0.56%	−10.45%	−11.01%

Note: This panel presents estimates for the number and percentage of infant deaths avoided by region under various climate scenarios. Births are from 2012.

Panel B. Impacts on adult earnings from early childhood exposure to $PM_{2.5}$

	Per capita income	No mitigation vs. 2001	Mitigation vs. 2001	Mitigation vs. no mitigation	No mitigation vs. 2001	Mitigation vs.2001	Mitigation vs. no mitigation
West	$44,589	−$30	$121	$151	−0.1%	0.3%	0.3%
Plains	$43,680	$15	$443	$429	0.0%	1.0%	1.0%
Midwest	$41,548	−$134	$759	$893	−0.3%	1.8%	2.1%
Northeast	$52,417	−$222	$913	$1,135	−0.4%	1.7%	2.2%
Southeast	$38,550	$85	$1,011	$926	0.2%	2.6%	2.4%
All	$44,455	−$30	$564	$594	−0.1%	1.3%	1.3%

Note: This panel presents estimates for the dollar and percentage change in adult earnings by region under various climate scenarios. Per-capita income is from 2012.

Panel C. Impacts on respiratory hospitalizations from contemporaneous ozone exposure

	No mitigation vs. 2001		Mitigation vs. 2001		Mitigation vs. no mitigation	
	BS	LM	BS	LM	BS	LM
West	0.0%	0.0%	-3.6%	−6.9%	−3.6%	−6.95%
Plains	0.8%	1.5%	−4.1%	−7.9%	−4.9%	−9.4%
Midwest	0.0%	0.0%	−4.9%	−9.4%	−4.9%	−9.4%
Northeast	−0.3%	−0.5%	−4.6%	−8.9%	−4.4%	−8.4%
Southeast	1.5%	3.0%	−8.0%	−15.3%	−9.5%	−18.2%
All	0.5%	1.0%	−4.6%	−8.9%	−5.1%	−9.9%

Note: This panel presents estimates for the percentage change in respiratory admissions by region under various climate scenarios.

Sources: BS = Timothy K. M. Beatty and Jay P. Shimshack, "Air Pollution and Children's Respiratory Health: A Cohort Analysis," *Journal of Environmental Economics and Management* 7 (2014): 39–57; LM = Adriana Lleras-Muney, "The Needs of the Army: Using Compulsory Relocation in the Military to Estimate the Effect of Air Pollutants on Children's Health," *Journal of Human Resources* 45 (2010): 549–90.

Figure 1. Percentage change in 2050 US infant mortality from PM$_{2.5}$ under two scenarios, by region

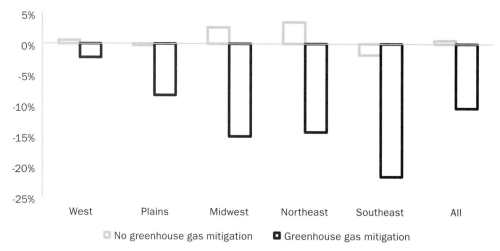

Note: This figure displays the percentage change in infant mortality rates, by region, from the projected change in PM$_{2.5}$ under scenarios of greenhouse gas mitigation and no greenhouse gas mitigation.

the Southeast. Given the small difference in PM$_{2.5}$ levels between no mitigation in 2050 and baseline values in 2001, we also find large infant mortality estimates for the mitigation versus no mitigation scenarios.

Adult Earnings

In panel B, we turn to projections of how early childhood exposure to PM$_{2.5}$ affects adult earnings. We use a procedure similar to the one we used for infant mortality: we obtain per capita income by region from the Bureau of Economic Analysis Regional Economic Accounts and multiply it by the estimated relationship between PM$_{2.5}$ and adult earnings and by the projected changes in PM$_{2.5}$. Following the study we discussed earlier about how pollution exposure after the 1970 Clean Air Act Amendments affected adult earnings, we estimate a 1.1 percent change in earnings from a 10-unit change in total suspended particles, and we scale this to obtain a 0.68 percent change from a 1-unit change in PM$_{2.5}$.[36] Under the no mitigation scenario, we again find small projected

impacts compared with the baseline year, with an estimated overall decrease in earnings of $30 per year per person. Once again, the estimates are considerably larger under a mitigation scenario compared both with the baseline and with no mitigation: $564 and $594, respectively, in additional earnings per person per year. The effects continue to be largest in the Midwest, Northeast, and Southeast, with estimates of more than $1,000 in additional earnings per person in the Southeast. The estimate for the entire United States suggests a 1.3 percent increase in earnings and up to 2.6 percent in the Southeast.

Hospitalizations

Here we look at how changes in ozone are projected to affect childhood hospitalizations for respiratory-related symptoms. Because we don't have a background rate of children's respiratory hospitalizations by region, we present only the percentage change in this outcome. To do so, we multiply the change in ozone by the percentage change from the best available estimates, giving estimates that range from a 1.03 to a 1.97 percent change in hospitalizations from a change in ozone concentration of 1 part per billion.[37]

The results, as panel C shows, indicate small to modest changes in respiratory hospitalizations without mitigation, ranging from a decrease of 0.5 percent in the Northeast to an increase of 3 percent in the Southeast. Overall, we see a net increase of 0.5 to 1.0 percent depending on the estimate used. Those modest effects suggest that the ozone increases expected under climate change are not likely to significantly increase respiratory hospitalizations among young children. Under a mitigation scenario, however, we again see large decreases in respiratory admissions, ranging from 3.6 percent in the West to 8 percent in the Southeast (with an overall estimate of 4.6 percent) under one set of assumptions; the decreases would be nearly twice as large

under a second set of assumptions. Comparing the mitigation scenario with no mitigation leads to even larger projected impacts.

Developing Countries

Our discussion thus far has focused almost exclusively on the most-developed countries. Hanna and Oliva discuss developing countries in detail; here we point out two key factors relevant to pollution. First, countries going through rapid development often witness considerably higher levels of pollution. A big question is whether those higher levels of pollution lead to greater health insults. Figure 2 shows air pollution levels over time for China, Mexico, and one city in the United States, Pittsburgh, focusing on PM_{10}. Although the pollution levels in China and Mexico are always higher than levels in the United States at the same point in time, the levels experienced in those countries today are not unlike historical levels in the United States. Contemporary pollution levels in

Figure 2. Trends in Air Pollution for Pittsburgh, China, and Mexico

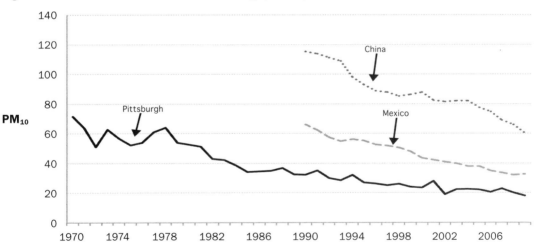

Note: All data are annual averages of daily measures of particulate matter less than 10 microns in diameter (PM_{10}), measured in micrograms per cubic meter.

Sources: Data for Mexico and China are averages across all major cities, obtained from the World Bank's database of World Development Indicators. Pittsburgh data from 1990 to 2009 are from the US Environmental Protection Agency's Air Quality System Data Mart. Data from before 1990 are courtesy of Cliff Davidson via Thomas Rawski; these data are total suspended particles multiplied by 0.55, which is the ratio of PM_{10} to TSP, where missing values for total suspended particles are imputed by using dustfall.

China and Mexico are similar to those found in Pittsburgh in the mid-1970s and mid-1990s, respectively. As such, studies based on historical pollution levels in the United States are likely to tell us something about current health and human capital impacts in developing countries.

Second, equatorial regions are expected to see larger heat effects from climate change, and they're also home to a much greater share of poorer nations, suggesting that increases in ozone from global warming are likely to be worse in poorer, equatorial nations. Mitigation is also likely to be more costly for those countries both because expenditures for mitigation would mean forgoing growth and because those countries have less capacity to regulate emissions, so they are less likely to experience mitigation's cobenefits. In fact, the Kyoto Protocol, the only ratified international treaty on climate change, exempted developing nations.

Those two factors suggest that even if the estimated pollution–health relationship is similar across nations, developing nations are likely to be hit by higher doses of pollution and thus suffer greater harm to child wellbeing.

Conclusions

Climate change, if it continues unabated, is expected to increase pollution concentrations in the future. Mitigation policies that reduce carbon emissions would not only offset that expected pollution increase but also further reduce pollution below current levels. Given children's sensitivity to pollution on a range of measures of wellbeing, this suggests that climate change and any policies to mitigate it may have significant effects on child wellbeing through changes in air quality. We have described some of the background

behind expected changes in air quality, reviewed quasi-experimental evidence that links the expected changes in $PM_{2.5}$ and ozone with several measures of child wellbeing, and performed some rough calculations to project how those changes in air quality might affect children.

Our calculations suggest that mitigating emissions that lead to climate change would likely produce significant improvements in child wellbeing. Infant mortality and respiratory diseases would decrease, and human capital and productivity would increase. Such improvements arise whether we compare mitigating emissions with the current situation or with a future scenario where no mitigation takes place. On the other hand, a scenario of no mitigation is unlikely to yield much change in wellbeing compared with the current situation. Though adaptation to temperature may moderate heat's direct effect on child wellbeing, adaptation is less likely to play a role when it comes to pollution. We have fewer technologies and biological responses that reduce the threat from pollution exposure.

Of course, our projections encompass many unknowns, and we must be cautious in taking them at face value. Projections of future climate are filled with uncertainty, as are projections of climate's relationship to emissions. How mitigation policies would affect pollution levels involves uncertainties as well. Moreover, technology may alter the ways we treat children throughout the life course. Given the need to act in the face of such uncertainty, we hope our estimates serve as a useful starting point.

ENDNOTES

1. Much of the material in this section is derived from US Environmental Protection Agency (US EPA), "Air Quality Criteria for Ozone and Related Photochemical Oxidants (2006 Final)," 600/R-05/004aF-cF (US EPA, Washington, DC, 2006), http://cfpub.epa.gov/ncea/risk/recordisplay.cfm?deid=149923, and US EPA, "2009 Final Report: Integrated Science Assessment for Particulate Matter," 600/R-08/139F (US EPA, Washington, DC, 2009), http://cfpub.epa.gov/ncea/risk/recordisplay.cfm?deid=216546.

2. Douglas Almond and Janet Currie, "Killing Me Softly: The Fetal Origins Hypothesis," *Journal of Economic Perspectives* 25 (2011): 153–72, doi: 10.1257/jep.25.3.153; David J. P. Barker, "The Fetal and Infant Origins of Adult Disease," *BMJ* 301 (1990): 1111, doi: 10.1136/bmj.301.6761.1111; and Thomas F. Bateson and Joel Schwartz, "Children's Response to Air Pollutants," *Journal of Toxicology and Environmental Health, Part A* 71 (2007): 238–43, doi: 10.1080/15287390701598234.

3. Arturas Petronis, "Epigenetics as a Unifying Principle in the Aetiology of Complex Traits and Diseases," *Nature* 465 (2010): 721–27, doi: 10.1038/nature09230.

4. Nebojsa Nakicenovic and Robert Swart, eds., *Special Report on Emissions Scenarios* (Cambridge: Cambridge University Press, 2000).

5. David Rind et al., "Use of On-Line Tracers as a Diagnostic Tool in General Circulation Model Development: 2. Transport between the Troposphere and Stratosphere," *Journal of Geophysical Research: Atmospheres* 104 (1999): 9151–67.

6. Daewon Byun and Kenneth L. Schere, "Review of the Governing Equations, Computational Algorithms, and Other Components of the Models-3 Community Multiscale Air Quality (CMAQ) Modeling System," *Applied Mechanics Reviews* 59, no. 2 (2006): 51–77, doi: 10.1115/1.2128636.

7. Georg A. Grell, Jimy Dudhia, and David R. Stauffer, "A Description of the Fifth-Generation Penn State/NCAR Mesoscale Model (MM5)," NCAR Technical Note NCAR/TN-398+STR (National Center for Atmospheric Research, Boulder, CO, 1994), doi: 10.5065/D60Z716B.

8. US EPA, "Assessment of the Impacts of Global Change on Regional US Air Quality: A Synthesis of Climate Change Impacts on Ground-Level Ozone US," 600/R-07/094F (US EPA, Washington, DC, 2009).

9. Ellen S. Post et al., "Variation in Estimated Ozone-Related Health Impacts of Climate Change Due to Modeling Choices and Assumptions," *Environmental Health Perspectives* 120 (2012): 1559–64, doi: 10.1289/ehp.1104271, and Lina Madaniyazi, "Projecting Future Air Pollution-Related Mortality under a Changing Climate: Progress, Uncertainties and Research Needs," *Environment International* 75 (2015): 21–32, doi: 10.1016/j.envint.2014.10.018.

10. Efthimios Tagaris et al., "Impacts of Global Climate Change and Emissions on Regional Ozone and Fine Particulate Matter Concentrations over the United States," *Journal of Geophysical Research: Atmospheres* 112 (2007): D14312, doi: 10.1029/2006JD008262.

11. US EPA, "Inventory of U.S. Greenhouse Gas Emissions and Sinks: 1990–2012," 430-R-14-003 (US EPA, Washington, DC, 2012).

12. Jeremy Avise et al., "Attribution of Projected Changes in Summertime US Ozone and $PM_{2.5}$ Concentrations to Global Changes," *Atmospheric Chemistry and Physics* 9 (2009): 1111–24, doi: 10.5194/acp-9-1111-2009.

13. Marcus Trail et al., "Sensitivity of Air Quality to Potential Future Climate Change and Emissions in the United States and Major Cities," *Atmospheric Environment* 94 (2014): 552–63, doi: 10.1016/j.atmosenv.2014.05.079.

14. Ashley Penrod et al., "Impacts of Future Climate and Emission Changes on U.S. Air Quality," *Atmospheric Environment* 89 (2014): 533–47, doi: 10.1016/j.atmosenv.2014.01.001.

15. Anastassia Manuilova et al., "Life Cycle Assessment of Post-Combustion CO_2 Capture and CO_2-Enhanced Oil Recovery Based on the Boundary Dam Integrated Carbon Capture and Storage Demonstration Project in Saskatchewan," *Energy Procedia* 63 (2014): 7398–7407, doi: 10.1016/j.egypro.2014.11.776.

16. Charles M. Tiebout, "A Pure Theory of Local Expenditures," *Journal of Political Economy*. 64 (1956): 416–24.

17. H. Spencer Banzhaf and Randall P. Walsh, "Do People Vote with Their Feet? An Empirical Test of Tiebout's Mechanism," *American Economic Review* 98 (2008): 843–63, doi: 10.1257/aer.98.3.843; Janet Currie, "Inequality at Birth: Some Causes and Consequences," *American Economic Review* 101, no. 3 (Papers and Proceedings) (2011): 1–22, doi: 10.1257/aer.101.3.1; Janet Currie, Michael Greenstone, and Enrico Moretti, "Superfund Cleanups and Infant Health," *American Economic Review* 101, no. 3 (Papers and Proceedings) (2011): 435–41; and Janet Currie and Reed Walker, "Traffic Congestion and Infant Health: Evidence from E-ZPass," *American Economic Journal: Applied Economics* 3 (2011): 65–90, doi: 10.1257/app.3.1.65.

18. Kenneth Y. Chay and Michael Greenstone, "Does Air Quality Matter? Evidence from the Housing Market," *Journal of Political Economy* 113 (2005): 376–424, doi: 10.1086/427462.

19. Paul N. Courant and Richard C. Porter, "Averting Expenditure and the Cost of Pollution," *Journal of Environmental Economics and Management* 8 (1981): 321–9, doi: 10.1016/0095-0696(81)90044-9; Winston Harrington and Paul R. Portney, "Valuing the Benefits of Health and Safety Regulation," *Journal of Urban Economics* 22 (1987): 101–12, doi: 10.1016/0094-1190(87)90052-0; and Timothy J. Bartik, "Evaluating the Benefits of Non-Marginal Reductions in Pollution Using Information on Defensive Expenditures," *Journal of Environmental Economics and Management* 15 (1988): 111–27, doi: 10.1016/0095-0696(88)90032-0.

20. For a full review, see Janet Currie et al., "What Do We Know about Short- and Long-Term Effects of Early-Life Exposure to Pollution?" *Annual Review of Resource Economics* 6: 217–47, doi: 10.1146/annurev-resource-100913-012610.

21. Ramona Lall et al., "Estimation of Historical Annual $PM_{2.5}$ Exposures for Health Effects Assessment," *Atmospheric Environment* 38 (2004): 5217–26, doi: 10.1016/j.atmosenv.2004.01.053.

22. Kenneth Y. Chay and Michael Greenstone, "The Impact of Air Pollution on Infant Mortality: Evidence from Geographic Variation in Pollution Shocks Induced by a Recession," *Quarterly Journal of Economics* 118 (2003): 1121–67, doi: 10.1162/00335530360698513, and Kenneth Y. Chay and Michael Greenstone, "Air Quality, Infant Mortality, and the Clean Air Act of 1970," Working Paper 10053 (National Bureau of Economic Research, Cambridge, MA, 2003).

23. Nicholas J. Sanders and Charles F. Stoecker, "Where Have All the Young Men Gone? Using Gender Ratios to Measure Fetal Death Rates," *Journal of Health Economics* (forthcoming).

24. Katharina Janke, Carol Propper, and John Henderson, "Do Current Levels of Air Pollution Kill? The Impact of Air Pollution on Population Mortality in England," *Health Economics* 18 (2009): 1031–55, doi: 10.1002/hec.1475.

25. Christopher R. Knittel, Douglas L. Miller, and Nicholas J. Sanders, "Caution, Drivers! Children Present: Traffic, Pollution, and Infant Health," *Review of Economics and Statistics* (forthcoming).

26. Eva O. Arceo-Gomez, Rema Hanna, and Paulina Oliva, "Does the Effect of Pollution on Infant Mortality Differ between Developing and Developed Countries? Evidence from Mexico City," Working Paper 18349 (National Bureau of Economic Research, Cambridge, MA, 2012).

27. Adriana Lleras-Muney, "The Needs of the Army: Using Compulsory Relocation in the Military to Estimate the Effect of Air Pollutants on Children's Health," *Journal of Human Resources* 45 (2010): 549–90, doi: 10.1353/jhr.2010.0016.

28. Matthew Neidell, "Information, Avoidance Behavior, and Health: The Effect of Ozone on Asthma Hospitalizations," *Journal of Human Resources* 44 (2009): 450–78, doi: 10.1353/jhr.2009.0018.

29. Timothy K. M. Beatty and Jay P. Shimshack, "Air Pollution and Children's Respiratory Health: A Cohort Analysis," *Journal of Environmental Economics and Management* 7 (2014): 39–57, doi: 10.1016/j.jeem.2013.10.002.

30. Jacqueline S. Zweig, John C. Ham, and Edward L. Avo, "Air Pollution and Academic Performance: Evidence from California Schools" (Department of Economics, University of Maryland, 2009).

31. Victor Lavy, Avraham Ebenstein, and Sefi Roth, "The Impact of Short Term Exposure to Ambient Air Pollution on Cognitive Performance and Human Capital Formation," Working Paper 20648 (National Bureau of Economic Research, Cambridge, MA, 2012).

32. Douglas Almond, Lena Edlund, and Mårten Palme, "Chernobyl's Subclinical Legacy: Prenatal Exposure to Radioactive Fallout and School Outcomes in Sweden," *Quarterly Journal of Economics* 124 (2009): 1729–72, doi: 10.1162/qjec.2009.124.4.1729; Sandra E. Black et al., "This Is Only a Test? Long-Run Impacts of Prenatal Exposure to Radioactive Fallout," Working Paper 18987 (National Bureau of Economic Research, Cambridge, MA, 2013); Prashant Bharadwaj et al., "Gray Matters: Fetal Pollution Exposure and Human Capital Formation," Working Paper 20662 (National Bureau of Economic Research, Cambridge, MA, 2014); and J. Peter Nilsson, "The Long-Term Effects of Early Childhood Lead Exposure: Evidence from the Phase-Out of Leaded Gasoline" (Institute for Evaluation of Labour Market and Education Policy, Swedish Ministry of Employment, Uppsala, 2009).

33. Nicholas J. Sanders, "What Doesn't Kill You Makes You Weaker: Prenatal Pollution Exposure and Educational Outcomes," *Journal of Human Resources* 47 (2012): 826–50, doi: 10.3368/jhr.47.3.826.

34. Adam Isen, Maya Rossin-Slater, and W. Reed Walker, "Every Breath You Take—Every Dollar You'll Make: The Long-Term Consequences of the Clean Air Act of 1970," Working Paper 19858 (National Bureau of Economic Research, Cambridge, MA, 2013).

35. Kenneth Y. Chay and Michael Greenstone, "The Impact of Air Pollution on Infant Mortality: Evidence from Geographic Variation in Pollution Shocks Induced by a Recession," *Quarterly Journal of Economics* 118 (2003): 1121–67, doi: 10.1162/00335530360698513; Knittel, Miller, and Sanders, "Caution, Drivers!" and Lall, "Estimation".

36. Isen, Rossin-Slater, and Walker, "Every Breath.".

37. Lleras-Muney, "Needs of the Army," and Beatty and Shimshack, "Children's Respiratory Health."

Implications of Climate Change for Children in Developing Countries

Rema Hanna and Paulina Oliva

Summary

Climate change may be particularly dangerous for children in developing countries. Even today, many developing countries experience a disproportionate share of extreme weather, and they are predicted to suffer disproportionately from the effects of climate change in the future. Moreover, developing countries often have limited social safety nets, widespread poverty, fragile health care systems, and weak governmental institutions, making it harder for them to adapt or respond to climate change. And the fact that many developing countries have high birth rates and high ratios of children to adults (known as high dependency ratios) means that proportionately more children are at risk there than in the developed world.

In this article, Rema Hanna and Paulina Oliva delve into climate change's likely implications for children in developing countries. Such children already face severe challenges, which climate change will likely exacerbate. In particular, most people in developing countries still depend primarily on agriculture as a source of income, and so anything that reduces crop yields—such as excessive heat or rain—is likely to directly threaten the livelihoods of developing-country families and their ability to feed their children. Poor nutrition and economic disruption are likely to lower children's scholastic achievement or even keep them out of school altogether. Children in developing countries also face more-severe threats from both air and water pollution; from infectious and parasitic diseases carried by insects or contaminated water; and from possible displacement, migration, and violence triggered by climate change.

How can we temper the threat to children in developing countries? Hanna and Oliva write that we should design and fund policies to shield children in developing nations from the harm caused by climate change. Such policies might include developing new technologies, inventing more-weather-resistant crops, improving access to clean water, increasing foreign aid during disasters, and offering more assistance to help poor countries expand their safety net programs.

www.futureofchildren.org

Rema Hanna is the Jeffrey Cheah Professor of South-East Asia Studies at Harvard University's John F. Kennedy School of Government. Paulina Oliva is an assistant professor in the Department of Economics at the University of California, Santa Barbara.

Prashant Bharadwaj of the University of California, San Diego, reviewed and critiqued a draft of this article

C limate change may be the "biggest global health threat of the 21st century."[1] As with many future events that are hard to predict, people disagree about the ultimate nature and extent of climate change. But many observers expect that Earth will warm to at least 2°C (3.6°F) over the preindustrial average; that rainfall patterns will change; that extreme weather events will become more frequent; that sea levels will rise, with increased flooding in coastal areas; and so forth. The other articles in this issue show that such changes may have serious repercussions for children and families worldwide.

Children are potentially much more vulnerable than adults to environmental factors (for example, heat, pollution, or famine) because they are both physically weaker and less able to dissipate heat. Moreover, we now have strong evidence that environmental influences during pregnancy and early childhood have persistent effects through adulthood. Simply put, healthier children grow into healthier, wealthier, more-educated adults.[2]

Although children worldwide may be at risk from climate change, its effects may be particularly severe for kids who live in poor nations. Temperature increases have a large effect on gross domestic product (GDP) in poor countries but little observable effect in rich ones.[3] The reason is partly that poor countries, on average, have warmer climates than richer ones do, and temperature changes may affect health and agriculture more severely in areas that are hotter to begin with. And because of their locations, developing countries are likely to face a disproportional share of extreme changes in weather.

Moreover, developing countries have weaker institutional structures. Weaker infrastructure and less-adequate health systems may make it harder to mitigate the effects of temperature. In the United States, electrification and greater access to health care have greatly reduced mortality from heat.[4] In developing countries, where energy infrastructure lags behind, we may not see a similar pattern. Developing countries also have weaker labor and credit markets, which may make it hard for families to adapt to losses caused by climate change. For example, a household that faces an agricultural loss caused by an increase in adverse weather may not have enough funds to sustain the family and also invest in agricultural inputs, such as seeds and fertilizer, for the following year. To manage their finances, families in a developed country might be able to get loans, both to have enough money for things like food, health care, and education and to ensure that they can plant again the following year. But in developing countries with limited access to banks and formal financing, such loans may be unavailable. Thus families might not only lose income from the crop loss today but also suffer sustained losses of income over time because they can't invest in future production. Government safety net programs may offer emergency help, but again, such programs are more limited in the poorest countries.

We devote this article, then, to exploring how climate change might affect the especially vulnerable children who live in poorer nations.

Effects on Children

Understanding how climate change will affect people is, in general, a challenging task. The task is further hampered by the fact that it's hard to disentangle climate effects from other characteristics that coexist with climate. For example, poor regions are likely to experience climate change effects sooner than wealthier regions are. Recent research in economics tries to predict the effects of high-frequency changes in weather, and we exploit that research here because it takes a large step forward in beginning to disentangle weather impacts from other characteristics. But that method could cause us to miss long-run and cumulative impacts that could be important—a particular problem in our case if we believe that the cumulative impacts of shocks to children in early life could produce lasting adult outcomes.

We face several additional challenges in trying to understand how climate change will affect children in developing countries. First, not all developing countries will face the same threats. Impacts may vary greatly from one region to another, and rural areas and cities may be affected very differently. For example, urban children and their families could suffer from rising food prices, while rural families could see their houses and livelihoods destroyed by flooding. Thus we will try to discuss a range of outcomes and places.

Second, the data that we're working with may not have been collected specifically for children in a household, or it may not include a comprehensive set of outcomes that we would care about in assessing impacts on children. For instance, studies on weather-related fatalities rarely include age.[5] As a result, in some cases, we will infer possible outcomes by combining what we know about effects on families with how we might expect children to be affected when their families face such situations.

Third, it's often hard to isolate the channel through which an impact occurs, because concurrent effects may interact with and compound one another. For example, health effects from malnutrition and dehydration could become much worse if flooding also knocks out essential health services. Or reductions in future work opportunities caused by a slowdown in economic growth might decrease the benefits of attending school, while, at the same time, rising rates of illness might increase the cost of school attendance. Therefore, although we separate potential mechanisms to make it easier to explain how they work, we also try to offer insights into those types of interactions.

Impacts on Health

Climate change may further endanger the already vulnerable health status of children in the developing world, because they will more often experience extreme heat, infectious diseases, and floods. Children in the highlands, who were previously unaffected by vector-borne illnesses (that is, illnesses such as malaria that are transmitted by insects and other pests) may become newly exposed to them. In addition, new health threats may appear, such as new illnesses that emerge from disturbed ecosystems or conditions previously uncommon among low-income youth, such as skin cancer.

Child health in the developing world is already substantially worse than in richer countries. For example, let's look at infant mortality, a leading indicator of child health and access to health care. In 2013, the infant mortality rate was 10 times higher in low-income countries than it was in wealthy ones: 53 vs. 5.3 deaths per 1,000 births, respectively. In poor countries, the main causes of child death often include infections and parasitic diseases, which are rarer in rich countries today. Because climate change is likely to exacerbate conditions that bring forth infections and parasites, the health of children in poor nations is likely to suffer substantially more than that of children in richer ones.

To understand the pathways through which climate change can affect health, we next describe each potential channel separately, and we provide insights into the importance of each channel based on available evidence.

Direct Effect of More Hot Days

As Joshua Graff-Zivin and Jeffrey Shrader write elsewhere in this issue, the more-frequent hot days and heat waves that accompany climate change may directly affect children's health through increases in rashes, heat exhaustion, temporary loss of consciousness (syncope), and heat stroke. Those impacts are likely to be more pronounced in the developing world because low-income countries will see a disproportional rise in warm days (defined as days above 30°C, or 86°F). Effects will vary by region, however: the percentage of warm days is projected to increase the most in the tropics, particularly in equatorial Africa, the Amazon, and the Malay Archipelago. India and areas of northern Africa will experience strong seasonal increases in warm days, and heat waves are projected to increase in the northwestern Sahara and most of South America.[6]

The effect on mortality of an additional warm day is seven times greater in rural areas of developing countries than it is in the United States. However, the United States experienced similarly high heat mortality before the use of air conditioning became widespread in the twentieth century. Thus the differences that we see between the United States and developing countries today can be attributed at least in part to technologies that are unavailable to the majority of people in the developing world. It's particularly worrisome that increases in mean annual temperature will occur at least two decades sooner in Africa than in other regions of the world: economic growth in Africa is unlikely to reach a level that can support widespread use of air conditioning and other adaptations by that point.

Water Shortages

Many scientists predict that climate change will lead to an increase in water shortages, although, again, the effects may vary substantially by region. Predictions for Africa, for example, foresee only a modest impact on water availability, although countries in the Zambezi River basin will see additional water shortages. In Asia, water shortages are hard to forecast because of low confidence in precipitation predictions, along with the uncertain effects that increasingly variable precipitation will have on water supply.[7]

Water scarcity may mean that people have less and lower-quality drinking water and that they have to spend more time and money to collect water from sources farther from their homes. Lack of access to sufficient sources of good-quality water—the type you would get from piped water systems, for example—has been linked to more-frequent and longer-lasting cases of diarrhea.[8] Droughts could also displace people from their homes, as we discuss later. In Asia, droughts could also cause forest fires and dust storms, which have

Figure 1. Top Causes of Death among Children under Five (2012)

WHO Africa Region	WHO Southeast Asia Region	United States
Acute lower respiratory infections (15.9%)	Prematurity (25.2%)	Congenital anomalies (19.4%)
Malaria (14.7%)	Acute lower respiratory infections (14.1%)	Prematurity (15.0%)
Prematurity (12.3%)	Birth asphyxia and birth trauma (11.4%)	Accidents/unintentional injuries (9.0%)
Birth asphyxia and birth trauma (10.9%)	Diarrheal diseases (9.8%)	Sudden infant death syndrome (6.0%)
Diarrheal diseases (10.3%)	Other communicable perinatal, and nutritional conditions (8.5%)	Maternal pregnancy complications (5.4%)

Note: WHO is the World Health Organization.

Sources: World Health Organization, "Global Health Observatory Data Repository," http://apps.who.int/gho/data/node. main.CM300REG6; National Center for Injury Prevention and Control, "10 Leading Causes of Death by Age Group, United States—2012," http://www.cdc.gov/injury/wisqars/pdf/leading_causes_of_death_by_age_group_2012-a.pdf; National Center for Health Statistics, "Deaths, Percent of Total Deaths, and Death Rates for the 15 Leading Causes of Death in 5-Year Age Groups, by Race and Sex: United States, 2012," http://www.cdc.gov/nchs/data/dvs/LCWK1_2012.pdf.

devastating effects on family income and health.

Infections and Vector-Borne Diseases

Climate change is likely to increase the incidence of infectious and vector-borne diseases. Because health care, sanitation, and coordinated pest control can greatly reduce human vulnerability to such diseases, they have largely been eradicated in the developed world. But they are still among the primary killers of children in developing countries (figure 1).

Climate change will likely increase the optimal conditions for infectious and parasitic diseases through more heavy rainfall, more flooding, and rising water temperature; for example, the association between heavy rainfall, high water temperatures, and cholera outbreaks has been well documented.[9] Such environmental changes are likely to affect the developing world disproportionally: Central Africa, Southeast Asia, and Central America, along with Peru, Ecuador, Colombia, and northeast Brazil, will likely experience an

increase in heavy precipitation, making all of them more susceptible to cholera outbreaks.[10] Bangladesh's high susceptibility to widespread outbreaks of cholera makes the large population of children there particularly vulnerable (about 1 in 10 experienced cholera in 2012, according to UNICEF).[11]

In addition to their short-run health effects, parasitic diseases may have long-term consequences for health and schooling, which may affect future income. Field experiments have shown that a 25 percent reduction in moderate to heavy infections of intestinal worms (such as hookworm, roundworm, whipworm, and the worms that cause schistosomiasis) reduced school absenteeism by one-fourth and had long-run impacts on adult outcomes.[12]

How climate change will affect vector-borne diseases is hard to predict. On one hand, in some regions where malaria currently flourishes, the optimal incubation temperature for the malaria parasite is likely to be exceeded. On the other hand, some areas that are now malaria free may become susceptible; many of the insects that transmit malaria to humans thrive in warm night and winter temperatures.[13] Although the overall pattern for vector-borne diseases is hard to predict, scientists foresee that malaria, dengue, and other vector-borne illnesses will expand to previously unaffected areas that will become suitable habitats for malaria-transmitting insects.[14] People whose immune systems have never been exposed to such parasites will likely be more vulnerable than people in historically exposed populations.

Flooding and Natural Disasters

Flooding and other natural disasters may substantially harm children's health, and children in the developing world may be more susceptible than the average population for two key reasons. First, the Intergovernmental Panel on Climate Change projects that climate change will make extreme precipitation near the centers of tropical cyclones more likely—and regions that experience tropical cyclones are disproportionately poor. Second, death rates from environmental disasters, including floods and windstorms, may be many times higher in low-income countries than in high-income countries. The current number of deaths per year from environmental disasters in countries with a per capita GDP near $2,000 (such as Bangladesh or Senegal) is 944, compared with 180 in countries with a per capita GDP above $14,000.[15] Research has also shown that income growth can initially increase the death toll from environmental disasters.[16] Thus poor countries whose per capita incomes will rise to around $5,000 in the next few decades will reach their peak vulnerability to environmental disasters at a time when such disasters become more common.

One of the reasons low-income countries are more vulnerable to environmental disasters is that they lack complete credit and insurance markets. Few people have private insurance for housing or crop loss, and households that lack such insurance would not have the money to rebuild or resettle after a disaster. Another option could be to borrow funds to get back on their feet after a disaster, but poorly functioning credit markets make that hard—or just very expensive—to do. International aid can help, but because of either lack of funding or the challenges inherent in providing aid in countries with limited institutional capacity and infrastructure to begin with, the donor community can't always respond proportionally to the human and physical toll.[17]

Air Pollution

Climate change may lead to higher concentrations of several air pollutants, including ozone and particulate matter. Elsewhere in this issue, Allison Larr and Matthew Neidell discuss climate change's direct effects on ozone and thus on children's health. Here we focus on the potential health effects of particulate matter, which may increase as wildfires and dust storms become more common in the developing world. First, as we've said, greater variability in precipitation patterns may increase drought in some regions in Asia and in eastern and southern Africa, making wildfires more common and more difficult to control.[18] Air pollution from forest fires can increase infant mortality and reduce general health, and the effects are much worse when the exposure occurs in the womb.[19] Studies of how wildfires affect adult health have found significant changes in prime-aged adults' ability to perform everyday activities, such as carrying heavy objects. Given that children are generally more sensitive to air pollution than adults are, we suspect that those health and productivity effects may extend to children as well.

Droughts can also create more air pollution through dust storms. Recent studies have shown that droughts in Africa and other arid regions can increase the amount of dust over large areas.[20] Dust storms and wildfires produce inhalable, coarse particles and a smaller share of fine particles, both of which are associated with increased mortality from heart disease and respiratory disease, especially among infants and the elderly. [21]

Other Potential Health Pathways

Climate change may affect health in developing countries through other pathways, such as previously unknown diseases and conditions that today are more common in the developed world. For example, rapid shifts in temperature and precipitation patterns can destabilize animal populations and lead to the emergence of new diseases, which is what happened with hantavirus—which causes dangerous pulmonary disease in humans—in the US Southwest after an El Niño event in the early 1990s.[22] However, predictions about emerging diseases are uncertain, and sound empirical evidence is scarce.[23] Nevertheless, the developing world, whose health systems are seldom able to fully manage even well-known and curable diseases in children, may find it particularly hard to cope with new infectious diseases. The 2014 Ebola outbreak in West Africa is a recent example of how the spread of pathogens can quickly overwhelm health systems.

Climate change may increase the incidence of diseases that are not currently big health problems in the developing world, such as melanoma, a type of skin cancer. Experimental studies on mice suggest that high temperatures exacerbate ultraviolet rays' impact on skin cancer.[24] Applying to humans the effects observed in mice (though doing so overlooks many biological and behavioral differences), one of these studies calculates that skin cancer could become 21 percent more common if global temperatures rise by 2°C, and 46 percent more common with a temperature increase of 4°C. Because melanoma is underreported in developing countries, its incidence is hard to assess. However, the International Agency for Research on Cancer suggests that melanoma is becoming more common in Africa and Southeast Asia.[25]

Income Loss, Food Insecurity, and Malnutrition

Several other articles in this issue review the link between climate change and agriculture. We'll take those articles as a starting point to discuss how agricultural losses—caused by warmer temperatures and increases in weather variability—could affect children's development.

According to the World Bank, 75 percent of the world's poor live in rural areas and depend on farming for a living either directly or indirectly. Lower yields of subsistence crops, reduced incomes from cash crops, and higher food prices would likely reduce the incomes of many of the world's rural poor. To make up for those income losses, families might borrow money or rely on government safety net programs. But developing countries, which tend to have imperfect credit markets and fewer formal social safety net programs, may be particularly sensitive to climate shocks: families often rely on informal insurance markets within their villages, and a climate shock that affects an entire region may cause those informal markets to collapse. In that case, families couldn't borrow money to make up for their income losses, making it harder to put food on the table.[26] Moreover, if climate shocks raise food prices or reduce urban wages (as we discuss later), children in nonagricultural families, too, may have less to eat.

Reduced income and lower purchasing power for food can affect children's and, ultimately, adults' health.[27] Credible empirical evidence supports the fetal origins hypothesis, whereby chronic degenerative diseases, as well as other health problems, can be traced back to mothers' nutrition during pregnancy. Similarly, malnutrition in the early stages of life can contribute to stunting, which is an indicator of adult health; it can also increase vulnerability to other health shocks. For example, recent research shows that Indian children tend to be tall, even taller than African children. But because parents invest less in the nutrition and health of subsequent children, Indian children born second tend to be much shorter than firstborns; children born third are even shorter, and so forth.[28] Similarly, we can understand how income affects children's nutritional status by looking at experimental studies that test whether giving parents cash affects their children's health. Such studies find mixed effects on cumulative child health as measured by height: cash transfers led to gains in children's growth in Mexico, Nicaragua, Ecuador, and Colombia but not in Brazil or Honduras. We need more research to understand why cash made a difference in some areas and not in others.[29]

When productivity losses make poor families even poorer, diminished nutrition isn't the only threat to children's health. Greater poverty may also make it harder for households to deal with relatively common health shocks: for example, having a child with a cleft palate can lead to enormous challenges for a poor family, even though cleft palate is a relatively common problem that is easily corrected in rich countries.[30]

Even short-term productivity losses can cause substantial health problems through moderate or chronic malnutrition. But extreme weather such as typhoons, hurricanes, and droughts can be disastrous, wiping out entire crops and, possibly, infrastructure such as housing, health centers, and schools. Following in the footsteps of Nobel Prize–winning economist Amartya Sen, who developed most of today's economic theories of the effects of famine, many researchers have documented how natural disasters and famine affect people in developing countries.[31]

Natural disasters have long-lasting effects on survivor's health.

Environmental disasters kill people directly, of course: one study of hurricanes estimated that from 1970 to 2002, they killed 2.47 million people and injured another 2.7 million.[32] Deaths can occur even after a disaster, as health services grow weaker, sanitation and other infrastructure suffers damage, and disease becomes endemic.[33]

Natural disasters also have long-lasting effects on survivors' health. Earlier, we discussed how reduced nutrition, both in the womb and early in life, can damage health even into adulthood. Massive food shortages during famine have even worse effects. For example, if the 1959–61 famine had never occurred, children born in 1959 in China would have been as much as three centimeters (about 1.2 inches) taller.[34]

Finally, a decline in health caused by reduced access to food that leads to malnutrition could exacerbate the other impacts of climate change. Children who are already in poor health may have a harder time fighting off infections even as climate change makes waterborne diseases more common. Sick children may also miss more days of school, and inadequate education can reduce long-run employability and wages.

In short, climate change will likely impair child nutrition and health, offsetting the gains that children in developing countries have made in recent decades.

Education and Human Capital

We've already touched on education, but the topic is important enough to merit its own discussion. Climate change may affect education through at least four mechanisms: shocks that affect income and wages, poor nutrition as a result of income losses, effects of natural disasters, and direct effects of climate changes (for example, pollution or heat).

First, reduced income might lower school enrollment and attendance because families might not be able to afford school fees or because children have to work to help provide for the family. Evaluations of programs that gave additional income to families in developing countries or directly helped them with school fees show that income changes have large positive effects on school attendance.[35] On the other hand, recent research shows that excessive rain

can improve school attendance by reducing wages, thus making jobs scarce for women and children.[36] Thus climate shocks, which affect both the labor market and wages at the same time, may have different effects than does loss of income alone. How climate change affects education may depend on the interplay between income losses to families and changes to children's wages.

Second, health declines caused by income loss—both in the womb and in early childhood—may affect children's school attendance. Taking birth weight as an indicator of mothers' nutrition and health, US children whose birth weight is low (defined as less than 2,500 grams, or about 5.5 pounds) are much less likely later in life to pass high-school-equivalency exams and to be employed.[37] Mothers' caloric intake is important, but so is their overall nutritional status during pregnancy: In Tanzania, for example, when iodine deficiency disorders were reduced by an intensive iodine supplementation program for mothers, children achieved 0.36 to 0.56 additional years of schooling.[38] Similarly, weather in early childhood has had long-run effects on schooling, particularly for girls.[39] For example, Indonesian girls whose childhoods are enriched by more rain—and thus higher yields of crops—are not only healthier and taller; they also attain more schooling. In contrast, there is no effect for boys, perhaps because when families face a loss, they adjust by reducing their investments in girls rather than boys.[40] Climate change, then, could affect girls and boys differently, thereby reducing the gains made in recent years toward closing the gender gap in education.

Third, extreme weather could cause famine and/or large-scale displacement, with massive impacts on human capital accumulation.

For example, men who were exposed to the 1959–61 famine in China during their mothers' pregnancies were 9 percent more likely to be illiterate; exposed women were 6 percent more likely to be illiterate. Those increases in illiteracy eventually translated to higher rates of unemployment for both men and women, as well as to changes in marital patterns.[41] Similarly, people exposed to the 1941–42 famine in Greece were less literate and attained fewer years of education.[42]

Schooling may also be affected when extreme weather damages infrastructure. For example, during the Yemeni airlift in 1949—when drought and prejudice in Yemen led to a campaign to fly 50,000 Jewish people to Israel—children (especially girls) who were placed in better physical environments (for example, with better sanitation, running water, and electricity) did better in school.[43] Another real worry is that an increase in extreme events could mean that more children's parents die. Among other harmful effects on children, a parent's death may also impede schooling: for example, children whose mothers die tend to attain fewer years of schooling and have less money for their education.[44]

Finally, environmental changes could directly affect whether children go to school at all and whether they learn while there. Heat has been associated with lower economic productivity in adults and could presumably also affect children's ability to learn.[45] Moreover, increased levels of pollution are associated with both lower school attendance and lower test scores.[46]

Displacement and Migration

Climate change may affect where people live. At the extreme, entire families and communities could be displaced by extreme

weather and massive crop losses. Displaced families are often put into makeshift camps with conditions that can be similar to those of refugee camps. That sort of displacement could exacerbate climate change's effects on food supply, access to health care, sanitation, and education.

On the other hand, permanent migration might reduce the adverse effects of a natural disaster: for example, massive migration may have mitigated the environmental catastrophe from land degradation during the American Dust Bowl of the 1930s.[47] However, the evidence from developing countries is less hopeful: Indonesia, for example, has seen little permanent migration to urban areas after natural disasters.[48] Similarly, in Bangladesh, there is little evidence of migration in response to massive flooding, suggesting that the lack of immediate funds coupled with an inability to borrow money to finance resettlement could make it hard for people to move away from disaster areas to places with greater employment opportunities.[49] Moreover, even if people do try to move, cities may not be able to absorb large numbers of migrants.

Research on a wide variety of developing countries confirms that households are more likely to migrate in response to temporary temperature and rainfall changes that are large enough to affect crops than they are in response to large-scale natural disasters.[50] Though migration may help mitigate income losses from climate shocks, it's unclear whether overall family income would fall or rise. On one hand, we know that there are barriers to migration and that overcoming those barriers could lead to better employment opportunities. Recent evidence also suggests that rainfall-induced migration leads to better work outcomes and mitigates long-run health effects.[51] However, others have argued that the urban sector of the economy could also suffer if a high share of industry is linked to processing agricultural goods, if a high proportion of jobs are in industries that rely on weather (for example, tourism), or if heat does indeed lower productivity.[52] In this case, migration might not be a cure for income loss.

Households are more likely to migrate in response to temporary temperature and rainfall changes than they are in response to large-scale natural disasters.

In terms of children specifically, the effects would depend on whether children move to cities with their parents or are left behind with other family members. If entire families migrate, the effects will depend on their financial situation. Further, if sudden increases in urban populations aren't matched by increases in social services, children's health and education may suffer. For example, sharp increases in urbanization in South Africa led to overly congested schools.[53] How would school overcrowding affect learning? Some evidence suggests that large class sizes impede learning, but other evidence from the developing world suggests that changes in class size don't matter much, perhaps because classes are too large already.[54]

For children who are left behind in rural areas, the evidence is mixed. Several studies have found that migration leads to better schooling outcomes for children who are left

behind.[55] On the other hand, another study, which compared families that won a lottery for a visa with families that did not, found no large, systematic effect on the health and education of children left behind. (However, the study's sample was relatively small, making it harder to measure impacts.)[56] Other research finds more nuance: for example, among people left behind in Mexico when family members migrate to the United States, infant mortality fell and birth weight increased, but investments in more continual, preventive health care for children fell.[57] Further research may be able to reconcile these conflicting studies and help us better understand the channels through which migration affects children.

Psychological Impacts

We know a good bit about how income shocks and climate disasters affect children's physical health, but less about the effects on their mental wellbeing. And we can't discuss the effects of climate change on children without discussing mental health. Mental health is important not only in its own right, but it can also affect other forms of human capital accumulation (for example, schooling) that we care about. Again, the impacts may vary depending on the nature and extent of the climate shock that a household faces, as well as the child's age.

Increased poverty from climate change could directly harm a child's mental wellbeing, with particularly detrimental effects if natural disasters also increase. For example, numerous studies have shown that children exposed to more natural disasters are more likely to suffer posttraumatic stress.[58] Moreover, among adults in developing countries, economic distress is strongly correlated with psychological distress and reduced decision-making ability.[59] Having psychologically compromised parents could harm a child's psychological development even further.

Recent research suggests that these effects can be long lasting. In Ghana, for instance, low cocoa prices in the year of a child's birth and in early childhood are correlated with higher incidence of severe mental distress once the children become adults; the channels driving that result may include reduced maternal health, worse decision making by stressed-out parents, and reduced physical health among children.[60] At the extreme end of the spectrum, a number of studies have shown that exposure to famine and war during pregnancy is associated with higher levels of antisocial behaviors and schizophrenia in adulthood.[61]

Violence and Children

Climate change may exacerbate domestic violence, raise crime rates, and increase the probability of conflict and war.

Household violence may increase because greater heat can spur aggression. Economic stress from climate shocks could also lead to increased violence; for example, rainfall shocks contribute to domestic violence and deaths during disputes over dowries in India, and job loss among US men is correlated with child abuse.[62] Extreme weather and natural disasters may also exacerbate household violence: in the United States, for example, hurricanes have been linked to a rise in inflicted traumatic brain injury in young children.[63] In addition, maternal stress from violence during pregnancy may lead to lower birth weight.[64]

Crime may be another product of climate change. Both low rainfall and high temperatures have been associated with increases in property crimes.[65] The ultimate effect on children will depend on the extent to which they are affected by crimes committed against the family (for example, loss of property or murder of a parent).

Bad economic times are also linked to an increase in child transactional sex—that is, the exchange of sex for money, goods, or services. Lack of data makes it extremely difficult to study this topic, but recent research has shown that among adult women, income losses increase the incidence of transactional sex and of risky sexual behaviors that men are willing to pay more for, whereas rising income reduces risky sexual activity in general among adolescent girls.[66] Moreover, rainfall shocks have been shown to increase the prevalence of HIV, which suggests an increase in higher-risk sexual behaviors.[67]

Finally, climate change may lead to greater civil conflict. Richard Akresh discusses climate change and conflict in detail elsewhere in this issue. Here we will note only that war could greatly exacerbate all of the effects on children that we've discussed so far by further reducing food security, increasing the incidence of family loss, driving mass displacement, interrupting school, and so on.

Mitigating Policies

In short, climate change can harm the growth and development of children in low-income countries through channels that are different from those present in the developed world. (See the article by Graff-Zivin and Shrader in this issue for more on how climate change can affect children in developed countries.) Of course, the extent of the problem will depend greatly on families' ability to engage in mitigating behaviors—that is, to undertake steps that would reduce their exposure to climate change—and on whether countries implement policies that help lessen the burdens families will face. But we don't know whether developing countries will be able to adapt in those ways. According to the World Bank, if developing countries aren't able to adapt to climate change, "certain climate scenarios may still cause regional disasters even if global production is not affected."[68]

The extent of the problem will depend greatly on families' ability to engage in mitigating behaviors and on whether countries implement policies that help lessen the burdens families will face.

Part of the challenge comes from the fact that developing countries have underdeveloped formal markets, weaker institutions, inadequate physical infrastructure, and lower incomes than do developed countries. For example, air conditioning can reduce exposure to very hot days that harm infant health. But globally, 1.2 billion households lack electricity. Even those that have electricity may face spotty service—particularly on hot days—and greater household spending on electricity may come at the cost of food and health-care spending on kids. Similarly, migration to urban areas may help compensate for rural job loss, but it's unclear whether the urban sector can absorb the influx. And migration itself may have adverse effects on children.

Other than the most obvious way to slow down and reduce the severity of climate change worldwide—reducing our carbon output—it is well worth our collective efforts to think about how to design and fund policies that can shield children from climate change's effects—particularly children in developing nations, who may be the most vulnerable. Such policies might include developing new technologies to expand electrification, inventing more-weather-resistant crops, improving access to clean water, increasing foreign aid during disasters, and offering more assistance to help poor countries expand their safety net programs. Investing in ways to help families adjust to the new situations and challenges arising from climate change may have long-run benefits. Not only will those investments affect children today, they may have long-lasting effects on human capital accumulation and, ultimately, on economic growth.

ENDNOTES

1. Anthony Costello et al., "Managing the Health Effects of Climate Change," *Lancet* 373 (2009): 1693, doi: 10.1016/S0140-6736(09)60935-1.

2. Douglas Almond and Janet Currie, "Killing Me Softly: The Fetal Origins Hypothesis," *Journal of Economic Perspectives* 25, no. 3 (2011): 153–72, doi: 10.1257/jep.25.3.153.

3. Melissa Dell, Benjamin F. Jones, and Benjamin A. Olken, "Temperature Shocks and Economic Growth: Evidence from the Last Half Century," *American Economic Journal: Macroeconomics* 4, no. 3 (2012): 66–95, doi: 10.1257/mac.4.3.66.

4. Douglas Almond, Kenneth Y. Chay, and Michael Greenstone, "Civil Rights, the War on Poverty, and Black-White Convergence in Infant Mortality in the Rural South and Mississippi," Working Paper no. 07–04 (Department of Economics, Massachusetts Institute of Technology, Cambridge, MA, 2006), and Alan Barreca et al., "Adapting to Climate Change: The Remarkable Decline in the U.S. Temperature–Mortality Relationship over the 20th Century," Working Paper no. 18692 (National Bureau of Economic Research, Cambridge, MA, 2013).

5. Sharon T. Ashley and Walker S. Ashley, "Flood Fatalities in the United States," *Journal of Applied Meteorology and Climatology* 47 (2008): 805–18; doi: 10.1175/2007JAMC1611.1.

6. Boris Orlowsky and Sonia I. Seneviratne, "Global Changes in Extreme Events: Regional and Seasonal Dimension," *Climatic Change* 110 (2012): 669–96, doi: 10.1007/s10584-011-0122-9.

7. Yasuaki Hijioka et al., "Asia," in *Climate Change 2014: Impacts, Adaptation, and Vulnerability. Part B: Regional Aspects*, ed. Vicente R. Barros et al. (Cambridge: Cambridge University Press, 2014), 1327–70.

8. Shanti Gamper-Rabindran, Shakeeb Khan, and Christopher Timmins, "The Impact of Piped Water Provision on Infant Mortality in Brazil: A Quantile Panel Data Approach," *Journal of Development Economics* 92 (2010): 188–200, doi: 10.1016/j.jdeveco.2009.02.006.

9. Xavier Rodó et al., "ENSO and Cholera: A Nonstationary Link Related to Climate Change?" *Proceedings of the National Academy of Sciences* 99 (2002): 12901–6, doi: 10.1073/pnas.182203999, and Anwar Huq et al., "Critical Factors Influencing the Occurrence of *Vibrio cholerae* in the Environment of Bangladesh," *Applied and Environmental Microbiology* 71 (2005): 4645–54, doi: 10.1128/AEM.71.8.4645–4654.2005.

10. Orlowsky and Seneviratne, "Global Changes."

11. UNICEF, "Bangladesh—Statistics," accessed January 26, 2015, http://www.unicef.org/infobycountry/bangladesh_bangladesh_statistics.html.

12. Edward Miguel and Michael Kremer, "Worms: Identifying Impacts on Education and Health in the Presence of Treatment Externalities," *Econometrica* 72 (2004): 159–217, doi: 10.1111/j.1468-0262.2004.00481.x, and Sarah Baird et al., "Worms at Work: Long-Run Impacts of a Child Health Investment," Working Paper no. 21428 (National Bureau of Economic Research, Cambridge, MA, 2015).

13. Paul R. Epstein, "Climate Change and Emerging Infectious Diseases," *Microbes and Infection* 3 (2001): 747–54, doi: 10.1016/S1286-4579(01)01429-0.

14. Willem J. M. Martens, Theo H. Jetten, and Dana A. Focks, "Sensitivity of Malaria, Schistosomiasis and Dengue to Global Warming," *Climatic Change* 35 (1997): 145–56, doi: 10.1023/A:1005365413932, and David J. Rogers and Sarah E. Randolph, "The Global Spread of Malaria in a Future, Warmer World," *Science* 289 (2000): 1763–66, doi: 10.1126/science.289.5485.1763.

15. Matthew E. Kahn, "The Death Toll from Natural Disasters: The Role of Income, Geography, and Institutions," *Review of Economics and Statistics* 87 (2005): 271–84, doi: 10.1162/0034653053970339.

16. Derek K. Kellenberg and Ahmed Mushfiq Mobarak, "Does Rising Income Increase or Decrease Damage Risk from Natural Disasters?" *Journal of Urban Economics* 63 (2008): 788–802, doi: 10.1016/j.jue.2007.05.003.

17. David Strömberg, "Natural Disasters, Economic Development, and Humanitarian Aid," *Journal of Economic Perspectives* 21, no. 3 (2007): 199–222, doi: 10.1257/jep.21.3.199.

18. Michael D. Flannigan, Brian J. Stocks, and B. Mike Wotton, "Climate Change and Forest Fires," *Science of the Total Environment* 262 (2000): 221–29, doi: 10.1016/S0048-9697(00)00524-6.

19. Seema Jayachandran, "Air Quality and Early-Life Mortality: Evidence from Indonesia's Wildfires," *Journal of Human Resources* 44 (2009): 916–54, doi: 10.3368/jhr.44.4.916.

20. Joseph M. Prospero and Peter J. Lamb, "African Droughts and Dust Transport to the Caribbean: Climate Change Implications," *Science* 302 (2003): 1024–27, doi: 10.1126/science.1089915.

21. C. Arden Pope III, "Epidemiology of Fine Particulate Air Pollution and Human Health: Biologic Mechanisms and Who's at Risk?" *Environmental Health Perspectives* 108 (2000): 713–23, doi: 10.2307/3454408, and Kenneth Y. Chay and Michael Greenstone, "The Impact of Air Pollution on Infant Mortality: Evidence from Geographic Variation in Pollution Shocks Induced by a Recession," *Quarterly Journal of Economics* 118 (2003): 1121–67, doi: 10.1162/00335530360698513.

22. Angela D. Luis et al., "The Effect of Seasonality, Density and Climate on the Population Dynamics of Montana Deer Mice, Important Reservoir Hosts for Sin Nombre Hantavirus," *Journal of Animal Ecology* 79 (2010): 462–40, doi: 10.1111/j.1365-2656.2009.01646.x.

23. C. Drew Harvell et al., "Climate Warming and Disease Risks for Terrestrial and Marine Biota," *Science* 296 (2002): 2158–62, doi: 10.1126/science.1063699.

24. Jan C. van der Leun and Frank R. de Gruijl, "Climate Change and Skin Cancer," *Photochemical & Photobiological Sciences* 1 (2002): 324–6, doi: 10.1039/b201025a.

25. Included countries are: for Africa, Algeria, Egypt, France (Réunion), Gambia, Libya, Malawi, Mali, South Africa, Tunisia, Uganda, and Zimbabwe and for Southeast Asia, Malaysia, the Philippines, Thailand, and Vietnam. See International Agency for Research on Cancer, *CI5: Cancer Incidence in Five Continents*, vols. V–X (Lyon, France: IARC, 1987–2013).

26. Shubham Chaudhuri and Christina Paxson, "Smoothing Consumption under Income Seasonality: Buffer Stocks vs. Credit Markets," Discussion Paper 0102-54 (Department of Economics, Columbia University, New York, 2002).

27. Janet Currie and Tom Vogl, "Early-Life Health and Adult Circumstance in Developing Countries," *Annual Review of Economics* 5 (2013): 1–36, doi: 10.1146/annurev-economics-081412-103704.

28. Seema Jayachandran and Rohini Pande, "Why Are Indian Children So Short?" (Women and Public Policy Program, John F. Kennedy School of Government, Harvard University, November 3, 2014).

29. Lia C. H. Fernald, Paul J. Gertler, and Lynnette M. Neufield, "10-Year Effect of Oportunidades, Mexico's Conditional Cash Transfer Programme, on Child Growth, Cognition, Language, and Behaviour: A Longitudinal Follow-Up Study," *Lancet* 374 (2009): 1997–2005, doi: 10.1016/S0140-6736(09)61676-7.

30. Janet Currie and Tom Vogl, "Early-Life Health and Adult Circumstance in Developing Countries," Working Paper no. 18371 (National Bureau of Economic Research, Cambridge, MA, 2012).

31. Amartya Sen, "Ingredients of Famine Analysis: Availability and Entitlements," *Quarterly Journal of Economics* 96 (1981): 433–64, doi: 10.2307/1882681.

32. Dean Yang, "Coping with Disaster: The Impact of Hurricanes on International Financial Flows, 1970–2002," *B.E. Journal of Economic Analysis & Policy* 8 (2008): 1–45, doi: 10.2202/1935-1682.1903.

33. See Jesse K. Anttila-Hughes and Solomon M. Hsiang, "Destruction, Disinvestment, and Death: Economic and Human Losses following Environmental Disaster," working paper (Social Science Research Network, Rochester, NY, February 2013), doi: 10.2139/ssrn.2220501.

34. Yuyu Chen and Li-An Zhou, "The Long-Term Health and Economic Consequences of the 1959–1961 Famine in China," *Journal of Health Economics* 26 (2007): 659–81, doi: 10.1016/j.jhealeco.2006.12.006.

35. Paul Gertler, "Do Conditional Cash Transfers Improve Child Health? Evidence from PROGRESA's Control Randomized Experiment," *American Economic Review* 94, no. 2 (2004): 336–41, doi: 10.1257/0002828041302109.

36. Manisha Shah and Bryce Millett Steinberg, "Drought of Opportunities: Contemporaneous and Long Term Impacts of Rainfall Shocks on Human Capital," Working Paper no. 19140 (National Bureau of Economic Research, Cambridge, MA, 2013).

37. Janet Currie and Rosemary Hyson, "Is the Impact of Health Shocks Cushioned by Socioeconomic Status? The Case of Low Birthweight," *American Economic Review* 89, no. 2 (1999): 245–50, doi: 10.1257/aer.89.2.245.

38. Erica Field, Omar Robles, and Máximo Torero, "Iodine Deficiency and Schooling Attainment in Tanzania," *American Economic Journal: Applied Economics* 1, no. 4 (2009): 140–69.

39. Paul Glewwe, Hanan Jacoby, and Elizabeth King, "Early Childhood Nutrition and Academic Achievement: A Longitudinal Analysis," *Journal of Public Economics* 81 (2001): 345–68, doi: 10.1016/S0047-2727(00)00118-3.

40. Sharon Maccini and Dean Yang, "Under the Weather: Health, Schooling, and Economic Consequences of Early-Life Rainfall," *American Economic Review* 99 (2009): 1006–26, doi: 10.1257/aer.99.3.1006.

41. Douglas Almond et al., "Long-Term Effects of Early-Life Development: Evidence from the 1959 to 1961 China Famine," in *The Economic Consequences of Demographic Change in East Asia, NBER-EASE*, vol. 19, ed. Takatoshi Ito and Andrew Rose (Chicago: University of Chicago Press, 2010): 321–45.

42. Sven Neelsen and Thomas Stratmann, "Effects of Prenatal and Early Life Malnutrition: Evidence from the Greek Famine," *Journal of Health Economics* 30 (2011): 479–88, doi: 10.1016/j.jhealeco.2011.03.001.

43. Eric D. Gould, Victor Lavy, and M. Daniele Paserman, "Sixty Years after the Magic Carpet Ride: The Long-Run Effect of the Early Childhood Environment on Social and Economic Outcomes," *Review of Economic Studies* 78 (2011): 938–73, doi: 10.1093/restud/rdq038.

44. Anne Case and Cally Ardington, "The Impact of Parental Death on School Outcomes: Longitudinal Evidence from South Africa," *Demography* 43 (2006): 401–20, doi: 10.1353/dem.2006.0022.

45. Geoffrey Heal and Jisung Park, "Feeling the Heat: Temperature, Physiology and the Wealth of Nations," Working Paper no. 19725 (National Bureau of Economic Research, Cambridge, MA, December 2013).

46. Janet Currie et al., "Does Pollution Increase School Absences?" *Review of Economics and Statistics* 91 (2009): 682–94, doi: 10.1162/rest.91.4.682, and Victor Lavy, Avraham Ebenstein, and Sefi Roth, "The Impact of Short Term Exposure to Ambient Air Pollution on Cognitive Performance and Human Capital Formation," Working Paper no. 20648 (National Bureau of Economic Research, Cambridge, MA, October 2014).

47. Richard Hornbeck, "The Enduring Impact of the American Dust Bowl: Short- and Long-Run Adjustments to Environmental Catastrophe," *American Economic Review* 102 (2010): 1477–1507, doi: 10.1257/aer.102.4.1477.

48. Pratikshya Bohra-Mishra, Michael Oppenheimer, and Solomon M. Hsiang, "Nonlinear Permanent Migration Response to Climatic Variations but Minimal Response to Disasters," *Proceedings of the National Academy of Sciences* 111 (2014): 9780–85, doi: 10.1073/pnas.1317166111.

49. Clark L. Gray and Valerie Mueller, "Natural Disasters and Population Mobility in Bangladesh," *Proceedings of the National Academy of Sciences* 109 (2012): 6000–05, doi: 10.1073/pnas.1115944109.

50. See, for example, Bohra-Mishra, Oppenheimer, and Hsiang, "Nonlinear Permanent Migration Response."

51. Taryn Dinkelman, "Mitigating Long-Run Health Effects of Drought: Evidence from South Africa," Working Paper no. 19756 (National Bureau of Economic Research, Cambridge, MA, December 2013).

52. Solomon M. Hsiang, "Temperatures and Cyclones Strongly Associated with Economic Production in the Caribbean and Central America," *Proceedings of the National Academy of Sciences* 107 (2010): 15367–72, doi: 10.1073/pnas.1009510107; Benjamin F. Jones and Benjamin A. Olken, "Climate Shocks and Exports," *American Economic Review: Papers & Proceedings* 100 (2010): 454–59, doi: 10.1257/aer.100.2.454; and Achyuta Adhvaryu, Namrata Kala, and Anant Nyshadham, "The Light and the Heat: Productivity Co-Benefits of Energy-Saving Technology" (University of Michigan, Ann Arbor, 2014).

53. Taryn Dinkelman and Sam Schulhofer-Wohl, "Can Migration Reduce Benefits of Spatial Programs? A Model of Congestion Externalities with Evidence from South Africa," Working Paper no. 700 (Federal Reserve Bank of Minneapolis, 2012).

54. Joshua D. Angrist and Victor Lavy, "Using Maimonides' Rule to Estimate the Effect of Class Size on Scholastic Achievement," *Quarterly Journal of Economics* 114 (1999): 533–75, doi: 10.1162/003355399556061, and Esther Duflo, Pascaline Dupas, and Michael Kremer, "Peer Effects, Teacher Incentives, and the Impact of Tracking: Evidence from a Randomized Evaluation in Kenya," *American Economic Review* 101 (2010): 1739–74, doi: 10.1257/aer.101.5.1739.

55. Ghazala Mansuri, "Migration, School Attainment, and Child Labor: Evidence from Rural Pakistan," Working Paper no. 3945 (World Bank, Washington, DC, June 2006).

56. John Gibson, David McKenzie, and Steven Stillman, "The Impacts of International Migration on Remaining Household Members: Omnibus Results from a Migration Lottery Program," *Review of Economics and Statistics* 93 (2011): 1297–1318, doi: 10.1162/REST_a_00129.

57. Nicole Hildebrandt and David J. McKenzie, "The Effects of Migration on Child Health in Mexico," Working Paper no. 3573 (World Bank, Washington, DC, April 2005).

58. Nilamadhab Kar et al., "Post-Traumatic Stress Disorder in Children and Adolescents One Year after a Super-Cyclone in Orissa, India: Exploring Cross-Cultural Validity and Vulnerability Factors," *BMC Psychiatry* 7, no. 8 (2007), doi: 10.1186/1471-244X-7-8.

59. Anandi Mani et al., "Poverty Impedes Cognitive Function," *Science* 341 (2013): 976-80, doi: 10.1126/science.1238041.

60. Achyuta Adhvaryu, James Fenske, and Anant Nyshadham, "Early Life Circumstance and Adult Mental Health," Working Paper no. 2014-03 (Centre for the Study of African Economies, Oxford, UK, January 2014).

61. See, for example, Richard Neugebauer, Hans Wijbrand Hoek, and Ezra Susser, "Prenatal Exposure to Wartime Famine and Development of Antisocial Personality Disorder in Early Adulthood," *Journal of the American Medical Association* 282, no. 5 (1999): 455–62, doi: 10.1001/jama.282.5.455, and David St. Clair et al., "Rates of Adult Schizophrenia following Prenatal Exposure to the Chinese Famine of 1959–1961," *Journal of the American Medical Association* 294, no. 5 (2005): 557–62, doi: 10.1001/jama.294.5.557.

62. Sheetal Sekhri and Adam Storeygard, "Dowry Deaths: Consumption Smoothing in Response to Climate Variability in India," Online Paper 407 (Department of Economics, University of Virginia, Charlottesville, March 2013), and Jason M. Lindo, Jessamyn Schaller, and Benjamin Hansen, "Economic Conditions and Child Abuse," Working Paper no. 18994 (National Bureau of Economic Research, Cambridge, MA, April 2013).

63. Heather T. Keenan et al., "Increased Incidence of Inflicted Traumatic Brain Injury in Children after a Natural Disaster," *American Journal of Preventive Medicine* 26 (2004): 189–93, doi: 10.1016/j.amepre.2003.10.023.

64. For example, Hani Mansour and Daniel I. Rees, "Armed Conflict and Birth Weight: Evidence from the al-Aqsa Intifada," *Journal of Development Economics* 99, no. 1 (2012): 190–99, doi: 10.1016/j.jdeveco.2011.12.005.

65. David S. Blakeslee and Ram Fishman, "Weather Shocks, Crime, and Agriculture: Evidence from India," working paper (Social Science Research Network, Rochester, NY, November 2014).

66. For example, see Sarah J. Baird et al., "Effect of a Cash Transfer Programme for Schooling on Prevalence of HIV and Herpes Simplex Type 2 in Malawi: A Cluster Randomised Trial," *Lancet* 379, no. 9823 (2012): 1320–29, doi: 10.1016/S0140-6736(11)61709-1.

67. Marshall Burke, Erick Gong, and Kelly M. Jones, "Income Shocks and HIV in Africa" (Paper 55392, Munich Personal RePEc Archive, Munich, April 2014).

68. Ariel Dinar et al., "Measuring the Impact of Climate Change on Indian Agriculture," Technical Paper no. 402 (World Bank, Washington, DC, 1998), 12.

Weighing the Costs and Benefits of Climate Change to Our Children

Simon Dietz, Ben Groom, and William A. Pizer

Summary

Our efforts to put the brakes on climate change or adapt to a warming climate present a fundamental tradeoff between costs borne today and benefits that accrue to the children and grandchildren of the current generation. In making investments today that affect future generations' prospects, we need to think carefully about how we value their welfare compared to our own.

A common economic formula recommends giving up only 5 cents today for every dollar of benefits 100 years in the future; we call this *discounting* the future. Underlying this approach is the assumption that future generations will be much better off than our own, just as we are much wealthier than our ancestors were. Would our descendants' agree with this approach? Are there reasons to put more value on future benefits?

William Pizer, Ben Groom, and Simon Dietz discuss three possible reasons that we might put a higher value on future benefits. First, people disagree considerably about the correct discount rate. Other plausible interpretations of society's preferences or observed data could increase the weight we place on future benefits by as much as a factor of five. Second, we may have failed to correctly value future climate change impacts, particularly those related to the loss of environmental amenities that have no close monetary substitutes. Third, we may not be properly valuing the risk that a warming climate could cause sudden and catastrophic changes that would drastically alter the size of the population.

Ultimately, the authors write, many of the choices about how we value future generations' welfare come down to ethical questions, and many of the decisions we must make come down to societal preferences—all of which will be difficult to extract from data or theory.

www.futureofchildren.org

Simon Dietz is a professor in the Department of Geography and Environment, director of the ESRC Centre for Climate Change Economics and Policy, and co-director of the Grantham Research Institute on Climate Change and the Environment at the London School of Economics and Political Science. Ben Groom is an associate professor in the Department of Geography and Environment at the London School of Economics and Political Science. William A. Pizer is a professor in the Sanford School of Public Policy and a faculty fellow in the Nicholas Institute for Environmental Policy Solutions at Duke University.

Charles Kolstad of Stanford University reviewed and critiqued a draft of this article.

Future generations are the current generation's children, grandchildren, and so on. That intergenerational perspective gives rise to extremely thorny questions about how to evaluate and make trade-offs between the wellbeing of current generations and the wellbeing of their descendants. In the context of climate change, we can't avoid intergenerational comparisons because greenhouse gas emissions today produce impacts that will last for hundreds of years. Therefore, we must analyze trade-offs over extremely long time horizons. In short, the payoffs from our own costly mitigation efforts will accrue to our children and their descendants. As will be made plain, to make decisions in the face of such dynamics, we must carefully analyze efficiency and equity. In particular, we can imagine asking whether our children will look back and take issue with how we valued their welfare compared with our own.

The principal economic tool for decision making is cost–benefit analysis (CBA). In a CBA, all current and future costs and benefits, or net benefits, in each period are given a weight and are then summed, with costs entered as negative benefits. Policy options with higher net benefits are generally preferred. Current costs and benefits have a weight of one. The weight placed on future costs and benefits is determined by a number known as the discount rate and, more specifically, in the case of societal rather than private decision making, the social discount rate (SDR). The SDR determines how quickly the weight placed on future costs and benefits diminishes with the time horizon being considered: the higher the SDR, the lower the influence of future costs and benefits on present values. When we consider long time horizons, as we must with climate change, small changes in the SDR can lead to extremely large differences in the weight we place on future costs and benefits.

What determines the SDR depends on how we conceive of social welfare across time and/or generations in the first place. The standard CBA approach is grounded in a welfare framework known as discounted utilitarianism (DU). In DU, welfare in future years and for future generations is added together, with future generations effectively viewed as extensions of ourselves further into the future (a *representative-agent* approach). A key feature of DU is that we value additional dollars less as we become richer. Coupled with the assumption that continued economic growth will leave our future selves (children and grandchildren) better off, this tends to support significant discounting of dollar-valued benefits in the future. But how much discounting?

Small changes in the social discount rate can lead to extremely large differences in the weight we place on future costs and benefits.

As we'll see, a typical application of the DU framework leads to weighting dollar-valued costs and benefits a hundred years in the future at roughly one-twentieth of the value of similar costs and benefits today. Some people, perhaps even our descendants themselves, might view such a weighting as incorrect or inequitable. Therefore, we explore a variety of reasons we might make the weighting more favorable for future generations.

Most significantly, scholars who work on DU disagree about which parameters we should use to reach the SDR and how those parameters should be calculated. One disagreement has been over whether to use a normative approach or a positive approach. Broadly speaking, the normative school asks the ethical question, "How *ought* we trade off our own welfare with that of our descendants?" The positive school asks instead, "Empirically, how *do* we trade off current and future welfare?" Within both schools, scholars further disagree about how to interpret the evidence and apply the ethical judgments that determine the SDR.

Beyond the question of parameters, a number of extensions and alternative conceptions of social welfare across time (that is, intertemporal social welfare) can affect future valuations. One key extension explicitly considers the significant uncertainty around future economic growth and welfare—in our case, economic growth and welfare distinct from climate change's effects. Another extension considers whether environmental resources can be substituted. We can also abandon the DU model altogether and consider other ways to assess social welfare across time and generations that are rooted in alternative conceptions of fairness and justice.

We could also imagine that the effects of climate change on human health and mortality could be so serious as to affect the size of the population, meaning that our choices about climate mitigation would affect not only how well off our descendants would be but also how many of them there would be. That possibility raises yet other

ethical issues, such as whether it's better to have large, subsistence-level populations or small, better-off ones. Thinking through such issues is a difficult task that has enormous consequences for the weight we place on our descendants when we evaluate intergenerational policies like climate mitigation.

The Intergenerational Trade-Off

The slow pace, or inertia, of the climate system's response to greenhouse gas emissions implies that an intergenerational trade-off lies at the heart of questions about how much to cut those emissions. (See the article in this issue by Michael Oppenheimer and Jesse Antilla-Hughes for more about the science of climate change.) Arguably, no research has presented the trade-off issue more starkly than the set of economic models built to simultaneously investigate the costs and benefits of reducing emissions and how those costs and benefits are distributed across time. We'll take the best-known model— the DICE (Dynamic Integrated Climate-Economy) model built by Yale economist William Nordhaus—and illustrate the important points by way of a few scenarios.[1]

Figure 1 plots the baseline level of aggregate consumption—essentially, how wealthy the world becomes over time in the absence of any action. Focusing on the "standard" case, we see the typical assumption that, over time, the world becomes much, much richer.

Figure 2 plots the net benefits of a particular mitigation scenario (relative to inaction, or, in other words, the baseline) over the next two centuries, according to DICE. The vertical axis shows the net benefits in each period as a share of consumption (top panel) and as valued in trillions of dollars (bottom panel) in that period; negative numbers indicate net

Figure 1. Aggregate Consumption under Standard and Catastrophic Climate Change Scenarios

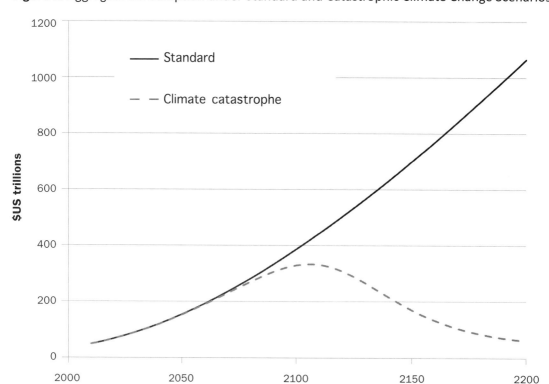

Source: A version of the DICE model built by Dietz et al., which extends Nordhaus's DICE-2013R model. See Simon Dietz, Christian Gollier and Louise Kessler, "The Climate Beta," Working Paper no. 215 [Centre for Climate Change Economics and Policy] and no. 190 [Grantham Research Institute on Climate Change and the Environment] (London School of Economics and Political Science, London, UK, 2015) and William D. Nordhaus, "Estimates of the Social Cost of Carbon: Concepts and Results from the DICE-2013R Model and Alternative Approaches," *Journal of the Association of Environmental and Resource Economists* 1 (2014): 273–312.

costs in that period. This particular mitigation scenario is intended to hold the increase in global mean temperature below 2° Celsius (3.6° Fahrenheit). The two different lines reflect different sets of assumptions about the costs and benefits of such a scenario.[2]

The "standard" case in figure 2 broadly reflects Nordhaus's usual parameter assumptions, which are typical of most research on the topic—at least until recently. The intergenerational trade-off in this case becomes immediately clear: for the rest of this century, society will have to sacrifice income—up to nearly 4 percent of baseline consumption in 2060—to avoid damages and adaptation costs from climate change,

which occur mostly after 2100. Absent any weighting to reflect time preferences, the cumulative net benefits of mitigation are larger than the net costs. That is, in the standard case, the positive area under the curve after 2100 exceeds the negative area above the curve before 2100. However, applying the sort of SDR that governments routinely use would substantially reduce the present value of long-term benefits compared with the near-term costs. The SDR that balances the present value of costs and benefits in this scenario—referred to as the internal rate of return—is 2.9 percent, which is slightly lower than the 3 percent rate that the US government used in a recent

Figure 2. Net Benefits of a Global Emissions Path to Avoid More than 2°C Warming

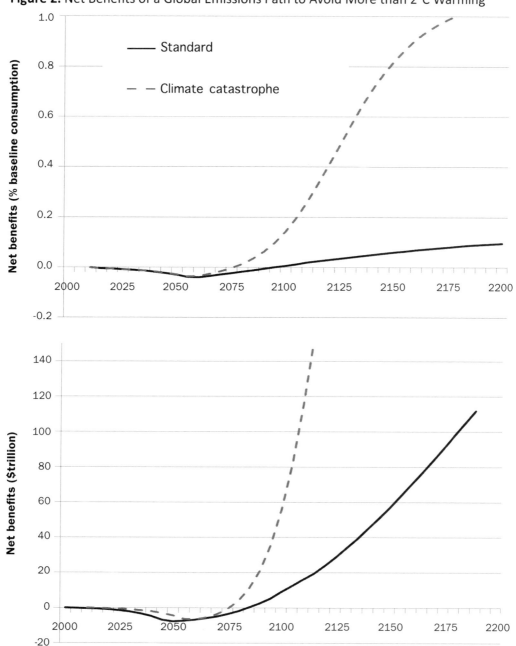

Source: A version of the DICE model built by Dietz et al., which extends Nordhaus's DICE-2013R model. See Simon Dietz, Christian Gollier and Louise Kessler, "The Climate Beta," Working Paper no. 215 [Centre for Climate Change Economics and Policy] and no. 190 [Grantham Research Institute on Climate Change and the Environment] (London School of Economics and Political Science, London, UK, 2015) and William D. Nordhaus, "Estimates of the Social Cost of Carbon: Concepts and Results from the DICE-2013R Model and Alternative Approaches," *Journal of the Association of Environmental and Resource Economists* 1 (2014): 273–312.

analysis of climate change benefits and much lower than the 4 to 5 percent assumed by Nordhaus himself.[3] In other words, under standard assumptions, the rate of return to a societal investment that would keep global mean temperature change below 2°C is less than what is required by typical SDR values. A global effort to reduce emissions by that much would fail a cost–benefit test, meaning that it would not increase social welfare.

Let's now explore how robust that result is. The "climate catastrophe" scenario in figures 1 and 2 combines a very sensitive response by the global mean temperature to rising atmospheric greenhouse gas concentrations with damages that rise particularly steeply in response to warming—a double whammy, if you like. As a result, human wellbeing initially grows but then falls back to current levels by the end of 2200. That situation contrasts sharply with the standard assumptions, wherein the economy grows by a factor of more than 10, with or without climate change (see figure 1). In the climate catastrophe scenario, the net benefits of mitigation that limits climate change to 2°C skyrocket (see figure 2); they are already more than 10 percent of consumption by 2100. In that case, not only does it make economic sense to keep global warming under 2°C; it makes sense to do a whole lot more.

Herein lies our main observation from the DICE model: the goal of stabilizing temperatures at 2°C doesn't pass a cost–benefit analysis that uses standard assumptions about climate change and an SDR of 3 percent, the rate suggested by the US government. A 3 percent rate implies that dollar impacts in 2115 are weighted at roughly one-twentieth the value of dollar impacts in 2015. Yet even with that kind

of weighting, assumptions of direr climate change consequences can overturn that result.

In this article, most of our interest centers on whether weighting consequences a hundred years in the future at roughly one-twentieth the value of consequences today is correct and/or fair. But before tackling that issue, we briefly step beyond DICE to ask, "What do we know about the costs of mitigation, as well as climate change's impacts and the benefits of mitigation?"

The Costs of Mitigation

What does it mean to say that mitigating climate change is costly? Ultimately, households and their children pay for mitigation through reductions in the welfare they enjoy. Policies to reduce emissions will raise the price of producing energy as we seek less-carbon-intensive alternatives. That means households will pay more not only for the energy they use but also for energy-intensive goods such as products made of steel and aluminum. In response, companies and households will switch from carbon-intensive, or dirty, production technologies to low-carbon, or clean, counterparts and/or look for ways to simply use less electricity. However, all of those things have welfare costs. The alternatives either cost more or entail loss of service or convenience. Though there may be negative-cost opportunities that can reduce emissions and raise welfare at the same time, most economists are skeptical that such opportunities will be plentiful or easy to capture.[4]

It's also tempting to imagine that costs to businesses somehow won't affect households. However, business losses come back to households in several ways, including lower income from stocks, reduced wages, or increased prices that work their way through the whole economy. For example, if the price of electricity goes up, so do the prices of aluminum and, in turn, aluminum products such as foil and cans.

It's helpful to understand those basic linkages not only to make the notion of mitigation costs tangible but also because the scholarship on mitigation costs follows various approaches and arrives at various ways to measure cost, not all of which are easily comparable. For instance, one popular way to roughly approximate mitigation costs is to (1) estimate the cost and potential to reduce emissions of each of a menu of technologies and options (for example, energy-efficient refrigerators or wind power), (2) sort them from least to most expensive, and (3) add them up until the desired level of abatement is reached.[5] That approach has the advantage of extensive detail about low-carbon technologies. At the same time, since all of those options are being estimated separately, they might not add up as a whole, because implementing some strategies might affect the cost of others. Perhaps the best example is how the emission-reducing benefits of using less electricity would decline if we switched to less-emission-intensive electricity sources.

By contrast, aggregate economic models emphasize relationships between energy prices and the supply and demand (from producers and consumers, respectively) for energy products. By integrating the behavior of such actors, an aggregate model ensures that everything adds up—but at the expense of retaining little detail about the various technologies for cutting emissions.

Stylized Facts

The extensive research on mitigation costs is dominated by simulation results from integrated economy-energy-climate models. *The Fifth Assessment Report* by the Intergovernmental Panel on Climate Change (IPCC) does a very good job of summarizing the vast majority this research.

- Most models predict that climate mitigation is costly and would reduce economic growth when considered against a "utopian" scenario wherein no mitigation takes place and climate change has no effect, but the reduction in growth prospects tends to be relatively small, except perhaps for the most stringent mitigation targets.[6] By 2050, the loss in consumption relative to a utopian scenario ranges from about 0.5 to just over 5 percent, depending on the depth of emissions cuts.

- Although it's useful to think of mitigation as a simple investment whereby we spend a onetime sum in the beginning to receive a stream of benefits in the future, mitigation is in fact an ongoing activity, and its global costs will rise over time. In this way, our children and their children will each face the dilemma of how to weight the costs they will endure to benefit future generations, even as they reap whatever benefits accrue from our own efforts.

- The global costs of mitigation increase with the stringency of the emissions target. Some evidence suggests that they increase more than proportionately.[7]

- Models' forecasts differ widely in what it would cost to achieve the same emissions target. And the differences increase as levels of required emissions reductions increase. That divergence has many causes, including different assumptions about population growth and economic growth, but a particularly important set of assumptions concerns the availability and costs of low-carbon technologies.[8]

- If key mitigation technologies aren't available at a reasonable cost (or aren't available at all), global mitigation costs could increase significantly. Carbon capture and storage (CCS) is a notable example. CCS is a technology for capturing the carbon dioxide from large emitting facilities and storing it in underground geologic formations. It makes continued fossil-fuel burning consistent with emissions targets in the short term; it can be combined with a range of emissions-generating technologies (that is, not just electricity generation); and it can even be combined with biofuels to yield negative emissions. But as of today, just 13 CCS facilities are operating in the world, and only one is attached to a power plant.[9] When we purposely eliminate CCS from a range of models, they predict that mitigation will cost much more.

- Delaying efforts to reduce emissions in the coming years will increase mitigation costs further in the future, partly because we'll have to make deeper cuts later on and partly because we'll have locked in carbon-intensive infrastructure in the intervening period. Many emissions are caused by very long-term investments that are in turn tied to very long-term infrastructure. For example, cars might have a useful life of 10 or 15 years, but the fueling infrastructure is more durable. If the task is simply to hit a given emissions target at the lowest cost,

too much delay is, consequently, a bad thing.

- Global mitigation costs increase if some countries don't pull their weight. In part, that's simply because some mitigation that could have taken place cost-effectively in those countries will now have to take place at a higher cost elsewhere. But it also reflects the phenomenon of carbon leakage: countries that lag in restricting emissions may attract carbon-intensive industries, thereby increasing aggregate emissions and making other countries work that much harder.[10]

- The costs of mitigation will vary from country to country, for two reasons. First, opportunities vary. Some countries are blessed with renewable resources, and others are not. Some countries are already building new infrastructure, and others would have to retire existing facilities before the end of their useful lives. That points to significant mitigation potential in large and fast-growing developing countries such as China and India. Second, national governments—both alone and in various multilateral settings—will make decisions about how to financially support efforts in poorer countries. Ultimately, the distribution of costs across countries will depend on some combination of where the mitigation opportunities exist, how much those countries are willing to spend to mitigate, and how much money other countries are willing to provide to meet the costs of mitigation.

- Estimates from integrated models don't include all of the factors thought to affect mitigation costs. Most models assume that, apart from climate change itself, the economy is otherwise functioning perfectly, or, if it isn't, the number of ways it could malfunction is at least severely limited. Fully incorporating imperfections into the functioning of the economy— something we can only imagine being able to do—could either increase or decrease global mitigation costs. One example is the cobenefits that mitigation would have for public health via reduced emissions of conventional air pollutants; in some parts of the world, those cobenefits could be very substantial, thus decreasing the cost of mitigation.[11] (For more about the relationship between emissions and health, see the article by Allison Larr and Matthew Neidell elsewhere in this issue.) On the other hand, economists have argued that carbon regulation would increase the cost of the existing tax system, thereby adding to the cost of mitigation.[12]

Costs of Climate Change

The costs of climate change fall into two categories: the costs of adapting to climate change (for instance, by increasing defenses against coastal flooding) and the costs of residual damage from climate change after adaptation, such as flooding from a storm surge that overtops those strengthened coastal defenses.

Costs can be further subdivided in a number of ways, two of which are helpful for understanding the nature of climate impacts. The first is simply to categorize costs by the sector of the economy in which they fall, which quickly leads to the conclusion that a few sectors, such as agriculture and forestry, are especially vulnerable to gradual climate change. However, increases both in weather's variability and in instances of extreme weather have the potential to affect a wider range of activities. For instance, Japanese automobile manufacturer Toyota suffered

disruption to its supply chain when Bangkok was flooded in 2011.

The second subdivision is between so-called market costs and nonmarket costs. Market costs are costs paid in the real economy, such as losses in agricultural output and increased expenditure on air conditioning. Nonmarket costs are impacts that are real but nonetheless aren't paid directly in the real economy—notably, the value most people would put on lost human health and damage to the natural environment beyond simple market losses. Not all research explicitly distinguishes between the two, but some important work has shown that nonmarket impacts, when rendered equivalent to market impacts by a technique called *shadow pricing*, are relatively substantial—perhaps greater than market costs.[13] We return to this topic at the end of the next section.

Stylized Facts

Research on the impacts of climate change is voluminous and, partly because those impacts are so diverse, much of it focuses on a particular impact. For example, one researcher might build a crop model to analyze agricultural impacts. By contrast, few economic models seek to aggregate impacts. The research as a whole was recently summarized in Working Group II's contribution to the IPCC's *Fifth Assessment Report*.

- The first few degrees of warming will bring costs to some and benefits to others (for example, increased agricultural productivity at high latitudes in the Northern Hemisphere). Consequently, models disagree on whether the initial global costs of climate change are positive or negative overall, though most find that they're negative. At warming of 2 or 3°C above the preindustrial level, which for many studies has become a benchmark, the small set of integrated models estimates a global cost in the range of minus 0.1 to 3 percent of gross domestic product relative to no climate change.[14]

- Tropical and subtropical developing countries are relatively more vulnerable to climate change. They're more exposed to adverse changes in climatic conditions; they're more sensitive to climate change because a larger share of their economic activity takes place in climate-sensitive sectors, particularly agriculture; and they have less capacity to adapt.[15]

- Beyond three degrees of warming, we understand little about the impacts of climate change, particularly at the aggregate level. Some integrated economic models continue to estimate small costs relative to the global economy, but others predict spiraling costs that would eventually lead to a global economic catastrophe.[16] The models agree, however, that losses accelerate as warming increases.

- No model covers all of the known effects of climate change. We can merely speculate on what would happen if we included those omitted variables, though most scholars agree that they would increase costs, because the omitted effects include some of the most worrying ones, such as climate-induced conflict.[17]

All of those observations about costs and benefits suggest that we should approach any estimates with caution. Nonetheless, most stakeholders and governments see value in trying to predict climate change's effects, even if the estimates are flawed. With a sketch in hand of such calculations concerning

today's costs and future benefits, we now turn to the question of impacts across time and generations. On what basis do we judge changes in our wellbeing versus the wellbeing of our descendants and their children?

Evaluating Our Descendants' Wellbeing

To decide whether investing for the future is somehow "better" or "worse" for society, we need ways to evaluate *better* and *worse*. It boils down to a definition of societal wellbeing across time and multiple generations against which to compare different courses of action. Only then can we evaluate whether the costs of mitigating climate change outlined in the previous section would be outweighed by the benefits to our descendants and whether the investment in future generations is "worth it."

Discounted Utilitarianism

The standard approach in cost–benefit analysis is to weight costs and benefits at different points in time using an SDR. But lurking behind the definition of an SDR is a larger notion of welfare, which recognizes that changes in income or dollars alone may not be the best way to measure the degree to which a particular person is better off. Instead, welfare economics defines individual wellbeing in terms of utility. The basic difference that such a definition of wellbeing introduces is that, although income and consumption contribute to wellbeing, extra income's contribution to wellbeing diminishes as an individual or society gets richer. Utility can also capture the idea that wellbeing may depend on things other than the market goods that we consume, such as clean air and good health.

But how should we aggregate welfare for many people—particularly those living at different points in time? That is, how do we add up and then compare the welfare effects of courses of action that may affect both today's society and future societies populated by our descendants? There are many ways we might do this, but the standard approach is to define the utility of an "average" person over a period of time—say, a year—in terms of consumption of market goods and, possibly, nonmarket goods such as environment and health. Those annual utilities of an average—or *representative*—agent are added together to obtain an overall measure of intertemporal social welfare (a number). Each generation and each person is assumed to have the same utility function. Thus, average utility is typically multiplied by the number of people alive in each period before current utility and future utility are added together. Future utility may or may not be discounted. This additive, representative-agent approach is discounted utilitarianism, and it is the standard approach involved in the welfare economics underpinning CBA and the economics of climate change.

Within the DU approach lie two essential issues that determine how much weight to place on the monetized costs and benefits accruing to future generations versus our own. The first issue is that society may place different weights on utility in future years. That's relatively uncontroversial when applied to an individual, because most people prefer to receive a net benefit earlier, all else equal. But when we extend the principle to different generations, questions of equity arise. For example, imagine that two generations—our own today and one in the future—enjoy the same level of income and hence of utility (in this standard approach). Moreover, a particular monetary benefit would lead to the same increase in utility for both. From today's perspective,

when aggregating and adding those utilities together to measure social welfare, we might wish to place less weight on the future generation's utility than on our own today. That is, all else equal, society might prefer a given monetary benefit if it is delivered to this generation rather than the next.

Two essential issues determine how much weight to place on the costs and benefits accruing to future generations. The first is that society may place different weights on utility in future years. The second concerns aversion to income inequality.

Alternatively, from the perspective of equal treatment of generations, we might not want to discount the future generation's utility at all when making the welfare calculation. This is the first essential issue of intergenerational equity that we must face when deciding how to evaluate the costs and benefits of climate mitigation, and it has caused a great deal of debate within the utilitarian tradition and beyond. We return to this debate later.

The second issue concerns aversion to income inequality. From a societal perspective, a given addition to income for a poor person is typically thought to raise welfare more than the same addition of income would for a rich person. An intervention (for example, a public infrastructure project or a climate change mitigation project) that yielded incremental income to the poor would then be worth more to society than would a project that yielded the same incremental income only to the rich. For example, consider an intervention that lowers present income by $1 in 2015 and raises future income by $1 in 2115. Let's say that the present society has an income of $10,000 per capita, and that the future society of our descendants has an income of $30,000 per capita. That is, income has grown over time, and the future society is richer as a consequence. In our example there is no inflation, so the income growth is real; for simplicity, imagine that we are considering only a single person at each point in time. Here, the considered intervention would lower welfare. Why? Because $1 in the future is worth less than $1 today, solely because the future is wealthier (has higher income) and we are averse to income inequality. This is the second reason we might wish to discount future costs and benefits. Of course, that wealth effect is a double-edged sword. If the future generation is poorer—that is, if growth is negative, as has been the case in many developing countries over the past 30 years—then $1 in the future contributes more to social welfare than $1 today does.

Typically, those two reasons for putting less weight on future generations combine to form an SDR that indicates the rate at which the weight we place on future generations' consumption declines the further we look into the future. We call it a social discount rate because the context is intertemporal *social* welfare rather than individual or household welfare. The DU approach leads to an SDR that is expressed by the so-called Ramsey rule, named after Frank Ramsey, an eminent mathematician and economist from the early twentieth century: the SDR equals *utility discounting* (expressed as the Greek letter rho, ρ),

added to the *wealth effect*, which is a measure of aversion to inequality (expressed as the Greek letter eta, η) multiplied by *income growth* (g). Thus, in the form of an equation, SDR = ρ + ηg. In this equation, ρ is known as the *pure rate of time preference* or *utility discount rate*, and it reflects the first reason for discounting the future: discounting future utilities. If SDR = ρ + ηg , it's easy to see that the SDR increases as any one of its components—the utility discount rate, growth, or inequality aversion—increases.

That may all sound rather abstract and stylized, but precisely those principles appear in government guidance on CBA throughout the world, and in the IPCC's *Fifth Assessment Report*, Working Group III, they represent one of the central ways of thinking about how to evaluate climate change.[18] The US government's report establishing a value for climate change damages discusses at length how to evaluate intergenerational decisions. Here, table 1 shows how other governments around the world calibrate the Ramsey rule for use in their domestic CBAs, along with analogous approaches from important reports on climate change.

Table 1 and the discussions in the IPCC and US reports suggest that 3 percent isn't an unreasonable choice for an SDR. However, if we want to examine critiques of setting the SDR at 3 percent (recall that this is the rate at which the typical climate change project would not pass a CBA test)—particularly critiques that would place higher weight on future welfare—we must turn to the evidence underlying the parameters that go into an SDR.

Estimating the Social Discount Rate

Where do the numbers in table 1 come from? Let's consider each of the parameters in turn. The essence of the pure time preference, ρ, can be understood by first thinking about

Table 1. How Governments and Reports Calibrate the Ramsey Rule

Country/ Study	Pure time preference (ρ)	Inequality aversion (η)	Growth (g)	Social discount rate (SDR)	Source
United Kingdom	0.5% (1%)	1%	2%	3.5% (1%)	HM Treasury (2003)
France	0%	2%	2%	4% (2%)	Lebègue (2005)
Stern	0% (0.1%)*	1%	1.3	1.4%	Stern Review (2007)
IPCC	0%	1–2%	2%	2–4%	IPCC (2013)
Nordhaus	2–3%	1%	2%	4–5%	Nordhaus (2007)

Notes: The rates in parentheses for the United Kingdom and France are the rates of discount for time horizons longer than 300 years. In the French case, the reduction occurs at 30 years. In the UK case, there is a stepped decline from 3.5 to 1 percent over that period.

Sources: HM Treasury, *The Green Book: Appraisal and Evaluation in Central Government* (London: HM Treasury, 2003; revised 2011); Intergovernmental Panel on Climate Change, *Climate Change 2013: The Physical Science Basis* (Cambridge: Cambridge University Press, 2013); Daniel Lebègue, *Révision du Taux d'Actualisation des Investissements Publics* (Paris: Commissariat Générale du Plan, 2005); William D. Nordhaus, "A Review of the *Stern Review on the Economics of Climate Change*," *Journal of Economic Literature* 45 (2007): 686–702, doi: 10.1257/jel.45.3.686; Nicholas Stern, *The Economics of Climate Change: The Stern Review* (Cambridge: Cambridge University Press, 2007).

*The figure in parentheses reflects the likelihood that society won't exist because of some catastrophic event, which Stern added to the pure time preference of 0 percent. The Stern SDR is an average of many different analyses contained in the *Stern Review.*

impatience. For instance, research has demonstrated empirically that children aren't always particularly good at deferring gratification in relation to things like, say, marshmallows.[19] They prefer to get their utility now rather than at even some very short time in the future: they are very impatient for marshmallows. That's an example of impatience at the individual level: individuals making their own decisions for their own benefit.

To evaluate societal projects, we need a measure of impatience that's appropriate for society as a whole. It must reflect the fact that decisions have implications not just for today's society but also for future, as yet unborn, generations. Some people argue that observing how people behave is the correct way to get such information. Others, particularly in the context of climate change,

argue that consulting ethical principles is more appropriate.

In the context of climate change and of long-run CBA in general, the pure rate of time preference is typically treated as a normative parameter, to be guided by ethical arguments. The utilitarian tradition argues for treating generations equally—that is, ρ = 0—on the ethical grounds that we should be impartial about when a person is born or when a society exists. That is, societies should be *anonymous*. The consequence of doing otherwise would be that generations in the distant future would be tyrannized, in the sense that a weight of zero would be placed on their utility and hence in the DU measure of intertemporal social welfare.

Just as there are ethical arguments for setting pure time preference at zero, there are ethical arguments for ρ greater than zero.[20] Nobel Prize–winning economist

Kenneth Arrow has discussed the trade-off between morality and self-regard as an ethical argument for treating current and future generations' utilities unequally.[21] His argument is that imposing equal treatment may tyrannize the present through onerous savings or investment requirements. In essence, when the utility discount rate is zero, increments to the utility of generations millions of years into the future have the same effect on social welfare as do increments today. Moreover, there are many of those generations! This would indicate that the current generation ought to invest in many more lower-return projects. However, the notion of self-regard proposes that individuals need not adhere to the morality of equal treatment if it comes at too great a cost to themselves. In particular, Arrow concludes that "the strong ethical requirement that all generations be treated alike, itself reasonable, contradicts a very strong intuition that it is not morally acceptable to demand excessively high savings rates of any one generation, or even of every generation."[22]

Another argument for discounting future utilities is the possibility that as a result of some external catastrophe, future generations may not exist at all. In that case, a separate term would be added to the pure rate of time preference to reflect the hazard rate of catastrophe.[23] This argument has found some support within the utilitarian tradition, although recently, some detractors have said that "from the ethical standpoint it may . . . seem questionable to make such a bet on the existence of future generations."[24]

How have recent studies of climate change approached the issue of where to set the value of ρ? The *Stern Review*—a highly influential report on the economics of climate change undertaken for the UK government—took the view that barring a small probability of global societal collapse of 0.1 percent per year, each generation's wellbeing should be treated equally: thus, $\rho = 0$ percent, but to that should be added a hazard rate of 0.1 percent. This choice contrasts with the UK Treasury guidelines on cost–benefit analysis referred to in table 1. Based on a variety of empirical studies, these guidelines argue that the risk of catastrophe in the UK is 1 percent per year. On top of that is a pure time preference of 0.5 percent, leading to an overall discount rate for utility of 1.5 percent.

Nordhaus, the developer of the DICE model, took a very different approach. He made the additional assumption that markets would equate the SDR in the equation SDR $= \rho + \eta g$ to the market rate of interest. He then calibrated the parameters (particularly ρ) around the market interest rate, using empirical estimates of g and η.[25] That led to ρ of 1.5 to 3 percent. Linking the calculation to observed market rates is sometimes referred to as a *positive* or *descriptive* approach to identifying the correct SDR. And we've covered but a few of the ways to estimate the pure rate of time preference.[26]

Within the Ramsey framework of SDR = $\rho + \eta g$, the parameter η reflects aversion to income inequality. Here we're thinking about potential inequality across generations. However, there are other interpretations of the parameter in different contexts. For instance, it might also be assumed to govern inequality aversion between individuals at the same point in time or inequality aversion across different risky states of the world.[27] Consequently, people have used different methods of estimating parameter η: for example, progressivity of income tax schedules (known as intratemporal inequality aversion), ethical introspection (intratemporal or intertemporal inequality aversion), international transfers of aid (international inequality aversion), observed consumption behavior at the aggregate or individual level (intertemporal substitution), experiments involving risk (risk aversion), and so on.

In the UK case, evidence to guide estimates of η comes from a variety of those sources.[28] The most recent estimates for the UK from observed behavior tend to suggest a value of around 1.5 to 1.6, whatever the type of data used.[29] Several experts have suggested a value of 2 on the basis of ethical considerations and personal introspection.[30]

Taken together, different perspectives on the parameters of the Ramsey rule naturally lead to different recommendations for an SDR. With expected annual growth of 2 percent, the UK selections of ρ = 1.5 percent and η = 1 lead to an SDR of 3.5 percent. In France, expected growth of 2 percent together with ρ = 0 and η = 2 has led to an SDR of 4 percent (see table 1). The US analysis ultimately proposed SDR values of 2.5, 3, and 5 percent, with 3 percent being the central case around which the report undertakes sensitivity analysis. All of this suggests that an SDR of 3 percent, with its consequent weight of one-twentieth for net benefits a hundred years in the future, can be criticized simply by disagreeing with the interpretation of evidence and the ethical rationale. A number at the lower end of the given examples—say, 1.4 percent—would apply a weight of almost one-fourth to those net benefits a hundred years in the future, counting them almost five

times as much against current costs as a 3 percent SDR would.

Discounted Utilitarianism Extended: Uncertainty about Growth

Even if we agree on an appropriate pure rate of time preference and a level of inequality aversion, the weight we place on future generations depends on the economic state in which we think our descendants will find themselves. In particular, the economic growth rate during the next hundred years and beyond is very uncertain, and the differences among the climate change scenarios in figure 1 illustrate that. How does the economic framework deal with uncertainty, and what are the implications for the way we account for future generations when we calculate CBA today?

Suppose our descendants will be faced with one of two possible states of the world at some point in the future—say, a hundred years from now. One is a "good" state, in which annual incomes are high, at $30,000, and the other is a "bad" state, in which annual incomes are only $10,000. A typical way to summarize today the welfare we expect in the future would be to simply take the average of the utilities associated with each state of the world. And a typical way of summarizing the welfare impact of an intervention that, say, raises income by one dollar would be to take the average change in welfare associated with each state of the world. This is the *expected utility*, which could then be added up over time to obtain our intertemporal welfare function, as in the DU approach.

How does this affect our evaluation versus simply using the average income of $20,000? It depends on another dimension of societal preferences, known as *prudence*, which refers to the idea that as the future becomes more uncertain regarding the best guess about income, the value of an additional dollar in the future increases. More uncertainty about income then leads to more savings; hence we call that effect prudence. Assuming prudence at the societal level, the effective SDR should be lower if we are uncertain about the state of the world that our descendants will inherit versus our best estimate of the average outcome. Moreover, the higher the level of uncertainty, the lower the SDR. Thus, the prudence effect would likely be higher over longer time horizons, where uncertainty about the effect of growth is greater. The idea that uncertainty is greater the further we look into the future actually justifies the use of a discount rate that is smaller for costs and benefits that occur in the future compared with today's costs and benefits: a *declining discount rate*.

The presence and degree of those prudence effects are, in general, determined by the same parameter that describes inequality (and risk) aversion, and for most reasonable values of that parameter, such aversion is often both present and large. Across countries, uncertainty about future growth would tend to justify a discount rate of less than 1 percent for long time horizons.[31]

There is no doubt that DU, declining discount rates, and related economic theories have been extremely influential in policy circles.[32] The guidelines of both the UK Treasury and the US Environmental Protection Agency have been heavily influenced by them.[33] The Norwegian government, too, in its advice on the time profile of discount rates that are to be applied to different time horizons (the term structure), refers to arguments about

uncertainty over the rate of return to capital.[34]

Table 1 shows that several governments have made this theory and its close relations a central part of their CBA guidelines. In France, the SDR declines from 4 to 2 percent after 30 years. In the United Kingdom, the SDR declines steadily over 300 years from an initial 3.5 percent to 1 percent. The United States uses a lower discount rate of 2.5 percent for intergenerational projects and to evaluate the social cost of carbon, which is the current value of all future damages arising from an additional ton of carbon emissions today.

So, in theory, uncertainty about future income levels increases the weight we place on our descendants' wellbeing. In practice, such uncertainty has been shown to be important for long-term policy making.[35] If uncertainty were to justify using a rate of 2.5 percent rather than 3 percent over the next hundred years, as suggested by the US government's analysis, our weight for net benefits a hundred years from now would change from one-twentieth of today's value to almost one-twelfth. But is that the only omission that the standard DU approach makes in its parsimonious approach to intertemporal decision making? When we put monetary values on many of the benefits of mitigating climate change, we are making certain assumptions about the value future generations will place on avoiding human and natural impacts—a topic to which we now turn.

Discounted Utilitarianism Extended: Environmental Goods and Services

When we evaluate courses of action today that will affect the wellbeing of our descendants in the future, we estimate both the monetized costs and benefits in each year and the weights necessary to compare those costs and benefits across time. As we noted in the previous section, nonmarket benefits such as health and environmental amenities aren't easily measured, but they could be quite large. Moreover, if future generations, otherwise equivalent to ourselves, simultaneously face a denuded environment and poorer health, the value they put on improving those amenities could be even larger than the value we put on similar improvements today. The environment and health are important dimensions of wellbeing. Thus, to evaluate how changes in those amenities are valued in the future, it's important to understand how they evolve over time alongside income and consumption.

Consider the following extension to the previous example, which looked at consumption growth and its effects on how we valued an additional dollar of income. Now consider two generations—the present and the future—whose wellbeing now depends on consumption *and* a measure of environmental services. Both have the same income levels, say, $20,000 per annum, and both consume identically. They differ only in the environmental services they each enjoy. Suppose that environmental services decline over time so that our descendants have 50 million hectares of forested land compared with our 200 million hectares (one hectare is about two and a half acres). How many dollars of consumption would each generation give up for an additional hectare of land?

If, like consumption, the added welfare from additional units of environmental services declines as the amount available rises, then due to land's increasing scarcity,

our descendants would probably be willing to give up more dollars of consumption for a hectare of land than would the current generation. So increments of environmental goods are worth more to our descendants than they are to us, and we would place different values on changes to the environment depending on when they happen in time. If that sounds a lot like the wealth effect that we discussed earlier, then it should—only this is an *environmental* wealth effect, where increasing scarcity has the opposite effect of raising, rather than lowering, the value of changes that occur in the future, all things equal.

But precisely how does this affect the valuation of our descendants' wellbeing? Empirical estimates suggest that the price of environmental goods could be rising at an annual rate 1 percent faster than consumption goods, an indication of their relative scarcity.[36] Evaluating our descendants' wellbeing in this way increases the prescribed urgency of climate mitigation policies when compared with other analyses.[37] For example, if along with our 3 percent discount rate we undervalued future benefits at 1 percent per year, it would be appropriate to use a 2 percent discount rate, thus weighting a mismeasured future net benefit in a hundred years at almost one-seventh of today's value rather than one-twentieth.

Ultimately, to properly evaluate how courses of action would affect our descendants, we must be careful to use a set of accounting prices in our CBA that reflect the relative scarcity of environmental or health goods in the future, rather than assuming that today's amenity values will remain the same. Differences in relative prices can be equivalently reflected in adjustments to the discount rate, downward for increasing scarcity of environmental resources. We need further work to understand whether current approaches have gotten that right.

Alternatives to Discounted Utilitarianism and Uncertainty

So far, we've focused on reasons that net benefits to future generations might be undervalued while staying within the standard welfare framework. But is this the only way to look at the problem? Does DU satisfy all the tenets of fairness that we might want to satisfy when taking a position on our descendants' wellbeing? That question is particularly relevant given uncertainty about the future in terms of both how the economy will evolve and the potential for calamitous climate change. Absent uncertainty, welfare analysis—whether or not it considers fairness—tends to be dominated by the general expectation that future generations will be much wealthier than our own and that climate change impacts will only put a dent in the degree to which they are wealthier but will not alter the general trend. In that landscape, a sharper focus on fairness would tend to disfavor those wealthy future generations.

With uncertainty, we confront the real possibility—whether small or not—that the future could be worse for future generations than for ourselves. In that landscape, a sharper focus on fairness could *favor* future generations. What might a sharper focus on fairness look like? Naturally, there are alternatives to DU both within and outside economics. In recent years, particularly since the *Stern Review* appeared, interest in different conceptions of intertemporal

welfare has been growing. Following are some examples to illustrate the point.

One approach is to simply increase aversion to inequality—specifically, aversion to the inequality that might occur for a future impoverished generation. In the DU framework, we often consider individual preferences to be appropriate sources of information about societal preferences, as we saw in our earlier discussion of how the parameters might be estimated. By simply asserting more inequality aversion or, somewhat equivalently, by adding aversion to unequal utility, we would raise the weight (relative to our own) placed on impacts for future generations that are worse off than our own. Prioritarianism, for instance, is an alternative to utilitarianism wherein, for reasons of fairness, the utility of generations that have the lowest utility levels receives more weight.

Of course, increased aversion to inequality also means lowering the weight (relative to our own) that we place on impacts for future generations that are better off than ours. Therefore, another concept would be a more nuanced form of increased aversion to inequality. Specifically, we could be averse to leaving a future generation worse off but not averse to future generations being better off. That concept pertains to the notion of sustainability. The sustainable discounted utilitarian approach is one example of how sustainability can be included in the analysis. Models using that approach have shown that taking sustainability into account could raise the level of willingness to pay for climate mitigation severalfold, reducing the effective SDR.[38]

A third possibility comes from recognizing that within the DU framework, aversion to inequality applies equally to inequality across time and generations as well as to inequality across risky outcomes (risk aversion). Recently, researchers have explored separating those two concepts when it comes to climate change.[39] Doing so lets us consider societal preferences that are more averse to climate risks—thus raising the value that future generations place on avoiding those risks—while maintaining the same relative weights between current and future generations based on average economic growth and/or the passage of time.

Finally, quite distinct from the question of uncertainty and aversion to risk and inequality, some researchers have begun to explore the question of population ethics related to climate change.[40] In most integrated assessment models, DICE included, mortality impacts are reflected by costing out lives through a method called *value of statistical life*. As the term suggests, value of statistical life is a statistical estimate, using observed or hypothetical behavior, of an individual's willingness to pay to reduce the risk of death.[41] Does that make sense, particularly when applied to the risk of large, catastrophic population impacts? To what extent are more people better than fewer if the larger population is worse off? Is there a critical, minimum level of utility below which life is not worth living?[42] Those and other questions are the topics of a new and evolving area of research, which presumably could lead to placing more weight on the consequences for future generations.

Conclusions

As we said at the outset, choices about climate change mitigation involve a tricky balance between the interests of current and future generations. Current generations largely bear the cost of mitigation; future

generations largely reap the benefits—though, at the same time, they face similar trade-offs with their own future generations. To the extent that we're interested in how climate change affects children, it's hard to get away from the fact that today's children will grow up to be a future generation, as will their children. For them, how we make intergenerational trade-offs is likely to mean as much as—and perhaps more than—how we modify the estimated costs and benefits for adults so that those costs and benefits are instead appropriate for children at the same moment in time.

For that reason, we've explored what economic analysis can tell us about the balance of those costs and benefits and why our future children might criticize that analysis. Using a well-known model of climate change mitigation costs and benefits, we estimated that avoiding a 2°C temperature increase would not (quite) pass a cost–benefit analysis. We based our estimate on a discount rate of 3 percent, the value recently suggested by the US government. Such a discount rate implies that monetized benefits a hundred years in the future receive a weight of about one-twentieth of the weight given to monetized costs today.

Why might that weight be wrong? We've explored three main reasons. First, people disagree considerably about the correct discount rate. Other plausible interpretations of society's preferences or observed data would increase that weight from one-twentieth to one-quarter—a factor of five. Even using the standard parameters but acknowledging that future economic growth is uncertain could change the weight to almost one-twelfth.

Second, we may have failed to correctly value future climate change impacts, particularly those involving the loss of environmental amenities that have no close monetary substitutes. One calculation suggests that accounting for those impacts might mean adjusting a future weight from one-twentieth to one-seventh.

Finally, we also examined how uncertainty and alternatives to the standard welfare approach might affect future valuation. Here the work is more recent and more speculative. However, properly valuing

catastrophic risks, and particularly the risk of major population changes, could alter the way we value impacts on future generations.

Ultimately, our goal has not been to provide a different or better answer to the question of how we should value future climate change impacts on our children. Instead, we have tried to explain how current economic analysis treats our children and our children's children in terms of intergenerational welfare. We've also tried to explain why current economic analysis might be wrong and, when possible, by how much, focusing on why an error might undervalue the future.

None of this should be interpreted as a failure of current analysis: policy making at any moment in time requires the best information and judgment available. We believe current efforts to balance climate change costs and benefits are valuable, though they may be only part of the answer. Ultimately, many of the choices come down to ethical questions, and many of the decisions come down to societal preferences—all of which will be difficult to extract from data or theory.

ENDNOTES

1 . See William D. Nordhaus, "Rolling the 'DICE': An Optimal Transition Path for Controlling Greenhouse Gases," *Resource and Energy Economics* 15 (1993): 27–50, doi: 10.1016/0928-7655(93)90017-O; William D. Nordhaus, *Question of Balance: Weighing the Options on Global Warming Policies* (New Haven, CT: Yale University Press, 2008); and William D. Nordhaus, "Estimates of the Social Cost of Carbon: Concepts and Results from the DICE-2013R Model and Alternative Approaches," *Journal of the Association of Environmental and Resource Economists* 1 (2014): 273–312, doi: 10.1086/676035. We acknowledge Louise Kessler's research assistance in running the DICE model.

2. Simon Dietz, Christian Gollier, and Louise Kessler, "The Climate Beta," working papers no. 215 [Centre for Climate Change Economics and Policy] and no. 190 [Grantham Research Institute on Climate Change and the Environment] (London School of Economics and Political Science, London, 2015).

3. Interagency Working Group on Social Cost of Carbon, US Government, "Technical Support Document: Technical Update of the Social Cost of Carbon for Regulatory Impact Analysis under Executive Order 12866" (May 2013), https://www.whitehouse.gov/sites/default/files/omb/inforeg/social_cost_of_carbon_for_ria_2013_update.pdf.

4. Michael E. Porter and Claas van der Linde, "Toward a New Conception of the Environment–Competitiveness Relationship," *Journal of Economic Perspectives* 9, no. 4 (1995): 97–118, doi: 10.1257/jep.9.4.97; Richard D. Morgenstern, William A. Pizer, and Jhih-Shyang Shih, "The Cost of Environmental Protection," *Review of Economics and Statistics* 83 (2001): 732–38, doi: 10.1162/003465301753237812.

5. Tomas Nauclér and Per-Anders Enkvist, *Pathways to a Low-Carbon Economy: Version 2 of the Global Greenhouse Gas Abatement Cost Curve* (New York: McKinsey & Company, 2009).

6. Simon Dietz and Cameron J. Hepburn, "Benefit–Cost Analysis of Non-Marginal Climate and Energy Projects," *Energy Economics* 40 (2013): 61–71, doi: 10.1016/j.eneco.2013.05.023; Massimo Tavoni and Richard S. J. Tol, "Counting Only the Hits? The Risk of Underestimating the Costs of Stringent Climate Policy: A Letter," *Climatic Change* 100 (2010): 769–78, doi: 10.1007/s10584-010-9867-9.

7. Valentina Bosetti, Carlo Carraro, and Massimo Tavoni, "Timing of Mitigation and Technology Availability in Achieving a Low-Carbon World," *Environmental and Resource Economics* 51 (2012): 353–69, doi: 10.1007/s10640-011-9502-x.

8. Elmar Kriegler et al., "The Role of Technology for Achieving Climate Policy Objectives: Overview of the EMF 27 Study on Global Technology and Climate Policy Strategies," *Climatic Change* 123 (2014): 353–67, doi: 10.1007/s10584-013-0953-7.

9. Global CCS Institute, "Large Scale CCS Projects" (2015), http://www.globalccsinstitute.com/projects/large-scale-ccs-projects.

10. Christoph Böhringer, Edward J. Balistreri, and Thomas F. Rutherford, "The Role of Border Carbon Adjustment in Unilateral Climate Policy: Overview of an Energy Modeling Forum Study (EMF 29)," *Energy Economics* 34 (2012), S97–S110, doi: 10.1016/j.eneco.2012.10.003.

11. Gregory F. Nemet, Tracey Holloway, and Paul Meier, "Implications of Incorporating Air-Quality Co-Benefits into Climate Change Policymaking," *Environmental Research Letters* 5 (2010): 014007, doi: 10.1088/1748-9326/5/1/014007.

12. Sergey Paltsev et al., "How (and Why) Do Climate Policy Costs Differ among Countries?" in *Human-Induced Climate Change*, ed. Michael E. Schlesinger et al. (Cambridge: Cambridge University Press, 2007), 282–93.

13. William D. Nordhaus and Joseph Boyer, *Warming the World: Economic Models of Global Warming* (Cambridge, MA: MIT Press, 2000).

14. Richard S. J. Tol, "Correction and Update: The Economic Effects of Climate Change," *Journal of Economic Perspectives* 28 (2000): 221–26, doi: 10.1257/jep.28.2.221.

15. Robert Mendelsohn and Michael E. Schlesinger, "Climate-Response Functions," *Ambio* 28 (1999): 362–66.

16. Martin Weitzman, "GHG Targets as Insurance against Catastrophic Climate Damages," *Journal of Public Economic Theory* 14 (2012): 221–44, doi: 10.1111/j.1467-9779.2011.01539.x.

17. Paul Watkiss, "Aggregate Economic Measures of Climate Change Damages: Explaining the Differences and Implications," *Wiley Interdisciplinary Reviews: Climate Change* 2 (2011): 356–72, doi: 10.1002/wcc.111.

18. IPCC, *Climate Change 2013: The Physical Science Basis* (Cambridge: Cambridge University Press, 2013).

19. Walter Mischel, Yuichi Shoda, and Monica L. Rodriguez, "Delay of Gratification in Children," *Science* 244 (1989): 933–38, doi: 10.1126/science.2658056.

20. Wilfred Beckerman and Cameron Hepburn, "Ethics of the Discount Rate in the *Stern Review on the Economics of Climate Change*," *World Economics* 8 (2007): 187–210.

21. Kenneth J. Arrow, "Discounting, Morality, and Gaming," in *Discounting and Intergenerational Equity*, ed. Paul R. Portney and John P. Weyant (Washington, DC: Resources for the Future, 1999), 13–21.

22. Ibid.

23. The mechanics of this process are discussed in Partha S. Dasgupta and Geoffrey M. Heal, eds., *Economic Theory and Exhaustible Resources* (Oxford: Cambridge University Press, 1979), 260–65.

24. Wolfgang Buchholz and Michael Schymura, "Intertemporal Evaluation Criteria for Climate Change Policy: The Basic Ethical Issues," Discussion Paper no. 11-031 (Centre for European Economic Research [ZEW], Mannheim, Germany, 2011), 16.

25. William D. Nordhaus, "A Review of the *Stern Review on the Economics of Climate Change*," *Journal of Economic Literature* 45 (2007): 686–702, doi: 10.1257/jel.45.3.686; William Nordhaus, *A Question of Balance: Weighing the Options on Global Warming Policies* (New Haven, CT: Yale University Press, 2008).

26. A recent survey of 200 experts in the context of long-term CBA shows the extent of disagreement on the utility discount rate. The minimum value was zero, which was also the modal value. The maximum value was 8 percent. For details, see Moritz Drupp et al., "Discounting Disentangled: An Expert Survey on the Determinants of the Long-Term Social Discount Rate," Working Paper 195 (Centre for Climate Change Economics and Policy, London School of Economics and Political Science, London, 2015).

27. For more on these concepts and how to measure inequality aversion, see Nicholas Stern, "The Marginal Valuation of Income," in *Studies in Modern Economic Analysis: The Proceedings of the Association of University Teachers of Economics, Edinburgh, 1976*, ed. Michael J. Artis and A. Robert Nobay (Oxford, UK: Basil Blackwell, 1977), 209–54; and Dasgupta, "Discounting." Empirical evidence suggests that individuals, even when considering intergenerational contexts, don't equate these concepts. See Håkon Sælen et al., "Siblings, Not Triplets: Social Preferences for Risk, Inequality and Time in Discounting Climate Change," *Economics: The Open-Access, Open-Assessment E-Journal*, 3 (2009–26): 1–28, doi: 10.5018/economics-ejournal.ja.2009-26.

28. See Stern, "Welfare Weights," and OXERA Consulting, "A Social Time Preference Rate for Use in Long-Term Discounting" (Oxford, UK, 2002).

29. Ben Groom and David Maddison, "Non-Identical Quadruplets: Four New Estimates of the Elasticity of Marginal Utility for the UK," Working Paper 121 (Centre for Climate Change Economics and Policy, London School of Economics and Political Science, London, 2013), looks at estimates of the elasticity of intertemporal substitution via analysis of the consumption function, inequality aversion via progressive tax rates, and Ragnar Frisch's wants-independence approach.

30. See Drupp et al., "Discounting Disentangled."

31. This calculation comes from Christian Gollier, "On the Underestimation of the Precautionary Effect in Discounting," Working Paper 3536 (CESifo, Munich, 2011), on the basis of a cross-country analysis of growth volatility.

32. For example, Martin Weitzman, "Gamma Discounting," *American Economic Review* 91 (2001): 260–71, and Martin Weitzman, "Why the Far-Distant Future Should Be Discounted at Its Lowest Possible Rate," *Journal of Environmental Economics and Management* 36 (1998): 201–8.

33. HM Treasury, *The Green Book: Appraisal and Evaluation in Central Government* (London: HM Treasury, 2003; revised 2011), and National Center for Environmental Economics, Office of Policy, US Environmental Protection Agency, *Guidelines for Preparing Economic Analyses* (Washington, DC: US Environmental Protection Agency, 2010).

34. There are issues concerning implementation and estimation, but these arguments have gained a lot of traction in policy. See Maureen L. Cropper et al., "Declining Discount Rates," *American Economic Review* 104 (2014): 538–43, doi: 10.1257/aer.104.5.538.

35. This is not an exhaustive list of justifications for a declining term structure of social discount rates. Indeed, many scholars point to the use of a declining term structure of discount rates for risk-free projects. For excellent surveys of the theory, empirics, and practice, see Kenneth J. Arrow et al., "Should Governments Use a Declining Discount Rate in Project Analysis?" *Review of Environmental Economics and Policy* 8 (2014): 145–63, doi: 10.1093/reep/reu008, and Christian Gollier, *Pricing the Future: The Economics of Discounting in an Uncertain World* (Princeton, NJ: Princeton University Press, 2012).

36. See Stefan Baumgärtner et al., "Ramsey Discounting of Ecosystem Services," *Environmental and Resource Economics* 61 (2015): 273–96, doi: 10.1007/s10640-014-9792-x.

37. Important references here include Thomas Sterner and U. Martin Persson, "An Even Sterner Review: Introducing Relative Prices into the Discounting Debate," *Review of Environmental Economics and Policy* 2 (2008): 61–76, doi: 10.1093/reep/rem024; Michael Hoel and Thomas Sterner, "Discounting and Relative Prices," *Climatic Change* 84 (2007): 265–80, doi: 10.1007/s10584-007-9255-2; and Hans-Peter Weikard and Xueqin Zhu, "Discounting and Environmental Quality: When Should Dual Rates Be Used?" *Economic Modelling* 22 (2005): 868–78, doi: 10.1016/j.econmod.2005.06.004.

38. Higher willingness to pay is shown in Simon Dietz and Geir B. Asheim, "Climate Policy under Sustainable Discounted Utilitarianism," *Journal of Environmental Economics and Management* 63 (2012): 321–35, doi: 10.1016/j.jeem.2012.01.003.

39. For example, Ravi Bansal, Dana Kiku, and Marcelo Ochoa, "Climate Change and Growth Risks (paper presented at National Bureau of Economic Research 2015 Summer Institute, Cambridge, MA, July 20–21, 2015), http://www.nber.org/confer//2015/SI2015/EEE/Bansal_Kiku_Ochoa.pdf, shows that such a model implies a significant cost of climate damages.

40. Antony Millner, "On Welfare Frameworks and Catastrophic Climate Risks," *Journal of Environmental Economics and Management* 65 (2013): 310–25.

41. For a review of value of statistical life in the context of climate change, see Maureen L. Cropper, "Estimating the Economic Value of Health Impacts of Climate Change" (paper presented at Research on Climate Change Impacts and Associated Economic Damages workshop, Washington, DC, January 27–28, 2011), http://yosemite.epa.gov/ee/epa/eerm.nsf/vwAN/EE-0566-110.pdf/$file/EE-0566-110.pdf.

42. See Marc Fleurbaey and Stéphane Zuber, "Discounting, beyond Utilitarianism," Economics Discussion Papers 40 (Kiel Institute for the World Economy, Kiel, Germany, 2014).

Mobilizing Political Action on Behalf of Future Generations

Joseph E. Aldy

Summary

Our failure to mobilize sufficient effort to fight climate change reflects a combination of political and economic forces, on both the national and the global level. To state the problem in its simplest terms, writes Joseph Aldy, future, unborn generations would enjoy the benefits of policies to reduce carbon emissions whereas the current generation would have to bear the costs. In particular, incumbent firms—politically influential fossil-fuel companies and fossil fuel–intensive industries, which are now reaping substantial returns from a status quo that fails to address climate change—might face significant losses from policies that discourage carbon emissions. On the other hand, insurgent firms—companies that are investing in low- and zero-carbon technologies—stand to gain.

Aldy analyzes durable, successful public policies in US history whose costs and benefits accrued to different groups—the 1935 Social Security Act, the 1956 Interstate Highway Act, and the 1970 Clean Air Act Amendments. Those policies differ from climate change policy in important ways, but they nonetheless offer lessons. For example, designing climate policy to deliver broad, near-term benefits could help overcome some of the political opposition. To do so might require linking climate change with other issues, or linking various interest groups. We might also win support from incumbent firms by finding ways to compensate them for their losses under climate change policy, or use policy to help turn insurgent firms into incumbents with political influence of their own. Finally, we might account for and exploit the veto points and opportunities embedded in our existing political institutions.

www.futureofchildren.org

Joseph E. Aldy is an associate professor of public policy at the John F. Kennedy School of Government at Harvard University, a visiting fellow at Resources for the Future, a faculty research fellow at the National Bureau of Economic Research, and a senior adviser at the Center for Strategic and International Studies. He is also the faculty chair for the Regulatory Policy Program at the Mossavar-Rahmani Center for Business and Government.

Matthew Kotchen of Yale University reviewed and critiqued a draft of this article. The author also thanks Janet Currie, Olivier Deschênes, Jon Wallace, and participants at the *Future of Children* "Children and Climate Change" conference at Princeton University for excellent comments.

From almost any perspective, our efforts to confront the risks posed by global climate change have been insufficient. Since the international community first negotiated a treaty focused on climate change in 1992, global carbon dioxide emissions have increased more than 60 percent.[1] President George H. W. Bush agreed to limit US emissions to 1990 levels by 2000, President Bill Clinton agreed to cut US emissions to 7 percent below 1990 levels by 2010, and President Obama has called for an economy-wide cap-and-trade program to lower emissions more than 80 percent by 2050, yet their stated intentions haven't produced substantive policy. Economic analyses suggest that the benefits of incremental reductions in greenhouse gas emissions greatly exceed the current explicit or implicit price to emit a ton of greenhouse gases by almost all emission sources around the world.[2] Environmental advocates call for limiting warming to no more than 2 degrees Celsius (3.6 degrees Fahrenheit); academics question whether such a goal is still feasible.[3]

The failure to mobilize sufficient effort to combat climate change reflects the difficult political economy (that is, the interplay between politics and economics) that characterizes the problem. Mitigation of emissions (1) yields a global public good that no individual, firm, or country has a strong incentive to produce unilaterally; (2) imposes near-term costs with benefits spread over centuries; (3) risks exposing domestic firms to adverse pressures from foreign competitors; (4) delivers unclear returns, given uncertainties about climate science, multilateral coordination, market behavior, and technological innovation; and (5) requires fundamental transformation of the energy foundation of modern industrial economies. Moreover, the distribution of climate change policy's benefits and costs varies across space and time, as well as among various political constituencies and special interests.

To grossly simplify the problem, the challenge is that future, unborn generations will enjoy the benefits of climate policy, whereas the current generation, in particular those reaping substantial returns from a status quo that fails to address climate change, will bear the costs. Even if that challenge could be overcome, what kinds of investments in protecting the global climate should we make? Nobel Prize–winning economist Thomas Schelling's observation on the eve of the 1997 Kyoto Protocol conference provides some context: "The future beneficiaries of these [climate change] policies in developing countries will almost certainly be better off than their grandparents, today's residents of those countries."[4] Like many other economists, Schelling says continued investment in productive physical capital and knowledge creation will make possible a better standard of living for future generations. In effect, unborn generations will enjoy the benefits of investments made today. Children alive today, however, may bear substantial costs associated with mitigating climate change. Given the discretionary nature of much public spending on children—relative to adults and, especially, older people—the costs borne by children today could be disproportionately large.

Thus investing in global climate protection may further enhance future generations' quality of life, but it comes with costs that merit consideration. First, investing in emissions mitigation may reduce the resources available to invest in other forms of capital that the future may value. Second, investment of any kind today represents forgone consumption among members of the current generation, including children.

The current dearth of meaningful investment in climate protection indicates that more climate investment is called for. But the increase in investment shouldn't be random. Going all in on climate protection would not necessarily make future generations better off. Instead, a prudent approach to investing capital, defined in a very broad sense (physical capital, human capital, environmental capital, social capital, etc.), can ensure that future generations enjoy a standard of living at least as good as that of the current generation. Maintaining if not increasing the capital stock in its broadest sense requires that we use analytic tools to identify the social returns on various kinds of investments—including investments in climate protection—and then translate the results of those analyses into policies that can guide shifts in current economic activity so as to maximize the social returns on investment in capital, writ large.

That formulation of the problem leads to the standard economist's prescription: "Get prices right." Putting a price on the damage that carbon emissions cause to the environment, the economy, and human wellbeing could align private returns on investment with social returns on investment. Such a prescription, however, must confront the political fact that the costs of changing prices would be borne primarily by the current generation, whereas the benefits would be enjoyed disproportionately by future generations. Moreover, the current costs are concentrated among politically influential firms whose existing capital imposes net adverse effects on the global

climate; economists call them *incumbent* firms. In contrast, as newcomers to the market, emerging, *insurgent* firms— those with new and potentially disruptive technologies intended to deliver low- and zero-carbon goods and services that could capture incumbents' market share—have less political power. Given that incumbent firms have long experience in using policy and regulatory processes to their own ends, designing a policy that would enhance the influence and investments of insurgent firms to deliver climate benefits to children today—as well as to future generations— represents a tall challenge.[5]

The Economics of Sustainability

To frame the political challenge of mobilizing effort on climate change, let's consider the returns on two different types of capital and the incentives for trying to influence policy. First, let's define business capital as appropriable physical and human capital associated with private firms. Second, let's define societal capital as a much broader concept that includes natural capital, such as the global climate; social capital; and knowledge, which can be thought of as a form of nonappropriable human capital.

Given current policies and laws, the agents responsible for managing business capital make decisions to maximize the return on that capital. They decide on procurement of equipment, hiring of personnel, marketing expenditures, and the like. They may also decide how to engage in policy debates. Industry attempts to shape, influence, and capture regulators and policy makers in order to maximize the returns on its capital.[6] This is true in an array of contexts, from antitrust policy to trade policy to environmental policy.

Why focus on firms?

Under climate change policy, firms will have to invest in new technologies to demonstrate compliance with government regulations. Because such compliance costs are typically concentrated in fossil fuel businesses and certain emission-intensive industries, those kinds of organizations—as they have in the past—will play very active roles by engaging political leaders of both parties as well as regulators in order to shape and/or delay climate change policies to accommodate their interests. Consumers' more disparate interests will likely motivate less political participation and lobbying than firms with assets at risk would undertake.

Some of the agents who manage incumbent firms may actively oppose policy proposals—such as regulating greenhouse gas emissions or pricing carbon—because, they say, such policies could reduce the return on their capital. Indeed, they may consider it their fiduciary responsibility to the owners of the firm to allocate resources to oppose climate protection policy. This stylized representation of "business capital" is characterized by (1) incumbents in the market economy (that is, those with existing capital) and (2) firms whose net effect on climate is adverse (on whom any regulation to reduce climate change risks would impose net costs).

Agents of insurgent firms may support climate protection policy proposals because such policies would expand markets for the goods and services they produce. Insurgent firms tend to be relatively new entrants, especially in energy markets, that are developing innovative and potentially disruptive technologies. They compete with the incumbents and aim to capture some of the incumbents' market share, which creates an incentive to try to influence policy.

In the context of climate, much of the incumbents' relevant business capital of fossil fuel extraction and energy production firms are assets whose value could fall—potentially dramatically—with emission mitigation policies. Coal-fired power plants, commercially developed oil fields, and natural gas pipelines all could become stranded assets if climate policy significantly reduced the use of fossil fuels. That possibility creates a strong incentive for the owners of such assets and their managers to oppose such climate change policies, absent some form of compensation. Because fossil fuels vary in their carbon intensity—for example, coal is almost twice as emission intensive per unit of energy as natural gas is—modestly ramping up climate change policy could benefit natural gas at the expense of coal. Over the longer term, as climate change policy becomes more ambitious, it could benefit renewable and nuclear energy at the expense of natural gas. This situation suggests that fossil fuel producers might not act as a monolithic bloc in opposing and/or shaping climate policy.

The second, broader type of capital effectively includes all resources left for the next generation.[7] Thus it includes the business capital described earlier as well as other forms of capital that markets either imperfectly or incompletely value, such as natural capital (including the global climate), social capital, and technological knowledge. This broader definition of capital is more closely associated with people's wellbeing than are narrower, market-oriented definitions.[8]

Policy Implications

Describing capital in this manner has several important policy implications. First, given the various kinds of capital under this broad umbrella, opportunities exist to substitute one kind of capital for another. Future generations might be better off with more climate-related capital and less energy-related physical capital; on the other hand, a small increase in climate capital and a dramatic decrease in physical capital could make them worse off. Investing in natural capital would mean forgoing investment in other kinds of capital. Related to that trade-off, investing the returns from drawing down one form of capital can ensure that consumption doesn't decrease across generations.[9] For example, the extraction of nonrenewable resources results in less nonrenewable resource capital. If those returns are consumed by the current generation instead of invested in other forms of capital, then the nonrenewable resources may deliver a short-term bump in consumption that will fall as the returns on resource extraction decline with the asset base. Likewise, if drawing down "climate" capital by burning fossil fuels yielded returns that were subsequently invested in new knowledge, then future generations might be no worse off than the current generation— even with some climate damages. It's unlikely, however, that the market is currently delivering optimal investment in line with such thinking.

The broad approach to capital that includes all resources left for the next generation has been referred to as the *economics of sustainability*. Though I won't explore in detail the ethics of our responsibilities to future generations (as well as to our contemporaries), a generally benign formulation of our obligations has been to leave the future with opportunities for consumption no worse than those our generation has enjoyed. Some economists

call this *weak sustainability*, because it allows for substitution across various kinds of capital; they contrast it to *strong sustainability*, which calls for maintaining capital in each category. Underlying the concept of weak sustainability is the idea that a small reduction in one type of capital can be offset by a small increase in another type of capital.

Second, as the stock of capital in any given category decreases, the returns to investment in that kind of capital are likely to increase. In other words, different kinds of capital are roughly interchangeable, but there are limits to substitution. A decline in climate capital that produced catastrophic impacts would make future generations worse off regardless of the returns on other forms of capital. A policy framework that accounts for how changes in each kind of capital alter the returns on incremental investments can account for those limits to substitution.

Third, given strong private incentives to invest in traditional business capital and very weak private incentives to invest in natural capital (combined with inadequate public policy to correct those incentives), the returns on incremental investment in climate protection likely exceed the returns on incremental investment in business capital. Policies that can better align incentives for investment in natural capital can help correct the imbalance, as described in the next section.

Fourth, uncertainty in returns on capital and potential differences in the uncertainty in returns across different types of capital will influence investment decisions. Typically, the greater the uncertainty (or variation) in returns, the larger the expected return necessary to justify an investment. Moreover, uncertainty about the benefits of a policy can reduce the level of public support and make it less likely that policy makers will take action.[10] Incumbents face a variety of uncertainties in a conventional business investment, but uncertainty regarding returns on climate policy is likely much greater, given uncertainties in the science, in technological innovation, in future policies, and in the extent to which other countries around the world will mitigate climate change.

Stakeholders can influence uncertainty. Some—in an effort to delay policy action and investment in climate-friendly technologies—may undertake communication campaigns that emphasize the uncertainties in climate change.[11] Others may call for investing more in the basic science and holding off on policy prescriptions until the research findings are realized; that was the Reagan Administration's approach to acid rain. Of course, businesses make investment decisions every day in the face of uncertainty and risk, which raises the question of why the uncertainty about climate change justifies putting off action. Indeed, businesses often look for ways to hedge risks when making decisions in uncertain environments. In the climate context, some have done so by simultaneously questioning the science of climate change—hoping to delay policy action—and investing in new resources and technologies (for example, shale gas) whose returns would likely increase under policies to mitigate climate change.

Finally, the prospect of abrupt or catastrophic climate change could result in large, discrete falls in consumption and wellbeing and violate that assumption in the weak-sustainability paradigm.[12] In such a case, a strong sustainability framework based on maintaining or enhancing the status quo

climate could be justified. The key question is how policy choices could influence the magnitude and/or likelihood of catastrophic climate change. For example, reducing uncertainty about the timing and scale of abrupt and catastrophic climate change could help spur the multilateral collective action necessary to avoid crossing a threshold into a climate catastrophe.[13] Yale economist William Nordhaus suggests that policy makers could react to the potential for catastrophic climate change by investing in geoengineering technology, such as by injecting sunlight-reflecting particles into the upper atmosphere to cool the planet and offset global warming.[14] Geoengineering to prevent catastrophic climate damages, although unproven and controversial, could effectively return the framework for climate policy to the marginal trade-offs in investment and consumption associated with weak sustainability.

Refocusing investment from traditional business capital to capital in the broader sense could promote sustainability. But to do so would require public policy intervention because private firms don't bear the societal costs that their emissions impose through climate change. How should we consider future generations' interests in developing such policies, and how should we engage the two kinds of business capital—incumbents and insurgents—in building political support for climate policy?

Cost–Benefit Analysis and Future Generations' Interests

Cost–benefit analysis is a decision tool that can evaluate various public policy options for correcting a market failure—such as greenhouse gas emissions—in much the same way that private investors assess options for allocating their savings. The policy maker who pursues the option that maximizes net social benefits delivers the outcome that would be expected in the market if it were not characterized by the market failure (that is, if private and social returns were identical). In practice, many cost–benefit analyses are narrow assessments of a specific policy in a specific sector. But we have a number of modeling approaches that permit dynamic evaluation of the economy-wide impacts of climate protection policies. As a result, we can clearly draw a connection from the outputs of a cost–benefit analysis—which could be described as a societal investment policy—to the economic sustainability framework outlined earlier.

In the context of a greenhouse gas mitigation policy, cost–benefit analysis typically shows (1) near-term costs associated with reducing emissions and (2) long-term benefits associated with reducing the risks posed by climate change. Given that most greenhouse gases have long atmospheric lifetimes—on the order of hundreds to thousands of years—the benefits of a climate change policy could accrue to many generations in the future. This framework permits an accounting of the streams of benefits and costs over time by applying a discount rate to convert benefits and costs that occur in various periods of time into a single, present-day measure. A discount rate reflects the fact that an individual typically values a dollar of consumption today more than a dollar of consumption in the future; for example, we could invest a dollar today, and its returns would provide more than a dollar in the future. A relatively low discount rate—which means that a dollar of consumption in the future is almost as valuable as a dollar of consumption today—effectively places greater weight on the impacts of climate

policy that affect generations in the distant future.

The Role of Discounting

The future benefits of any climate policy thus depend on the choice of discount rate. Economists have had a long and robust debate on the appropriate discount rate for long-term policy problems.[15] Some support a *prescriptive* approach on ethical terms, effectively arguing that all generations should be treated equally, with the permissible discounting to reflect changes in wealth and how the incremental value of consumption declines at higher levels of wealth. Others support a *descriptive* approach based on revealed preferences in markets in which rates of return on investment could guide the discounting of societal benefits and costs from climate policy intervention. Complicating the considerations under these very different schools of thought are the implications of uncertainty in determining the appropriate discount rate. As a result, an analyst can draw from a range of plausible discount rates in evaluating the economic impacts of climate policy. (For more on choosing a discount rate that accounts for the interests of future generations, see the article in this issue by Simon Dietz, Ben Groom and William Pizer.)

In choosing a discount rate, the stakes are large. Table 1 shows how the present value of $1,000 in climate damage occurring in 2050 varies by a factor of more than 30—from $19 to $623—depending on a choice among four different discount rates. Similarly, the present value of $1,000 in year 2100 damages ranges from 5 cents to $311, and the present value of $1,000 in year 2200 damages ranges from near zero to $77.

Table 1. Present Value of $1,000 in Climate Damages Occurring in 2050, 2100, and 2200 under Various Discount Rates

$1,000 in Damages Occurring in Year	Discount Rate			
	1.4%	2.5%	3.0%	5.0%
2050	$623	$269	$99	$19
2100	$311	$39	$3	$0.05
2200	$77	$0.82	$0.004	~$0

When former World Bank chief economist Nicholas Stern used a discount rate of 1.4 percent in his 2006 review of the economics of climate change for the government of the United Kingdom, the majority of the present value damages from climate change (that is, the benefits of mitigating climate change) reflected benefits enjoyed after the year 2200.[16] To characterize the benefits of mitigating greenhouse gas emissions, the US Interagency Working Group on Social Cost of Carbon produced estimates of the social cost of carbon—the dollar value of reduced climate change damages associated with reducing carbon dioxide emissions by 1 metric ton (1,000 kilograms, or about 1.1 US tons).[17] Those estimates have been used by federal regulatory agencies whose rulemaking affects carbon dioxide emissions, including the Environmental Protection Agency (EPA), the Department of Energy, and the Department of Transportation. The Interagency Working Group's two reports presented social-cost-of-carbon estimates for three discount rates: 2.5 percent, 3 percent, and 5 percent. The 2015 social cost of carbon at the 2.5 percent rate is $58 per metric ton of carbon dioxide, which is more than 50 percent greater than the social-cost-of-carbon estimate for that year based on a 3 percent discount rate and almost five times greater than the estimate at the 5 percent discount rate. Those results are not necessarily

surprising: the National Research Council has said the social cost of carbon can plausibly vary by a factor of 100, with the choice of discount rate determining one-tenth of that variation.[18]

Because the social cost of carbon distills the impacts of climate change into a single measure of marginal damages associated with carbon dioxide emissions, that social cost can guide the design of welfare-maximizing public policies. Just as an investor in business capital pursues investment until the return on the last dollar of investment is equal to the return of the next-best alternative investment, a policy maker can pursue climate protection policy until the marginal cost of emission mitigation is on par with the societal return on that mitigation: the social cost of carbon. Thus, mitigation policies with marginal costs equal to the social cost of carbon—for example, a carbon tax in line with the social cost of carbon—would maximize net social benefits.

In practice, public policies appear to deviate significantly from the guidance that cost–benefit analysis could supply. With the exception of a few carbon tax programs in northern Europe and the Canadian province of British Columbia, most policies that affect greenhouse gas emissions do not explicitly set prices (or marginal costs) on emissions. Some governments—such as the European Union,

California, Quebec, and several cities in China—employ carbon dioxide cap-and-trade programs. (A cap-and-trade system constrains the aggregate emissions of regulated sources by creating a limited number of tradable emission allowances—whose sum is equal to the overall cap—and requiring that those sources surrender allowances to cover their emissions.[19]) The dramatic volatility in allowance prices in such markets, especially in the European Union Emissions Trading System, indicates that, in all likelihood, the marginal cost of compliance rarely equals the social cost of carbon.[20] Examination of policy instruments around the world suggests that explicit and implicit carbon prices under such policies vary by a factor of 100.[21]

The variation in carbon prices could reflect differences in how governments evaluate the benefits of their climate protection programs. Given the uncertainty in the social cost of carbon, it's possible that failure to coordinate on a single estimate of the benefits has resulted in policies that reflect the tremendous variation in marginal costs. It's more likely, however, that special interests have influenced the policy debates, which have yielded a vast array of nth-best public policies in lieu of a carbon tax. That influence can take several forms.

Engagement of Stakeholders

First, insurgent firms might push for public policies that subsidize and/or mandate their innovative technologies. They may have strong interest in policies that could, in the context of the broad capital framework presented previously, produce excess investment in their technologies. For example, some possible renewable power policies have implicit carbon prices 10 times greater than the US government's estimate

of the social cost of carbon at a 2.5 percent discount rate.[22] Incumbent firms might not oppose such policies if they perceived that policy implementation would weaken political resolve for more-comprehensive and more-ambitious policies, such as a carbon tax.

Second, certain special interests might attempt to use public support for climate protection policies as a rationale for their preferred policies, even if those policies would have negligible impacts on the global climate. For example, biofuel producers have claimed that their output can substitute for carbon-intensive petroleum products. In practice, the vast majority of biofuels sold in the United States are corn ethanol blends, which, over their life cycles, yield very small carbon dioxide emission benefits compared with gasoline manufactured from crude oil.

Third, incumbents might support public policies that impose more-substantial regulatory requirements—and hence greater costs—on new sources of emissions.[23] Such so-called vintage-differentiated regulation has been used in many contexts, including vehicle pollution standards and power plant pollution regulations.[24] The incumbents may claim that it would be unfair to set strict standards on their existing assets because that would effectively change the rules of the game relative to when they made their initial investments in those assets. They also sometimes claim that it would be less expensive to impose requirements on new capital, as opposed to retrofitting existing capital. In effect, vintage-differentiated regulation can extend the lifetimes of existing, pollution-intensive capital because the cost of new capital is higher under the regulation. Imposing a single, common carbon price on emission sources would eliminate the inefficiencies of vintage differentiation and establish a level playing field for both existing and new capital. But the prospect of a level playing field is exactly what spurs incumbents to push for the vintage differentiation approach.

> *The Baptists, who opposed Sunday liquor sales for moral reasons, and the bootleggers, who opposed Sunday liquor sales for business reasons, found common cause in policy debates.*

Fourth, and most important, is what Bruce Yandle, former executive director of the Federal Trade Commission, calls the *bootleggers and Baptists* phenomenon.[25] The Baptists, who opposed Sunday liquor sales for moral reasons, and the bootleggers, who opposed Sunday liquor sales for business reasons, found common cause in many state and local policy debates. The key characteristics of such coalitions are that the moral champion sets the policy objective and the business champion determines the implementation. For example, in the climate policy context, environmental groups might call for ambitious emission mitigation goals, and some businesses might support them conditional on their being able to influence the policies designed to implement the goals. As a result, a simple economy-wide carbon tax could be rejected in favor of a much more complicated suite of policies that conveys returns to (at least some) incumbent firms, perhaps in a relatively opaque manner.

When Can Future and Current Generations' Interests Coincide?

We might be able to design climate change policies that can draw support from various special interests in the current generation, including (some) incumbents and insurgents. To provide background for those opportunities, I identify insights from other policy contexts and point out important differences between those contexts and climate change.

Other Policy Contexts: Insights and Differences

A successful climate change policy will transform the energy foundation of industrial economies. That transformation will require a long-term, comprehensive commitment in the United States and in economies worldwide. As we've seen, the political challenge reflects the near-term costs, borne by one group, coupled with the long-term benefits, enjoyed by other groups. In that regard, climate change differs from other major policy reforms in American history. Let's consider a few examples.

The innovation of public pensions through the 1935 Social Security Act provided almost immediate economic benefits for then current retirees as well as the promise of retirement benefits for all workers once they attain retirement age. Through a payroll tax, all workers bear the costs of participating in Social Security, but on retirement, those workers all enjoy the returns of having done so. Moreover, creating an age-specific program gave older populations strong incentive to mobilize politically to sustain the public pension program. Older people can lobby and have lobbied for similar programs throughout the developed world as a result of successful special interest political competition.[26]

The Interstate Highway Act of 1956 called for a 40,000-mile network of high-speed freeways across the United States, which in turn created substantial numbers of construction jobs in every state and congressional district, delivering broad near-term economic benefits. In addition, the Interstate Highway System fulfilled important needs in terms of homeland defense and the military threat posed by the Soviet Union. That infrastructure investment led to rapid growth in the transportation of goods and people during the following decades. Moreover, the freeways were financed through gasoline and diesel taxes—which are effectively user fees—so that many of those enjoying the benefits also bore much of the costs.

The Clean Air Act Amendments of 1970 and the Clean Water Act of 1972 established ambitious standards, new regulatory authorities, and extensive enforcement tools to clean up the nation's poor air and water quality. Media images of a river catching fire and of cars driving with headlights on during the middle of a cloud-free but highly polluted day illustrated the environmental crisis that motivated a broad political response through those laws. Americans' everyday experience with poor air and/or poor water quality dramatically increased the importance of the problems and drew attention to the need for policy remedies. In contrast to climate change policy, which is intended to prevent a future environmental crisis, those laws aimed to correct existing environmental degradation and, in some places, a current environmental crisis.

Those three examples—of social insurance, infrastructure investment, and environmental policy—pinpoint some of the major characteristics of long-term, durable, and successful public policies. First, each one remedied a publicly salient contemporary crisis or threat. Second, each one shows how near-term benefits can be enjoyed broadly across the country. Third, in the case of Social Security and the Interstate Highway System, there were few private sector incumbents that could be adversely affected by the public policies. The absence of private old-age insurance and private freeways served as the motivation for those public interventions.

The case of climate change differs in all three aspects. First, when it comes to climate change, the task today is to prevent rather than remediate. Second, most of the benefits of climate policy will accrue in the coming decades and even centuries. Third, climate change policy could easily reduce the value of an extensive array of fossil fuel capital and resource stocks.

Implications for Climate Change Policy

Climate change differs in another important way from those three public policy examples. Old-age pensions, freeway construction, and local air and water quality are distinctly domestic challenges, but climate change is a global problem that will require multilateral coordination. Although in this article I've focused on the US political economy, the same issues play out in other countries and shape the conduct of climate-related international relations. The question of who bears the cost of climate change mitigation has served as one of the primary factors limiting the progress of multilateral climate negotiations.[27] The prospect that the United

States could impose costly, unilateral emission mitigation policies while its trade partners fail to implement climate change policy has caused US manufacturers to worry about losing competitiveness, even if the empirical evidence suggests quite modest impacts.[28] Moreover, many developing countries claim that their current economic development needs—including education and public health benefits for today's children—trump the need for them to invest in climate mitigation. Some developing countries have indicated they would undertake substantial emission mitigation only once they have raised the wellbeing of their populations to satisfactory levels.

Despite the differences, though, insights gained from successful policies in other domains could help meet the political economy challenge of climate change policy. For example, designing climate policy to deliver broad, near-term benefits could help overcome some of the political opposition. To achieve that might require linking climate policy with other policy issues or linking various interest groups. Prominent events such as Hurricane Sandy and heat waves might also be cited to focus public interest on tackling the climate change problem. And if climate policy can pass Congress, then Congress's inertia may create an institutional bias for sustaining climate policy.

Given those insights, let's consider a few examples of how policy could alter the difficult political economy of climate change and produce meaningful action.

Policy Choice and Design

The political need for near-term benefits, coupled with the bootleggers-and-Baptists phenomenon, suggests that climate policy could be tailored to compensate owners of capital who might bear the costs of protecting the climate. For example, a greenhouse gas emission cap-and-trade program could be designed in a way that secures support from a broad array of the owners of private capital. Faced with the choice of surrendering an allowance or reducing emissions, companies would place a value on an allowance that reflects an emission-reduction cost they could avoid by surrendering an allowance. Regardless of how the allowances are distributed initially, trading can ensure that allowances are put to their highest-valued uses: covering the emissions that are most costly to reduce and providing an incentive to undertake the least costly reductions.[29]

By setting a binding cap on emissions and establishing tradable emission allowances, the government would effectively create an asset with substantial value. Various analyses that model proposed economy-wide cap-and-trade programs for the United States suggest that the value of allowances could range from $100 billion to $300 billion annually.[30] At least in the early years of a cap-and-trade program, that value would likely exceed the direct costs borne by owners of capital in complying with the program. One analysis showed that giving about 15 percent of emission allowances to US fossil fuel producers would leave their profits unchanged under a cap-and-trade program.[31] Moreover, strategic allocation of allowances could elicit support from industry for a cap-and-trade regime.[32] The American Clean Energy and Security Act of 2009 (H.R. 2454), also known as the Waxman–Markey bill, which passed the US House of Representatives, received the support of the US Climate Action Partnership, a coalition of businesses and environmental organizations that includes about 20 major corporations in the energy, manufacturing, and services sectors. The bill gave away

> ## About Waxman–Markey
>
> The American Clean Energy and Security Act of 2009 (H.R. 2454), also known as the Waxman–Markey bill, introduced in March 2009, called for an economy-wide cap-and-trade program for greenhouse gas emissions. The program would have established binding emission caps that would have lowered US greenhouse gas emissions to 17 percent below 2005 levels by 2020, with further reductions each year until reaching 83 percent below 2005 levels by 2050. Though the bill passed the House of Representatives in June 2009, and a modified version—the Kerry–Boxer bill—passed the Senate Environment and Public Works Committee in November 2009, the bill did not receive a floor vote in the Senate and thus failed to become law.

allowances at no cost to a vast array of users, slowly transitioning to an auction system over several decades.

By modifying implementation to secure political support from incumbents, such an approach might risk forgoing socially valuable investment that future generations would prefer. For example, channeling some of the value of emission allowances to finance research and development could significantly lower the long-term costs of emissions mitigation and yield returns to other sectors of the economy. Revenues from climate policy could also be used to reduce the burden of existing taxes (more on that later).

Strategically Linking Interest Groups

I've shown that tailoring climate policy to deliver direct economic value to incumbent firms could compensate them for the costs of such policies and thus reduce or eliminate their opposition. An alternative approach could take the value created under climate policy and dedicate it to tax reform.[33] The government could set either a tax in terms of dollars per ton of carbon dioxide emissions from sources covered by the tax or—more likely—a tax on the carbon content of the three fossil fuels (coal, petroleum, and natural gas) as they enter the economy. The revenues raised by the carbon tax (or, similarly, by an auction of emission allowances under a cap-and-trade program)

could be used to elicit strong support from a broader business constituency. Writing elsewhere, I've proposed using carbon tax revenues as part of a larger reform of the tax code coupled with eliminating greenhouse gas regulation under the Clean Air Act.[34] Business stakeholders interested in corporate tax reform and lowering the marginal tax rate on corporate income could find that proposal appealing.

A potential drawback to this approach is that it would distribute the benefits of tax reform to a much broader group of business interests than only those directly affected by climate policy. Companies may not support direct subsidies if they can't effectively limit who receives the subsidies, as in the case of an across-the-board cut in the corporate income tax rate.[35]

Carbon taxes also face a great deal of resistance. Despite economists' enthusiasm for such taxes, the general public and the American political system have been less receptive. A carbon tax makes the cost of environmental policy much more obvious than conventional regulatory approaches do, which could in turn impose political costs on politicians seeking reelection. Moreover, a tax imposes costs on concentrated, influential, and resourceful business interests, such as oil, gas, and coal companies. Finally, few environmental groups have embraced a carbon tax because they worry that it would be less effective in reducing emissions than conventional regulations would.

In contrast, a carbon tax has received support in other countries. Scandinavian governments, as well as the government of the province of British Columbia, have implemented such a tax. Differences in political institutions, in public attitudes toward the environment, and in the emission intensity of the resource base (for example, about 90 percent of British Columbia's power comes from hydroelectric dams) help explain the greater support for a carbon tax in those economies than in the United States. Nonetheless, the majority of the world's population lives in developing countries that subsidize the consumption of fossil fuel–based transportation, fuels, and electricity.[36] The difficulty of reforming fossil fuel subsidies reflects political obstacles similar to the pricing of carbon through a carbon tax. The global trend, however, is toward greater interest in and support of policies that price carbon.[37] Because the emerging international climate policy regime focuses on countries' making unilateral emission mitigation pledges subject to periodic review, such domestic policy reforms could become the foundation for international coordination to protect the global climate. Indeed, the structure of international climate policy reflects, in large part, domestic political constraints in the major economies participating in the climate negotiations.

Alternatively, policy designers could aim to draw support from across multiple generations. Public opinion polls tend to show that younger people have stronger interest than older people do in addressing climate change, and older people have stronger interest in supporting Social Security and Medicare. Climate policies that

integrate those interests could attract a broad political constituency across generations.[38] For example, the tax or auction revenues from climate policy could fill funding gaps in other government programs, such as Social Security or Medicare. In 1997, staff of the Council of Economic Advisers analyzed how revenues from a carbon dioxide cap-and-trade program could offset forecast funding shortfalls in Social Security.

Strategically Linking Issues

The marketing of climate policy could focus on ancillary benefits enjoyed by the current generation. Politicians advocating for climate change mitigation policies often note that improved local air quality also improves respiratory health and reduces the risk of death.[39] For example, in his 2013 Georgetown University speech, President Obama said, "So today, for the sake of our children, and the health and safety of all Americans, I'm directing the Environmental Protection Agency to put an end to the limitless dumping of carbon pollution from our power plants, and complete new pollution standards for both new and existing power plants." In August 2015, through the so-called Clean Power Plan, the US Environmental Protection Agency issued the standards Obama called for in that speech. In its economic evaluation of the regulation, the EPA estimated year-2030 climate benefits of $20 billion and public health benefits ranging from $14 billion to $30 billion from reducing local air pollutants.[40]

Yet the argument that climate policy could also improve health faces political and policy obstacles. Some opponents of climate policy agree on the value of improving local air quality but question whether greenhouse gas mitigation policies represent the most effective way to deliver those benefits. For example, they might argue that if reducing fine particulate pollution yields major health benefits, then environmental policy should target particulates directly. A report by the Organisation for Economic Co-operation and Development found that the local air quality cobenefit of mitigating carbon dioxide emissions may not motivate large developing countries to implement ambitious climate change policies, because directly controlling air pollution appears to be less costly in those countries.[41] Moreover, many policies that directly target conventional air pollutants do not necessarily reduce—and in some cases may increase—carbon dioxide emissions. Installing scrubbers on coal-fired power plants, for example, imposes an energy penalty that effectively increases the emissions of carbon dioxide per kilowatt-hour of power generated.

In the 2009 debate over the Waxman–Markey bill, politicians often described it as a "jobs bill" that would promote US energy independence. For example, at the end of the floor debate on the bill, Speaker Nancy Pelosi's entire speech was "Jobs, jobs, jobs, jobs." On the other side of the debate, opponents decried the bill as part of a broader pattern of "job-killing regulations." In practice, neither of those rhetorical positions is on target. Pricing carbon is unlikely to serve as a credible substitute for economic stimulus, and empirical analyses suggest that the potential for job losses in energy-intensive manufacturing—the sectors most likely at risk under climate change policy—is quite modest and is swamped by other factors affecting the same labor markets, such as technological innovation and trade policy.[42] Nonetheless, advocates for US climate policy continue to point to the job creation opportunities associated with insurgent technologies.

Making Insurgents into Incumbents

Subsidizing energy efficiency and renewable energy can, over time, increase the size and the potential clout of the insurgent-business constituency. For example, the US solar industry recently claimed that it employs more workers than the US coal industry. The growth of the solar industry reflects a variety of market and policy factors, including very generous support for solar power through the American Recovery and Reinvestment Act of 2009. Several new utility-scale solar facilities have been supported through government-subsidized loan guarantees. All solar investment benefits from accelerated depreciation and a capital subsidy in the form of a grant or an investment tax credit. Those policies have also significantly contributed to the growth of the US wind power industry, which has more than doubled its installed capacity since 2008.[43]

Owners of capital with large investment positions in novel energy technologies have a vested interest in policies that create markets for those innovations.

Likewise, the ramping up of clean energy investment, especially in Silicon Valley, south of San Francisco, has helped promote support for climate protection policies. Owners of capital with large investment positions in novel energy technologies have a vested interest in policies that create markets for those innovations. As a result, during the public debate about the future of California climate policy around the 2010 ballot proposition 23—which would have effectively ended California's efforts to design and implement climate change policies, including a cap-and-trade program—incumbent big oil companies made substantial donations to support the proposition, and major investors in clean energy ventures made substantial donations to oppose it. The proposition's opponents raised almost three times as much in donations as the proponents did, reflecting the political and economic strength of clean energy capital in California.

Finally, investing in research and development for new technologies can change the economic calculus for future policies. Encouragement of innovation can deliver new knowledge, new technologies, new processes, and new products whose existence is irreversible. A major R&D program today could lower the costs of mitigation policies tomorrow by increasing the range of commercial low- and zero-carbon technologies. Indeed, the August 2015 EPA Clean Power Plan set more-ambitious carbon dioxide targets for the US power sector than the EPA had proposed earlier—partly because the costs of new renewable power-generating technologies had fallen.[44] Those declining costs reflect a number of things, including a multidecade history of public sector support for renewable energy R&D and subsidies that have contributed to scale economies and learning by doing.

Institutions and Durable Climate Policy

In their scholarship on environmental policy, economists have sometimes assumed away the importance of institutions.[45] Nonetheless, the political institutions through which climate policy is made can significantly affect

the influence of various constituencies and the outcome of policy debates. In particular, the design and implementation of policy-making institutions can create veto points and opportunities for people engaged in climate policy debates.

Let's consider a few illustrations from the process of drafting new statutes in Congress and writing rules in regulatory agencies before examining how to design a durable climate policy by exploiting existing institutional frameworks. In Congress, committees play the initial roles in writing, rewriting, and voting on bills. The composition of committee memberships is not random but reflects the interests of specific members as well as the interests of their constituents and campaign backers. For example, the composition of the House Energy and Commerce Committee affected the design and revision of the 2009 Waxman–Markey bill as well as the committee's voting.[46] In particular, the disproportionate representation of energy-producing districts affected the way allowances were allocated; for example, a set-aside of free allowances for petroleum refineries was necessary to secure the votes of several members with refineries in their home districts.

Various stakeholders' political influence with members of specific committees can affect the types of policies those stakeholders support. Some stakeholders have developed strong relationships with committees whose jurisdiction constrains the kinds of policies they write into bills. For example, the preference for cap and trade in US climate policy debates—at least relative to a carbon tax—may reflect environmental advocates' preference for working with environmental committees (such as the Senate Environment and Public Works Committee and the House

Energy and Commerce Committee) than with tax-writing committees, which they view as less green and controlled by incumbent business interests.[47]

The voting rules in Congress—particularly in the Senate, with its de facto supermajority vote requirement under today's filibuster procedures—also influence the characteristics of policy. For example, two colleagues and I simulated support for a national clean energy standard in the House and Senate and contrasted it to what would be expected under a national referendum (that is, majority rule) based on survey data.[48] The 60-vote threshold to defeat a filibuster in the Senate suggests that only a very low-cost, modest clean energy standard would pass that chamber—in contrast to what would be possible under simple majority-rule voting in the Senate. Given young voters' greater support for policies to reduce greenhouse gas emissions relative to that of older voters, voter turnout among younger generations could change the composition of Congress and make it more inclined to consider climate change legislation.[49] Of course, other factors could constrain that influence, such as the construction of congressional districts; the extent to which any voters, young or old, vote based primarily on a candidate's position on climate change; and the campaign finance landscape.

Alternatively, the executive branch could use its statutory authority to draft new regulations on climate policy the way the EPA did with the Clean Power Plan.[50] That regulation illustrates the many institutions involved in climate policy—and the many opportunities for delaying or vetoing it. First, the EPA proposed the rule and solicited comment in 2014. It received more than 4 million public comments, and that feedback shaped the final rule. Second, the EPA's final rule, issued in August 2015, gave Congress the opportunity to strike down the regulation under the Congressional Review Act. Third, several coal companies opposing the rule filed lawsuits on the same day that the EPA issued the final rule, and legal scholars anticipate an important and potentially lengthy judicial review process. Finally, the Clean Power Plan includes a very important role for the states in developing their own plans for reducing power-sector carbon dioxide emissions. That reflects the nature of federalism in general in American public policy and particularly for climate policy (under the Clean Air Act, the statutory authority for this regulation), which can influence incentives and create opportunities for policy innovation as well as establish another veto point for opponents of climate policy.[51]

Building a durable, long-term climate policy will require accounting for and exploiting existing political institutions.[52] The veto points raise barriers to realizing meaningful climate policy in the first place. For example, the failure to pass national cap-and-trade legislation in the Senate in 2010 precipitated the development of the regulatory approach by way of the 2015 Clean Power Plan. Of course, the veto points built into American political institutions can also serve to maintain climate policy should it become the new status quo. Securing a long-lived political constituency for a climate policy would help it last. Given the strong bias for the status quo in American political institutions, this would mean, first, bringing together a sufficiently strong political coalition to change policy from the status quo and then maintaining that coalition to defend the new status quo once climate policy has taken effect. The design of climate policy, including the design and implementation of new institutions and the use of existing institutions, could facilitate such a defense. Incorporating flexibility—to permit modifications of policy as new information arrives—may also ensure strong political support and policy durability, so long as we don't introduce new veto points into the process.

Conclusions

Mark Twain allegedly said, "Everybody talks about the weather, but nobody does anything about it." The risks posed by climate change have for decades elicited political rhetoric but little substantial policy action. That political outcome is not surprising given that the benefits of climate policy disproportionately accrue to future generations and that the costs are disproportionately borne by current generations—and concentrated among select incumbent firms in the fossil fuel industries.

I've used a stylized capital framework to illustrate both how to frame the current generation's obligations to future generations and the political economy challenges of mobilizing action to address climate change. Owners of existing business capital—especially the large incumbent firms—have strong incentives to oppose climate policy. Their private interests diverge from the larger societal interests to maximize the return to all forms of capital, including natural capital. Ensuring that today's children as well as their children and their children's children will grow up to enjoy a level of

wellbeing and consumption no worse than what today's generation experiences requires a public policy response that promotes a broad approach to investment in all forms of capital.

Today's children, as well as future generations, lack a voice in climate policy debates. But we can design policy approaches that attempt to drive action consistent with their interests. The key challenge lies in crafting policies that mesh the interests of the current generation with those of future generations. I've presented several such approaches, drawing from both economic research and real-world policy debates. Indeed, incumbent firms' preference for policies that maximize private returns can be used to design climate policies that deliver some near-term benefits in exchange for meaningful climate change mitigation. Alternatively, a successful climate policy design could link issues or link interest groups in a way that builds support in a policy space broader than just climate change. Finally, policy support of insurgent firms with low-carbon, disruptive technologies could eventually transform those organizations into politically potent incumbents that could challenge the fossil fuel firms. Tailoring climate policy to mollify the incumbents that oppose it and to boost the potential of the insurgents to build broad political support will be necessary if we are to mobilize successful political action to combat climate change.

ENDNOTES

1. Corinne Le Quéré et al., "Global Carbon Budget 2014," *Earth Systems Science Data Discussions* 7 (2014): 521.

2. William D. Nordhaus, *The Climate Casino: Risk, Uncertainty, and Economics for a Warming World* (New Haven, CT: Yale University Press, 2013).

3. David G. Victor and Charles F. Kennel, "Ditch the 2°C Warming Goal," *Nature* 514 (2014): 30–31, doi: 10.1038/514030a.

4. Thomas C. Schelling, "The Cost of Combating Global Warming," *Foreign Affairs* (December 1997): 13.

5. George J. Stigler, "The Theory of Economic Regulation," *Bell Journal of Economics and Management Science* 2 (1971): 3–21, doi: 10.2307/3003160.

6. Ibid.

7. Robert M. Solow, "Sustainability: An Economist's Perspective" (paper presented at the 18th J. Seward Johnson Lecture to the Marine Policy Center, Woods Hole Oceanographic Institution, Woods Hole, MA, June 4, 1991).

8. Partha Dasgupta, *Human Well-Being and the Natural Environment* (Oxford: Oxford University Press, 2001).

9. John M. Hartwick, "Intergenerational Equity and the Investing of Rents from Exhaustible Resources," *American Economic Review* 67 (1977): 972–74; John M. Hartwick, "Substitution among Exhaustible Resources and Intergenerational Equity," *Review of Economic Studies* 45 (1978): 347–54; National Research Council, *Nature's Numbers: Expanding the National Economic Accounts to Include the Environment* (Washington, DC: National Academies Press, 1999).

10. Benjamin I. Page and Robert Y. Shapiro, "Effects of Public Opinion on Policy," *American Political Science Review* 77 (1983): 175–90.

11. Naomi Oreskes and Erik M. Conway, *Merchants of Doubt: How a Handful of Scientists Obscured the Truth on Issues from Tobacco Smoke to Global Warming* (New York: Bloomsbury Publishing USA, 2011).

12. Martin L. Weitzman, "On Modeling and Interpreting the Economics of Catastrophic Climate Change," *Review of Economics and Statistics* 91 (2009): 1–19, doi: 10.1162/rest.91.1.1.

13. Scott Barrett and Astrid Dannenberg, "Climate Negotiations under Scientific Uncertainty," *Proceedings of the National Academy of Sciences* 109 (2012): 17372–6, doi: 10.1073/pnas.1208417109; Scott Barrett and Astrid Dannenberg, "Sensitivity of Collective Action to Uncertainty about Climate Tipping Points," *Nature Climate Change* 4 (2014): 36–9, doi: 10.1038/nclimate2059.

14. William D. Nordhaus, "Economic Policy in the Face of Severe Tail Events," *Journal of Public Economic Theory* 14 (2012): 197–219, doi: 10.1111/j.1467-9779.2011.01544.x.

15. Kenneth J. Arrow et al., "Intergenerational Equity, Discounting, and Economic Efficiency," in *Climate Change 1995: Economic and Social Dimensions of Climate Change*, ed. James P. Bruce, Hoesung Lee, and Erik F. Haites (Cambridge: Cambridge University Press, 1996), 129–44; Nicholas H. Stern, *The Stern Review: The Economics of Climate Change* (London: HM Treasury, 2006); William D. Nordhaus, "A Review of the *Stern Review* on the Economics of Climate Change," *Journal of Economic Literature* 45 (2007): 686–702, doi: 10.1257/jel.45.3.686; Martin L. Weitzman, "A Review of the *Stern Review* on the Economics of Climate Change," *Journal of Economic Literature* 45 (2007): 703–24; Simon Dietz and Nicholas Stern, "Why Economic Analysis Supports Strong Action on Climate Change: A Response to the *Stern Review's* Critics," *Review of Environmental Economics and Policy* 2 (2008): 94–113, doi: 10.1093/reep/ren001; Kenneth Arrow et al., "Determining Benefits and Costs for Future Generations," *Science* 341 (2013): 349–50, doi: 10.1126/science.1235665.

16. Stern, *Stern Review*.

17. Interagency Working Group on Social Cost of Carbon, *Technical Support Document: Social Cost of Carbon for Regulatory Impact Analysis under Executive Order 12866* (Washington, DC: United States Government, 2010); Interagency Working Group on Social Cost of Carbon, *Technical Support Document: Technical Update of the Social Cost of Carbon for Regulatory Impact Analysis under Executive Order 12866* (Washington, DC: United States Government, 2013); William A. Pizer et al., "Using and Improving the Social Cost of Carbon," *Science* 346 (2014): 1189–90.

18. National Research Council, *Hidden Costs of Energy: Unpriced Consequences of Energy Production and Use* (Washington, DC: National Academies Press, 2010).

19. Joseph E. Aldy and Robert N. Stavins, "The Promise and Problems of Pricing Carbon: Theory and Experience," *Journal of Environment and Development* 21 (2012): 152–80, doi: 10.1177/1070496512442508.

20. Joseph E. Aldy and W. Kip Viscusi, "Environmental Risk and Uncertainty," in *Handbook of the Economics of Risk and Uncertainty*, vol. 1, ed. Mark J. Machina and W. Kip Viscusi (Oxford: North-Holland, 2014), 601–49.

21. Joseph E. Aldy and William A. Pizer, "Alternative Metrics for Comparing Domestic Climate Change Mitigation Efforts and the Emerging International Climate Policy Architecture," *Review of Environmental Economics and Policy* 10 (2016): 3–24, doi: 10.1093/reep/rev013.

22. Joseph E. Aldy and William A. Pizer, "The Employment and Competitiveness Impacts of Power-Sector Regulations," in *Does Regulation Kill Jobs?* ed. Cary Coglianese, Adam M. Finkel, and Christopher Carrigan (Philadelphia: University of Pennsylvania Press, 2014), 70–88.

23. Stigler, "Theory of Economic Regulation"; Robert N. Stavins, "Vintage-Differentiated Environmental Regulation," *Stanford Environmental Law Journal* 25 (2006): 29–63.

24. Howard K. Gruenspecht, "Differentiated Regulation: The Case of Auto Emissions Standards," *American Economic Review* 72 (1982): 328–31; Garth Heutel, "Plant Vintages, Grandfathering, and Environmental Policy," *Journal of Environmental Economics and Management* 61 (2011): 36-51.

25. Bruce Yandle, "Bootleggers and Baptists in Retrospect," *Regulation* 22, no. 3 (1999): 5–7.

26. Casey B. Mulligan and Xavier Sala-i-Martin, "Gerontocracy, Retirement, and Social Security" (Working Paper no. 7117, National Bureau of Economic Research, Cambridge, MA, May 1999).

27. Joseph E. Aldy and Robert N. Stavins, eds., *Architectures for Agreement: Addressing Climate Change in the Post-Kyoto World* (Cambridge: Cambridge University Press, 2007); Scott Barrett, *Environment and Statecraft: The Strategy of Environmental Treaty-Making* (Oxford: Oxford University Press, 2003).

28. Joseph E. Aldy and William A. Pizer, "The Competitiveness Impacts of Climate Change Mitigation Policies," *Journal of the Association of Environmental and Resource Economists* 2 (2015): 565–95, doi: 10.1086/68330.

29. Robert W. Hahn and Robert N. Stavins, "The Effect of Allowance Allocations on Cap-and-Trade System Performance," *Journal of Law and Economics* 54 (2011): S267–94, doi: 10.1086/661942; W. David Montgomery, "Markets in Licenses and Efficient Pollution Control Programs," *Journal of Economic Theory* 5 (1972): 395–418, doi: 10.1016/0022-0531(72)90049-X.

30. US Energy Information Administration, "Energy Market and Economic Impacts of H.R. 2454, the American Clean Energy and Security Act of 2009," SR-OIAF/2009-05 (Washington, DC: Department of Energy, 2009).

31. A. Lans Bovenberg and Lawrence H. Goulder, "Neutralizing the Adverse Industry Impacts of CO_2 Abatement Policies: What Does It Cost?" in *Behavioral and Distributional Effects of Environmental Policy*, ed. Carlo Carraro and Gilbert E. Metcalf (Chicago: University of Chicago Press, 2001), 45–90.

32. Robert N. Stavins, "A U.S. Cap-and-Trade System to Address Global Climate Change" (Hamilton Project discussion paper, Brookings Institution, Washington, DC, 2007).

33. Gilbert E. Metcalf, "A Proposal for a U.S. Carbon Tax Swap" (Hamilton Project discussion paper, Brookings Institution, Washington, DC, 2007).

34. Joseph E. Aldy, "The Case for a U.S. Carbon Tax," *Oxford Energy Forum* 91 (2013): 13–16.

35. Stigler, "Theory of Economic Regulation."

36. Joseph E. Aldy, "Policy Surveillance in the G-20 Fossil Fuel Subsidies Agreement: Lessons from Climate Policy," *Climatic Change*, forthcoming.

37. Joseph E. Aldy, "Pricing Climate Risk Mitigation," *Nature Climate Change* 5 (2015): 396–98.

38. Antonio Rangel, "Forward and Backward Intergenerational Goods: Why Is Social Security Good for the Environment?" *American Economic Review* 93 (2003): 813–34, doi: 10.1257/000282803322157106.

39. Allison Larr and Matthew Neidell, "Pollution and Climate Change," *Future of Children* 26, no. 1 (2016), 91–111.

40. US Environmental Protection Agency, "Regulatory Impact Analysis for the Clean Power Plan Final Rule," EPA-452/R-15-003 (Research Triangle Park, NC: Office of Air and Radiation, US EPA, 2015).

41. Johannes Bollen et al., "Co-Benefits of Climate Change Mitigation Policies: Literature Review and New Results" (Economics Department Working Papers no. 693, Organisation for Economic Co-operation and Development, Paris, 2009).

42. Aldy and Pizer, "Employment and Competitiveness Impacts"; Olivier Deschênes, "Climate Policy and Labor Markets," in *The Design and Implementation of US Climate Policy*, ed. Don Fullerton and Catherine Wolfram (Chicago: University of Chicago Press, 2011), 37–49; W. Reed Walker, "The Transitional Costs of Sectoral Reallocation: Evidence from the Clean Air Act and the Workforce," *Quarterly Journal of Economics* 128 (2013): 1787–1835.

43. Joseph E. Aldy, "A Preliminary Assessment of the American Recovery and Reinvestment Act's Clean Energy Package," *Review of Environmental Economics and Policy* 7 (2013): 136–55, doi: 10.1093/reep/res014.

44. US Environmental Protection Agency, "The Clean Power Plan: Key Changes and Improvements from Proposal to Final," http://www.epa.gov/cleanpowerplan/fact-sheet-clean-power-plan-key-changes-and-improvements.

45. Dallas Burtraw, "The Institutional Blind Spot in Environmental Economics," *Daedalus* 142, no. 1 (2013): 110–18, doi: 10.1162/DAED_a_00188.

46. Michael Cragg et al., "Carbon Geography: The Political Economy of Congressional Support for Legislation Intended to Mitigate Greenhouse Gas Production," *Economic Inquiry* 51 (2013): 1640–50, doi: 10.1111/j.1465-7295.2012.00462.x.

47. Nathaniel O. Keohane, Richard L. Revesz, and Robert N. Stavins, "The Choice of Regulatory Instruments in Environmental Policy," *Harvard Environmental Law Review* 22 (1998): 313–67.

48. Joseph E. Aldy, Matthew J. Kotchen, and Anthony A. Leiserowitz, "Willingness to Pay and Political Support for a US National Clean Energy Standard," *Nature Climate Change* 2 (2012): 596–99, doi: 10.1038/nclimate1527.

49. Jon A. Krosnick and Bo MacInnis, "Does the American Public Support Legislation to Reduce Greenhouse Gas Emissions?" *Daedalus* 142, no. 1 (2013): 26–39, doi: 10.1162/DAED_a_00183.

50. US EPA, "Clean Power Plan."

51. Burtraw, "Blind Spot."

52. Ann E. Carlson and Robert W. Fri, "Designing a Durable Energy Policy," *Daedalus* 142, no. 1 (2013): 119–28, doi: 10.1162/DAED_a_00189.